D1582163

GUINNESS
AMAZING FUTURE

GUINNESS PUBLISHING

Managing Editor
Mark Fletcher

Research Editor
Gill Moodie

Editors
Hephzibah Anderson
Mark Beasley
Ian Fitzgerald
Sarah Taylor

Contributors
Belinda Archer
Elaine Brass
Brigitte Engler
Brian Ford
Tim Furniss
Max Glaskin
Martin Godfrey
Hari Kunzru
Manu Luksch
Armin Medosch
Sandip Shah
Karl Shuker

Proof Reader
Sue Harper

Indexer
Sue Harper

Art Director
Damian Jaques

Designer
Adam Kelsey

Picture editor
Ellen Root

Cover Design
Max Ellis

Pre-Production Manager
Patricia Langton

Colour Origination
Essex Colour

Printed and bound
Printer Industria Grafica, Barcelona

Paper
Printed on wood-free, chlorine-free
and acid-free paper

Publishing Director
Ian Castello-Cortes

British Library cataloguing-in-Publication
Data
A copy of this book is available from the
British Library

ISBN 0-85112-051-2

GUINNESS

AMAZING FUTURE

GUINNESS PUBLISHING

CONTENTS

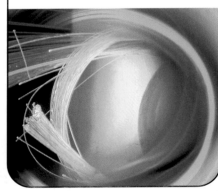

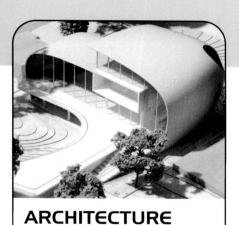

ARCHITECTURE

ENVIRONMENT

NEW SCIENCES

HEALTH

SPACE

SCIENCE FICTION

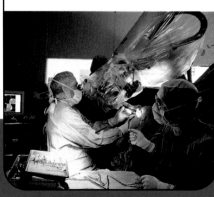

As we reach the end of the millennium we all have both a sense of trepidation and excitement at what the next century will bring. *Guinness Amazing Future* offers you a glimpse into this new world. Inside you'll find hundreds of true stories to do with scientific research that will change the way we live, work and think in the future.

The book has been designed for easy access to all subject matters, from medicine to warfare across architecture and environment. Unusual subjects are covered, including Cult TV, Techno Utopias, Cyber Art and Hackers, which although little known or understood at the moment will without doubt become areas of enormous importance in the next hundred years.

Our team of future experts has scoured the world looking for breakthrough stories to bring you. And our graphics team has designed an interactive design using colour-coded spreads each with its own icon. Each section opens with a brief introduction including a fun and fascinating techno-babble box revealing the meaning of some of the world's strangest new expressions.

In a hundred years time some of us could be living in space, or commuting to Australia for work, or enjoying a fit and healthy life at a hundred and fifty. If you want to find out more about your future read on.

How To Use This Book

Special Boxes
Highlight amazing facts and statistics about the future.

Spread titles
Each spread has its own specially-designed icon.

Futurescope
A selective look at the future, pointing out some of the more outrageous and astounding predictions.

Techno-Babble
We explain new, bizarre words.

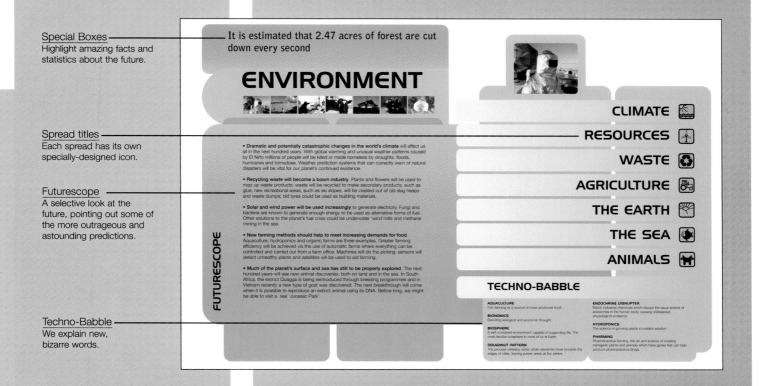

Past/Future
Forgotten past inventions and discoveries are contrasted with incredible predictions for the future.

News flashes
Headlines for at-a-glance access to the key elements of the story.

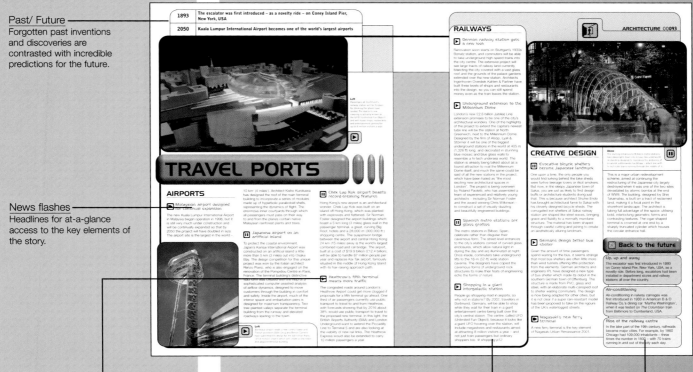

The Three Symbols
Breakthroughs of today
R & D for tomorrow
Projects for the future

 Today
Tomorrow
The Future

Cross-references
Easy-to-use cross-references with the page number and spread title of linked topics.

Back to the future
A look back in time to some of the world's forgotten scientific breakthroughs, inventions and failed marketing opportunities.

Canada's West Edmonton mall has 20,000 parking spaces and 325,000 light fittings

LIFESTYLES

- **Fruit and vegetables will become more colourful and bigger** thanks to biotechnological techniques that allow scientists to alter the genetic make-up of foods. It will be perfectly normal to eat pipless apples and melons.

- **Extreme sports will become increasingly popular** as kids look for new ways to mix sport and danger. Street luge – lying down on your back on a sort of enlarged skateboard while you plummet down steep roads at over 100 mph with only your feet for brakes – is already a growing sport in California. Skysurfing, ice climbing and skiboarding may all be Olympic sports in the next century.

- **Shopping is destined to become a home-based pastime** with the Internet allowing direct and easy access to thousands of outlets. Even visiting the local supermarket will be made as convenient as possible. Intelligent shopping trolleys, smart cars and smell-identification systems will allow the shopper simply to go into a store, take what they want and walk out again. The cost will be deducted automatically from the shopper's card as they pass the checkout point.

- **Customised clothes will soon be possible**. Fashion will become increasingly technical and specific to the wearer. New techniques in measuring people's bodies will allow for all clothes to be made to measure, even jeans. There will even be garments that can adapt to the outside temperature – keeping us warm in the cold and cool in the heat – and fabrics that are impervious to the worst stains.

- **We will take our holidays in space or under the seas**. Purpose-built underwater hotels and zero-gravity sports centres will cater for our 21st century needs. The typical holiday journey will no longer be a charter flight to Spain, but a shuttle to the Moon.

- **Virtual sex partners will eliminate the danger of catching sexually-transmitted diseases**. One day, we may be able to control our moods by using tonics and pills; sober-up drugs will be available to counteract the effects of drinking too much alcohol. However, it remains to be seen whether people will embrace such a sterile world.

FUTURESCOPE

FOOD

SHOPPING

FASHION

SPORT

HOLIDAYS

TECHNO-BABBLE

BROCHUREWEAR
A product that is aggressively marketed though publicity brochures, but does not actually exist yet.

COOLHUNTER
One who researches cutting-edge fashion and ideas and sells them to companies who want to be hip and trendy.

GASTRONAUT
A bold and adventurous eater, who is prepared to experiment with a host of wonderful and exotic foodstuffs.

HEDON
The unit of pleasure.

RAW FOODISM
Extreme vegetarianism, in which food is consumed without any form of cooking. Special types of raw foodists include fruitarians, who only eat fruit and sproutarians, who like sprouts and greens.

REALITY FIGHTING
An extremely violent sport, akin to bare-knuckle fighting. A no-holds barred combat, with kicking, choking and head-butting.

SMART DRUGS
Nutritional supplements that act as vitamins for the brain.

WHITE CARD
A smart card that includes data to suit particular needs.

1961	American astronauts on *Mercury* flights in space eat foods in semi-liquid form out of aluminium toothpaste-type tubes for the first time
2004	Robots developed by NASA allow farmers to plough their fields, sow seed and harvest crops directly from the farm office

Left
Biotechnology, the technique which allows scientists to transfer DNA, can develop new plant and fruit varieties. The FLAVSAVR tomato, grown by Calgene Inc. of California, USA, is designed to stay firm after being harvested.

FOOD

NEW FOODS

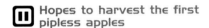 Hopes to harvest the first pipless apples

At the Horticulture Research Institute in East Malling, UK, plans are currently in place to harvest the first palatable pipless apples. The Institute has produced coreless hybrids by crossing well-known apples like Red Pippins with the more obscure seedless varieties, Spencer Seedless and Wellington Bloomless from the USA.

The future for chocolate might be bendy

The manufacturer Nestlé is currently developing a new bendy chocolate that will be able to be made into different shapes. During the Gulf War the American chocolate production company Hershey supplied American troops with chocolate bars that were designed not to melt and therefore survive in the desert heat.

The cow that can supply humanised milk

Although cow's milk features heavily in many people's diet, some find it difficult to digest. PPL Therapeutics, UK, have unveiled Rosie, a cow who is able to produce 'humanised milk'. Rosie can supply milk which contains a human breast milk protein alpha-lactalbumin which is more nutritious and is easily digestible.

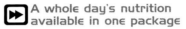 A whole day's nutrition available in one package

One day, grocery stores may offer 'total nutrition' packages containing several types of fresh produce that are designed to give a person a day's worth of complete nutrition based on their individual body weight. In 1996, in Phoenix, USA, a grocery store offered hermetically sealed, separate plastic packages each containing a selection of fresh melon and red grapes. In New York, NetGrocer already offers an on-line grocery service. In the future, no doubt, people will be able to get 'total nutrition' packages based on their own personal needs, delivered to their homes via the Internet.

Investigations into soil show that it may be good to eat

Although many peoples around the globe traditionally eat soil, modern science has remained very sceptical, until now. Tests by scientists from Toronto University and York University, Canada, have revealed that soil eaten by people in Zimbabwe and China does indeed contain the nutrients claimed by its advocates. Zimbabwe soil, supposed to be good for the stomach, was found to contain kaolinite, a major ingredient in the western treatment of diarrhoea. Yellow soil, eaten in China's Hunan Province during famines, contained manganese, vanadium, iron and other vital nutritional elements.

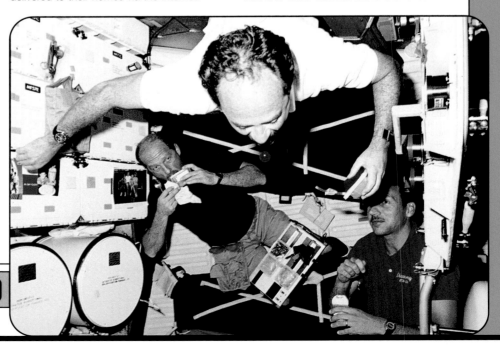

Right
American astronaut John M Lounge chases a bubble of strawberry drink which escaped during a meal on the space shuttle *Discovery* mission STS-26 in 1988. Space food uses the world's most advanced techniques in food preservation and packaging.

BIOTECHNOLOGY

▐▐ Genetically modified tomatoes last longer and taste better

In May 1994, the USA Food and Drug Administration announced it had developed a new tomato, the FLAVSAVR, through biotechnology. Via gene manipulation, the tomato has had its polygalacturonase (PG) – a naturally occurring enzyme in tomatoes – suppressed. PG breaks down pectin, an enzyme found in cell walls, and causes ripe tomatoes to soften. The FLAVSAVR can therefore stay ripe longer.

▶ Superchickens that could be immune to salmonella

The Roslin Institute in Edinburgh, UK, is breeding a race of 'superchickens' – the Ross 308 – using gene maps to identify the chicken's chromosomes. The Chickmap project aims to create the ideal chicken – a stronger, faster-growing bird, immune to salmonella and with even leaner meat. They will also need less feed and produce less manure, so making free-range farming more commercially viable. @ *agriculture p128*

▶▶ New bananas could help in the fight against hepatitis B

Biotechnologists at the Boyce Thompson Institute for Plant Research at Cornell University in New York State, USA, are genetically engineering a banana to produce an antigen found in the outer coat of a hepatitis B virus. These bananas will contain vaccines that could provide developing countries with cheap medicine delivered not as raw bananas, but conveniently in purée form similar to baby food.

Above
Today, hydroponic techniques are used as an alternative to traditional growing methods in areas where there is little rainfall. Here, young lettuce plants are being grown under sodium vapour lamps using hydroponic techniques.

▶▶ Anti-cancer agents found in strong-tasting sprouts

Scientists at Norwich Research Park, Norwich, UK, believe that chemicals called glucosinolates, which are largely responsible for the strong taste and smell of brussels sprouts, are important anti-cancer agents. Scientists and plant breeders are working together to create sprouts that are not too bitter to eat but still retain the beneficial health qualities of these chemicals.

Above
Three massive greenhouse biomes are being constructed as part of the Eden Project in Cornwall, UK. The planthouses will be used to explore ways of growing plants in the future. The Centre will be completed in 2000.

FOOD PRODUCTION

▶ World's largest greenhouse to be built in Cornwall, UK

The Eden Project is a £106 million scheme in St Austell, Cornwall, UK, to construct the world's largest plant house in a 15 hectare (37 acre) china clay pit. Research will focus on global solutions to the problems of conservation and sustainable agronomic development. The Project will consist of Mediterranean, tropical rainforest and desert biomes. @ *resources p124*

▶ Snail droppings to be used as fertilizer in Israel

In the Negev Desert, Israel, scientists have built ridges in the desert enabling them to catch droppings from rock-eating snails. The droppings contain soil-enriching nitrogen which helps soil fertility and so promotes crop growth.

▶ Robot farmhands developed by NASA to plough fields

A hay-cutting robot that allows farmers to harvest crops using unmanned machines has been developed by NASA, the Carnegie Mellon University, Pennsylvania, USA, and a farm machine manufacturer, New Holland. Within seven years, the researchers say, farmers will be able to plough their fields, sow seed and harvest crops from an office. A prototype, which uses computerised technology pioneered in robotic space vehicles, is already cutting crops in Imperial Valley, California, USA. @ *robots p28*

♻ Back to the future

Sky Lab

Sky-Lab Foods, Inc., NY, USA, was formed in 1978 to market food packages modelled on the NASA meal system. The company makes freeze-dried foods, which are reconstituted using water, and 'retorch pouch' meals which need no reconstitution, only heating.

Jadinon pumpkins

In 1989, Jean-Pierre Jadinon, the director of Promagri, France, developed a pumpkin the size of a melon so as to help employees working in a canning factory who always had to carry large pumpkins. Research and successive selection from more than 150 *Cucurbitaceae* seeds from California, USA, and New Zealand was undertaken to produce the 'Merveille de Tourinnes'.

Edible plates

In 1991, edible plates made from compressed oatmeal were marketed in Taipei, Taiwan, allowing eating to continue after the meal.

Flavoured vegetables

In April 1997, British frozen food chain Iceland was selling chocolate-flavoured carrots, cheese-and-onion-flavoured cauliflower and peas that tasted like baked beans. This was backed by the Cancer Research Campaign in an effort to encourage children to eat more vegetables. But by 1998 the chain store withdrew the line due to lack of sales.

Left
The Swatch Bar is an up-to-the-minute café inside the Swatch Time Ship, the watch company's flagship store in New York, USA. Designed by Daniel Weil of Pentagram Design Ltd, the shop has been planned to resemble a piece of machinery, deliberately mimicking the Swatch watches' colourful, modern design.

SHOPPING

RETAIL SYSTEMS

▶ Self-service with the intelligent shopping trolley

In some countries Express Checkout Systems are already in operation, consisting of one cashier desk overseeing two or more scanning stations. The goods are scanned by the customers themselves and then placed on a conveyor belt. Big supermarket chains are evaluating studies about the 'intelligent shopping cart' which would automatically read the prices of goods as they are collected from the shelves. In this way buyers constantly know how much they are spending, and there would be no waiting time at cashiers.

⏸ Smart packaging to detect contaminated food

A research team at the University of California, USA, has developed smart packaging, with specialized molecules programmed to change colour if the food becomes contaminated with a virus such as *E. coli*. Another smart packaging device tells customers if frozen food has been warmed up, which can lead to forms of food poisoning such as salmonella. The warning consists of an area of the packaging containing diacetylene monomer, which starts off clear but darkens if the package is warmed up.

▶ Advanced data tags scan trolley loads

Britain's Centre for the Exploitation of Science and Technology is asking retailers to use radio frequency identification tags to broadcast product information. If they agree, scanners would be able to calculate the total cost of products directly from the customer's stacked trolley and shoplifting could be eliminated. Flying Null Limited, a company from Cambridge, UK, is developing a new data tagging system which holds up to 16 bits of information and can be read from a distance of up to 2 m (6 ft). Many retailers believe that the future of tagging is in incorporating the security tagging into the packaging itself. British company Sensormatic is currently developing a plastic CD case which incorporates the security tag.

▶ Auto selecting with the interactive car locater

If a recently launched system works, car salesmen could soon be replaced by a touchscreen car locater system. The first CarLand store in West Thurrock, UK, allows buyers to use an interactive touchscreen system to choose the car they want, according to price, make and colour. The CarLocator kiosk then issues a colour printout with detailed information on suitable cars, before the customer inspects them in the superstore.

▶ Intelligent ink for shorter queues

In 1997 the company Philips, based in Eindhoven, the Netherlands, announced the development of an intelligent ink which

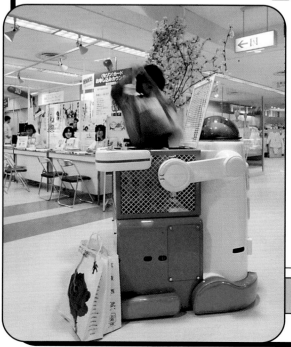

Left
Seibu, a Japanese department store, is the world's first fully-automated shop, where robotic shopping trolleys greet customers on arrival and follow their progress at a discreet 70 cm (2 ft).

contains polymers into which information about the product can be coded. This could be incorporated into the labelling and read by an electronic eye at the till.

▶ Grocery scanner aids shoppers with allergies

Two British inventors have developed a hand-held grocery scanner which will warn customers of products which would cause an allergic reaction. Called Inside Trak, the scanner checks a database of ingredients to ensure the product conforms to the shopper's dietary requirements. If inappropriate, an alternative product would be suggested on the small built-in display screen. The inventors are hoping it will encourage manufacturers to improve ingredient information on labels.

▶ Everything you need on one smart card

Smart cards, consisting of a tiny computer chip in a plastic card, are set to replace magnetic strip cards and could be used in multifunctional ways for the retail trade. They would incorporate all your personal information, including bank account details, benefit rights and health records. Apart from enabling cashless payments, they could also include supermarket loyalty card schemes, storing up personal bonus points to be used when you pay for your shopping. Mondex, owned by Mastercard International, will be one of the first cards to allow for multiple uses, and could even act as a travel card, cellphone key and soccer season ticket. @ *money p30*

▶▶ The whiff of high-tech checkouts

US inventor Alan Gelperin of Princeton, New Jersey, USA, has patented a time-saving invention to be used on busy supermarket checkout counters. NCR Corporation in Dayton, Ohio, has been assigned to manufacture the device, which can recognize fruit and vegetables by their smell. As air is wafted past the unpackaged produce a sensor is activated which creates a pattern according to the smell. The pattern is then compared with references and the price is calculated from the weight and rung up on the till.

HOME SHOPPING

⏸ Virtual shopping on the Internet

Thanks to the Web it is now possible to do your weekly grocery shopping without leaving the house. In the UK, Tesco already has a dozen virtual superstores which deliver to customers in London and Leeds. In the USA, Peapod and Choice Mail, in association with major grocery chains, will deliver groceries throughout the US as well as in Canada and South Africa. As it is the case that one in four car journeys in the UK is for shopping, it seems virtual shopping could have a significant impact on traffic. @ *net culture p40*

▶▶ New software takes auctions into the next millennium

Scientists working at the Artificial Intelligence Institute in Barcelona, Spain, have created a virtual fish auction. The software being developed mimics the traditional auctioning activities at fish markets – although, luckily, it is as yet unable to reproduce the unfragrantly fishy smells – and guarantees that all participants are treated equally. It is envisioned that the software will eventually be used for the virtual auctioning of many other goods, such as art or property, or even houses – which can already be virtually viewed on some estate agents' web sites.

▶ Phones to compile virtual shopping lists

By 2000 shoppers could be preparing their own virtual shopping lists simply by scanning bar codes with a phone or a pen. Symbol Technologies, which introduced self-scanning to UK supermarkets, can incorporate a scanner into a mobile phone or ballpoint pen, so that when the cereal or toothpaste runs out, a simple swipe across the bar code stores the information for the next shopping trip. When the scanner is within range, supermarket staff will pick up the information and prepare the orders in time for your arrival. Codes could also be scanned from mail order catalogues and ordered from the company by PC or phone.

⏸ Web site enables shoppers to find the best deal

A US web site is enabling on-line bargain-hunters to find the lowest price for the

Above
Wild at Heart in Ledbury Road, London, UK, is a flower shop with a difference. Designed by Future Systems, it has a deliberately organic feel, with the surfaces and walls inside bent into fluid shapes to reflect the shapes of the flowers themselves.

products they want. Infospace's Ultimate Product Search provides consumers with a comprehensive price comparison service on anything from books and clothes to household appliances. Bargain-hunting consumers simply choose a category and a product name and they are provided with a list of prices and an availability check from different retail outlets. They are then given the opportunity to complete the transaction right away.

♻ Back to the future

Silicone breasts

In 1962, women were able to shop for body parts for the first time. In that year the Dow Corporation of Michigan, USA, invented silicone breast implants, which, despite recent health scares, are still readily available today.

Self-service shopping

In 1956 self-service shops were introduced, paving the way for the growth of supermarket chain stores. At first, critics predicted pilfering, overspending and the squeezing out of the specialist small shop keeper.

Sell-by date

In 1942, the first 'sell-by date' was used on food, when the company Lyons put one on a carton of coffee. The practice spread and eventually became standard for most kinds of foodstuff in the UK.

Left
Designers often try to anticipate trends. Models applaud Japanese designer Issey Miyake at the end of the 1997/98 winter ready-to-wear collection he presented in Paris, France, in March 1997.

FASHION

FUTURISTIC FASHION

U2 wear superhero costumes for their Pop Mart tour

Belgian designer Walter van Beirendonck, creator of the Wild & Lethal Trash (W & LT) label, grabbed the spotlight with his futuristic designs for U2's Pop Mart tour. Van Beirendonck based the costumes on a muscle print which was personalised to fit each performer with a superhero theme. Bono became 'Bonoman', 'Muscleman' and 'Fly 2000' while guitarist The Edge was transformed into the 'Electronic Cowboy'.

Liquid-resistant denim and neoballistic nylon

The British designers Adam Thorpe and Joe Hunter, behind the label Vexed Generation, use computer graphic programs for drawing patterns and textile designs. They have created a denim coated with neoprene – usually used in wetsuits – which is resistant to oil, dirt and water. They have also developed a neoballistic nylon fabric which is resistant to fire, water and knife attacks.

Fashion show of the future features interactive clothes

A cyberfashion show was held at the Massachusetts Institute of Technology (MIT) Media Lab's Wearables Symposium at Cambridge, Massachusetts, USA, in 1997. The show, hosted by Star Trek's Leonard Nimoy, featured a jacket fitted with a tiny music synthesizer and a 'firefly' dress made of electricity-conducting fabric, decorated with tiny lights that flashed with every move of the model. Also on show was a ruby and diamond brooch that glowed in rhythm with the wearer's heartbeat.

Where shirts become skirts and T-shirts become dresses

The darling of the Spring-Summer 1998 Paris Collection, 24-year-old US designer Jeremy Scott, has a bright future with his

Right
Light-emitting plastics, such as polyphenolane vinylene (ppv), are polymers which emit light when a voltage is set up across them. They can be made to emit light of any colour and possibly could be used in clubwear of the future.

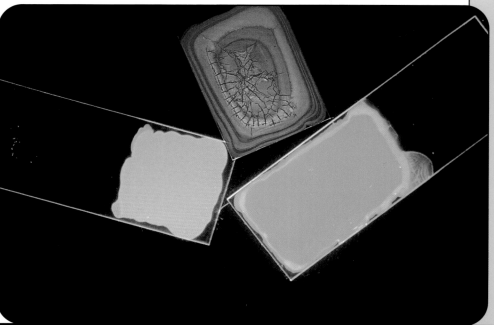

all-white collection. Within this collection, Scott designed shorts that became skirts and dresses that sculpt the body with the look of corrugated iron. He also caught the eye of the fashion world with an item of clothing which combined the function of a jersey, T-shirt and dress all in one garment. It had strategically placed holes so that it could be swung around and worn from many different angles.

▶ Fashion of the future is brought to the big screen

Jean-Paul Gaultier's exotic style found perfect expression in the costume designs for Luc Besson's film, *The Fifth Element*. Gaultier's designs looked forward to a future of haute couture, and attracted almost as much attention as the film itself. Set in the 23rd century, the film featured Bruce Willis in a skin-tight rubber T-shirt with an open back and supermodel Milla Jovovich, who played the Fifth Element, in a white 'bandage' dress, while Gary Oldman, as the evil Zorg, sported a striped bodysuit and a multi-coloured reflective dinner shirt. To add to the futuristic ambience, the film also featured an automated cupboard in a floating hotel which created clothes to fit the specific size of each guest.

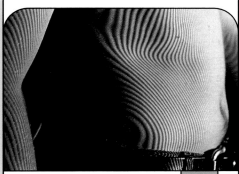

Above
A 'holographic tailor' projects a pattern of parallel stripes onto a man's torso. The pattern is scanned into a computer by a camera from three angles providing exact personal measurements in under three seconds.

SMART FASHION

⏸ Chemical treatment creates wool that doesn't itch

Japanese clothing company Kurabo Industries has devised a technique for making wool less scratchy. The fibres are chemically treated to break down their tight spiral structure. This exposes the soft inner fibres and allows individual strands to be stretched, resulting in a wool that is softer, lighter and able to retain its strength and water resistance. @ *materials science* p160

▶ The smart clothes that could be used as camouflage

Sarah Taylor, at the Scottish College of Textiles, is experimenting with weaving fibre-optic strands with translucent nylon to create fabrics which can transmit information and emit light. She has been approached by Britain's Ministry of Defence for whom intelligent clothing would be

useful in the future as camouflage, being able to adapt to different environments. Taylor is aiming to produce a safe material for wall hangings and club wear which shines and even gives off sparks. @ *warfare* p68

▶ Space-age pyjamas that monitor a sleeping baby

Babies are in for an early introduction to the world of information technology with the advent of 'intelligent' pyjamas, which have been designed to warn parents, via an onboard alarm system, when their infant may be at risk from such threats as cot death. In many developed countries, sudden infant death syndrome (SIDS) is the most frequent cause of death in children between two and 12 months old. The pyjamas were originally devised to monitor the breathing patterns and heartbeats of sleeping astronauts.

▶ Bespoke jeans could be available for everyone

Tailoring clothing to the masses could soon become a reality as automation in the garment industry increases. If demand continues to rise, it will soon be possible for companies to sell customized clothing to the masses on a regular basis. At the moment, a 'personal pair' of Levi's women's jeans can be ordered with three weeks' notice through the Custom Clothing Technology Corporation and Levi stores in the USA. The stores in the UK and USA will make a pair of custom denims after taking the customer's measurements and feeding the information into a computer.

⏸ The system that determines the comfort levels of clothes

A system developed in 1997 by British company Coverplus takes customized clothing to very sophisticated levels indeed. It can determine how comfortable clothes are by measuring the temperature and humidity inside the layers of clothing using special data loggers. The information is then fed into a computer program devised to pinpoint the optimum combination of design and fabric to produce the best fit and comfort for the customer.

▶ Tape measure could soon be replaced by a digital scanner

One innovation in the textile industry which could speed up the advance of customized clothing is the digital scanner, which experts believe will replace the tape measure within the next decade. While Adidas has already taken the plunge and is currently testing a digital foot scanner, the Textile and Clothing Technology Corporation is working on the

Above
This *Lingua Trekka* outfit, from MIT, contains neckline microphones and speech recognition software that can understand and then translate speech instantaneously through tiny speakers. The chest pieces house a computer screen and keyboard that provide a continuous environmental response.

development of a full-body scanner. The scanner works by shining light on the body in a special booth and recording how light falls. It then sends the exact shape of the body to the manufacturer to produce clothes with exact body measurements.

♻ Back to the future

Velcro inspiration

Georges de Mistral patented Velcro in 1956. He saw the need to create an alternative fabric fastener after the faulty zip on his wife's dress had jammed one evening. A couple of months later, while hunting in a Swiss forest, his inspiration came when he noticed that burrs had stuck to his dog's coat. Today it is estimated that every year enough Velcro is produced to stretch twice around the Earth.

Short skirts

In 1925, the arrival of the short skirt outraged conservative society. The Archbishop of Naples was so incensed by the new skirt length that he blamed the shorter skirt for provoking God's anger, which manifested itself in the form of an earthquake in Amalfi, Campania, in southern Italy.

Nudity as fashion

In 1970, US fashion designer Rudi Gernreich predicted that in the future, people's inhibitions about nudity would eventually disappear and men and women would go about bare-chested if the weather permitted.

SPORT

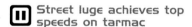 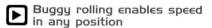 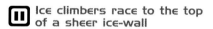

EXTREME SPORTS

Street luge achieves top speeds on tarmac

An extension of the Olympic sport ice luge but conducted on a twisting tarmac course, street luge involves a skater sitting and lying down on a board to maximize speed. It took off in the USA in the early 1990s and became one of the most exciting events of the Summer X Games, an Olympic style extreme games, which was first started in 1995. Now street lugers are using lighter boards with shorter wheel bases which allow for better manoeuvring and top speeds of up to 104 km/h (65 mph).

▶ Buggy rolling enables speed in any position

Jean-Yves Blondeau from Paris, France, has invented a more extreme form of street luge he calls buggy rolling. It involves wearing a plastic armour over a latex bodysuit that comes complete with 31 wheels attached to the feet, knees, elbows, hands, hips and back that allow the competitor to skate in absolutely any position in order to maximize speed, from lying down flat to kneeling.

Ice climbers race to the top of a sheer ice-wall

Climbing an artificial ice-cliff which is cooled from within by liquid nitrogen was one of the most extreme events in the Winter X Games held in Crested Butte, Colorado, USA, in Jan 1998. Attached to a safety rope, climbers compete against each other in the speed event which involves climbing a sheer wall of ice as fast as possible. The 1998 World Champion was Will Gadd from the USA, who beat South Korea's Seung Kwon Chung in the head-to-head final race.

Skydivers and formation flyers invent skysurfing

Skysurfing was developed in the 1980s when skydivers and freefall formation flyers started experimenting with Boogie boards. This new sport only caught the attention of the public in 1991 when a Reebok TV commercial featured Frenchman Patrick de Gayardon, generally considered to be the

 Left
Former Olympic skier Trace Worthington from Park City, Utah, USA, during the new skiboarding competition at the Winter X Games in Crested Butte, Colorado, USA, Jan 1998.

father of the sport. Nowadays, a skysurfer will always make a dive with a free-falling cameraman so that the video footage can be beamed down to audiences and a panel of judges.

▶ Golf is taken to the extreme with radical golf

Radical golf turns a game of patience and strategy into a game of brute strength and speed. Players strap one or two clubs to a backpack and set off on a quest to see who can finish a course in the fewest number of strokes and the shortest time, running from stroke to stroke and avoiding the other competitors' balls.

▶▶ Accrobranching: the new sport to hit the tree-tops

Accrobranching is a new pastime involving leaping from branch to branch at the very top of the forest tree canopy. The sport is mainly practised by tree surgeons who have only their agility and strength to keep them from falling. The only harnesses and ropes they use are those which help them get to the top.

▶ New sport is invented by lawn-chair balloonist

Cluster ballooning was invented by accident in 1982 when former US Air Force pilot Larry Walters attached helium-filled weather balloons to a garden chair and found himself floating 3,353 m (11,000 ft) above San Pedro, USA, until he was rescued by a helicopter. Walters, now famous as the 'lawn-chair balloonist', claimed he merely wanted to hover over his girlfriend's house but was soon receiving sponsorship to repeat the feat. In June 1997, US balloonist John Ninomiya reached 3,050 m (10,000 ft) and covered 22.5 km (14 miles) strapped to a cluster balloon.

⏸ Surfers can ride the perfect wave with flowboarding

Flowboarding was invented by surfer Tom Lochtefeld when he created the Flow Rider, a massive pumping machine which creates the perfect artificial wave. Flowboarding is practiced in waterparks where huge artificial waves are generated and maintained for surfers to ride, without the risks of pollution and sharks, giving them more time and space for creative expression.

⏸ The race where competitors must fend for themselves

Endurance adventure races, in which individuals or teams have to navigate through the wilderness are on the increase. The Alaska Mountain Wilderness Classic involves hiking, river crossing and pack-rafting through 210 km (130 miles) of grizzly bear country to McKinley Village, USA. There is also the annual Marathon Des Sables in Morocco which is a running and walking race over 200 km (124 miles) of the Sahara Desert. Competitors are required to be entirely self-sufficient, carrying food, water, compasses, maps, and clothing with them throughout their trip.

TECHNO SPORTS

⏸ Robotic mice compete to navigate around a maze

A micromouse, an autonomous robot no bigger than 25 cm² (10 in²), competes with other robots to be the first to find its way through a maze. The first maze-solving machine was built by Dr Claude Shannon at the Massachusetts Institute of Technology in 1950, to understand the behaviour of laboratory rats in a maze, hence the term 'micromouse'. Micromouse contests became popular at computer shows and academic conferences in the early 1980s, and today hundreds of universities, companies and hobbyists compete worldwide. @ robots p28

▶ Robot Wars: where robots must fight to the end

Started by US artist and animator Marc Thorpe in 1994, Robot Wars is an event held annually in San Francisco, USA, in which contestants build remote-controlled robots for combat. Limited by weight and safety guidelines, the robots are left in a ring to slug it out until the last one standing is declared the winner. The first UK Robot Wars Championship, held in 1998, also included robotic soccer matches and an obstacle course with four House Robots to spice up the contest.

⏸ Radio- and computer-controlled car racing

Radio-controlled car racing has a massive following in Japan and the USA, and is on the rise in Europe where radio-controlled rally cars, Formula 1, stock cars and off-road four-wheel drive cars compete. The top drivers compete on a professional basis

Above
Skysurfing developed out of the sport of skydiving. Here, several skydivers perform freefall feats of aerial acrobatics before eventually opening their parachutes.

with cars up to a fifth the regular size. Controlled by a radio transmitter, or more recently, by computer, these cars are powered by specialised batteries and built exclusively for speed. A Honda Accord Street Weapon made by Californian-based Team Losi is able to accelerate from 0–48 km/h (0–30 mph) in 2.5 seconds and has a top speed of 644 km/h (400 mph).

♻ Back to the future

Skateboarding
Urban legend has it that skateboarding was invented in the 1950s by two Californian surfers who nailed roller skates to a board, but the sport didn't take off till 1973 when the development of the polyurethane wheel provided the necessary speed and agility.

Rollerblading
Rollerblade skates were first demonstrated in London, UK, in the 1820s, but didn't catch on at the time. More recently, ice-hockey player Scott Olson, from Minneapolis, USA, and his brother, Brennan, developed Rollerblades as a means of continuing to practise ice-hockey during summer. Unfortunately, the Olsons sold the Rollerblade company, founded in 1980, before the sport became popular later in the same decade.

Skysurfing
In Dec 1995, champion US skysurfer Rob Harris was killed in a skydiving accident while filming a Canadian TV commercial, with his free-falling cameraman Joe Jennings. This brought to an end a partnership which had performed over 10,000 dives and dominated the sport for years.

1936	Billy Butlin opens his first holiday camp in the UK
2074	It is estimated that the entire **US** population can take a holiday at the same time in **Las Vegas, USA**

Left
Hawaii-based architects WAT&G have designed a holiday resort on – and off – the coast of Oahu Island, Hawaii, USA. The resort will be partly based offshore, some 100 m (328 ft) out to sea and 13m (40ft) under it. Each offshore room will have a high-tech underwater fantasy theme, resembling the sets from *20,000 Leagues Under the Sea*.

HOLIDAYS

NOVELTY TRIPS

 **Tourists will flock to watch the end of the world**

As the millennium approaches, the biblical site of Armageddon is set to attract millions of pilgrims to the Holy Land. An 'intellectual theme park' is being built at Israel's Mount Megiddo, which is Hebrew for Armageddon, the place where many believe the final battle between Good and Evil will take place. In co-operation with computer giant IBM, Israel will invest millions of pounds in 14 new visitor centres.

Underwater exploration with private sub

A new class of manned submersible, known as Deep Flight, has inspired interest in the

Below
The Seagaia resort in Miyazaki, Japan, is one of the world's most advanced holiday complexes. Its centrepiece is the Ocean Dome, the world's largest indoor water park at 300 m long (984 ft), 100 m (328 ft) wide and 38 m (124 ft) high.

underwater tourism market. Graham Hawkes's winged craft looks more like a deep sea diving suit than a small submarine and uses battery-powered thrusters to manoeuvre in any direction at depths of up to 1,000 m (3,280 ft). Hawkes believes his craft will have a major impact on the largely undeveloped territory of underwater exploration and raises the possibility of new sports – underwater aviation or hydro-acrobatics.

The world's first underwater hotel opens in Florida

The Jules Undersea Lodge, off the coast of Key Largo, Florida, USA, is the world's first underwater hotel. At present, guests have to scuba dive to it, but in future subsea hotels could cruise the deep, surfacing to pick up guests, or be linked to land by covered walkways. By 2000, tourists could be checking in to the U-Sea Marine Habitat, Hawaii, which has 80 rooms on four underwater levels, parking for 150 cars, a visitors' observatory, restaurants and a sundeck. The underwater tourist industry is already estimated to be worth more than $144 million (£90 million) per year.

Theme parks in Las Vegas hotels

It was estimated in the US magazine *Newsweek* that by 2074 the entire population of the US will be able to holiday at the same time in Las Vegas, USA. The Luxor Hotel, like many other hotels in Las Vegas, is also a model for future entertainment centres, comprising a hotel, casino and indoor theme park. Virtual reality rides have replaced roller coasters and housed inside an enormous glass pyramid is a 10-storey obelisk, ancient temples, restaurants and shops. Guests can even take trips down the River Nile.

TECHNOLOGY IN TOURISM

Smart cards set to take off in a big way

American Express and Continental Airlines have issued several thousand business fliers with 'smart cards' embedded with

the user's personal preferences and other information. The test cards are inserted into a Continental smart card reader, which has a touch screen and prompts that allow passengers to switch flights, upgrade to first class, change seats, confirm One Pass numbers for mileage credits and obtain boarding passes and receipts.

❚❚ High-tech hotels to become standard in future

Hotel guests could one day expect automated check-in desks and Internet sockets in their rooms to be as common as air conditioning. The increased demand among business travellers for additional services when they travel means voicemail, Internet access and office centres may soon become standard in hotels.

❚❚ Internet takes on role of travel agents

You can now book your holiday on the Net or via interactive video. Thomas Cook has been testing a 24-hour telephone/TV interactive travel service in Ipswich, UK, which shows flights, maps and video clips. TravelWise is an Internet search engine for travel programs, such as Passport Online, that enables users to look for Net-based holiday deals updated on a daily basis.

HOLIDAYS IN SPACE

▶ Tour operators are offering a space cruise

Zegrahm Space Voyages was set up in 1997 to offer space travel packages. Their space tour will involve a week-long astronaut training experience, culminating in a 90-minute flight to 100 km (62 miles) above sea level to experience a short period of weightlessness. Selected tour operators around the world are already taking bookings for the first commercial departure on 1 Dec 2001 at a cost of $88,000 (£55,000) a seat.

▶▶ Space Cruiser will propel tourists into space

US contractor AeroAstro LLC is building a craft to take tourists into space. Unlike the space shuttles currently in use, a jet-propelled plane will carry the tourist capsule to 15,240 m (50,000 ft), at which point the Space Cruiser vehicle will detach and continue up to astronaut altitude. Six passengers will be aboard the 18-m (60-ft) long delta-winged craft, powered by rocket and jet engines and capable of a maximum speed of 3,700 km/h (2,300 mph).

Above
Professor Benjamin Britton of Cincinnati University, USA, makes a virtual visit to the Lascaux Caves, France, painted by Cro-Magnon Man 17,000 years ago. As the caves are closed to the public, VR trips there provide a useful alternative.

▶▶ Lottery for the ultimate holiday

At present, a ticket into space costs about £5 million, which is the price two Japanese businessmen paid to join a Russian space trip in 1996. But the fare could come down to as little as the price of a lottery ticket if a suggestion from Buzz Aldrin, the second man to walk on the moon, is considered. Feeling that recreational space travel should not be the exclusive domain of the rich, he proposes an international lottery which would generate development funds and guarantee space trips for ordinary people.

▶ Space-flavoured theme park cleared for lift off

The FuturePort Experience being built in Long Beach, California, USA, will be an entire theme park devoted to space. More than just an entertainment complex, it will consist of rides and exhibits designed to excite the public's interest in space while educating them about new space projects. The first phase opens in 1999 at a cost of $169 million (£106 million), and hopes to attract 2 million visitors in the first year.

▶▶ X-prize offered for tourist spacecraft

Over a dozen contestants have entered a $10 million (£6.25 million) competition, known as the X-prize, on offer for contestants challenged with developing truly out-of-this-world tourism. The X-prize's purpose is to promote the development and flight of spaceships able to provide low-cost commercial transport for humans who want to travel into space. The winning craft must have the capacity to carry three people 100 km (62 miles) above the Earth and must be 90% reusable.

▶▶ Japanese corporation plans space hotel

The Shimuzu Corporation, one of Japan's biggest construction companies, wants to build a £17.5 billion orbiting space hotel. The main body would be made up of a dozen lavishly refurbished space shuttle fuel tanks, each 31 m (102 ft) long and 8 m (26 ft) wide, with room for 200 guests each paying around £40,000 for a three-day trip.

♻ Back to the future

'Hello Campers!'

In 1936, the UK's first holiday camp was opened by Billy Butlin in Skegness, UK. The 'Butlins' camps attracted the British working classes, who were receiving paid holidays for the first time and who had not yet discovered the joys of the package holiday abroad.

First passenger flights

In 1935, the British airline Imperial Airways began passenger flights from London to Brisbane in Australia. As this was before the age of jet travel, the journey took ten days, with several lengthy stopovers, but was still a much quicker option than sailing by boat.

Jet airlines

Sir Frank Whittle's jet engine was first used in WWII fighter planes. After the War, the technology was used to develop the world's first jet airliner, the UK-built De Havilland Comet in 1949, which beat Boeing's US-built jet planes into the air by several months.

The desktop PC of the year 2000 will be over 8000 times faster than the first generation of PCs

WORK

- **It will no longer be necessary to commute to and from work**. Instead, everything will be done from home. There are already an estimated 10 million telecommuters – people who work from home – in the world today. In future, all one will need is a computer, a communication system of some sort, and perhaps a robot.

- **Cash, cheques and even credit cards will all become things of the past** as people learn to use e-cash. The idea of carrying around wads of cash will simply be seen as absurd since all transactions will be carried out automatically. Of course, different sorts of virtual transaction systems will be used: virtual money and e-cash on the Internet and smart cards in shops. With the new way of buying and selling goods it will become imperative to have safe and foolproof identification systems. Iris-recognition systems that can read people's eyes will replace the personalised pin number and cryptography will ensure that money is safe during electronic transfers.

- **The Internet has enormous potential to change the way we do business**. Already, it is possible to find out all the latest news and play the stock market using Net pages. In addition, the Net will offer comprehensive guides to everything from holidays to films, enormous digital libraries and even virtual bodies that medical students can dissect from their bedrooms.

- **Global wireless mobile phones will offer unlimited phone access** – in the desert, at sea, in the jungle – and better battery technology will mean that they will be able to be used without recharging for days at a time. Voice-controlled phones with almost invisible earpieces and throat microphones will do away with the need for handsets. Meanwhile, developments in video-phones and even holographic phones will give us the opportunity to talk face to face with our business colleagues all over the world.

- **Secretaries, receptionists and cleaners will no longer be needed** as they are replaced by robots that have been trained to clean, type and answer the phone. In fact, the office will be a sort of smart space where everything is automated: light, temperature, and telephone systems. But even more exciting is the prospect of your office preventing you from getting bored and so making sure you are always working to your best ability.

COMPUTERS

COMMUNICATION

INFO POOLS

ROBOTS

MONEY

TECHNO-BABBLE

BREAK-OUT SPACE
An area of a modern office designed for informal meetings.

CUBE FARM
An open-plan office based around a series of cubicles.

DOG-COLLAR WORKER
Graphic artists and designers.

DOWNAGING
Lowering the average age of employees at the office by replacing older workers with younger ones.

EYE SERVICE
Working only when the boss is looking.

GOLD COLLAR WORKER
A super-employee, skilled in multiple areas of their work.

HOT DESKING
The tendency of modern offices not to have set desks for their freelance and contract staff, but to provide desk-spaces on a as-needed basis. A result of network computing.

MARZIPAN LAYER
The layer of the office just under the management level.

PRAIRIE DOGGING
Sudden commotion in an open-plan cubicle-based office, which causes all other workers to suddenly look up from their desks.

SOHO
Small office, Home office, those small businesses centralised around one or two computers and often run from a bedroom.

TRAINING TOURIST
Someone who takes training classes so as to avoid the office.

1947	IBM chairman, Thomas J Watson, predicts a world market for about five computers only
2010	Robotic pet computers become all-round personal assistants

Left
Researcher Thad Starner wearing MicroOptical spectacles linked to a tiny computer. Data are projected onto the lens allowing him to read information whilst looking around. A small on-board camera can recognize people he meets and provide data on them.

COMPUTERS

NEW COMPUTERS

⏸ The computer programs that can recognise human speech

Big computer companies like Microsoft are investing in the development of speech recognition technology which can speed up all computer functions from text inputting to facilitating computer use for disabled groups such as blind and paralysed people. Prof. James Allen of Rochester University, Rochester, New York, USA, has developed an artificial intelligence program that is designed to recognise human speech, including words that are mispronounced and muffled and even malapropisms. Most speech recognition programs are limited by only being able to recognise clearly pronounced words in short sentences.

▶ Computers with virtual screens and keyboards

German-based electronics company Siemens is developing a new 'virtual' computer that has no screen, keyboard or mouse and is controlled by hand gestures. An image of a screen and keyboard is projected onto a flat surface, and the hand movements are picked up by cameras which then operate the computer like a mouse would. To make a telephone call, the user makes a specific gesture and a virtual telephone keypad appears on the desk; to write a letter, a virtual keyboard is used.

▶▶ Computers that are controlled by brainwaves

Though still in its infancy, research into controlling computers by thought is a popular field of research among everyone from the US military, who are investigating pilots controlling aeroplanes by thought, to Japanese scientist Masahiro Kahata who is pioneering an Interactive Brainwave Visual Analyser. Kahata's device consists of a box worn on a headband that holds electrodes which measure electrical activity in the brain and have been used to make limited moves in a games console. Prof. Emanuel Donchin from the University of Illinois, Chicago, USA, has developed a thought-controlled typewriter which can type at a speed of 2.3 characters per minute through the user spelling out words in their head. @ *techno utopias p176*

▶ Walking adds energy to the new shoe computer

In 1993, Microsoft chief Bill Gates predicted that conventional computer work stations would eventually be replaced by pocket-size computers able to transmit and receive messages, aid navigation, as well as assist with conventional computing. The Massachusetts Institute of Technology's (MIT) Media Lab in Cambridge, USA, has developed a shoe computer that uses the low-level electrical impulses emitted by the body. The shoes act as processors for a network and are partly powered by the energy generated when walking. MIT has also developed wearable computers complete with headsets which can be hooked up to networks through wireless modems, enabling e-mail to be retrieved and read on the way to work.

▶▶ Cyber pets can do the shopping and book a holiday

Dr Ian Pearson, a futurologist working for British Telecom's Applied Research and Technologies Laboratory, UK, has predicted that by 2010 personal computers will take

Left
Each binary digit in the Bit-Serial Optical Computer (BSOC) is represented by a pulse of infra-red laser light 4 m (13 ft) long. The pulses go round a 4 km (2.48 miles) loop of optical fibre some 50,000 times per second.

the form of robotic pets. The computer pet will do the shopping, banking and book flights for holidays. Dr Pearson foresees that the computer pet could also become as common as the personal computer.

▶ Supercomputer could carry out virtual bomb tests

IBM is building a supercomputer for the US government's Energy Department, capable of a trillion calculations a second, that was scheduled to be finished at the end of 1998. This is part of the US government's plan to build the most powerful machine in the world, capable of 10 trillion calculations a second, by 2004. It is hoped that the IBM computer will be powerful enough to learn the characteristics of nuclear weapons and the devastation they produce so that it can be used for virtual bomb tests.

⏸ The Saxex program can play jazz just like Charlie Parker

Intelligent computers gained worldwide recognition when the IBM supercomputer Deep Blue beat Russian chess grandmaster Gary Kasparov in May 1997. Scientists at the Artificial Intelligence Research Institute in Barcelona, Spain, have developed an artificial intelligence program which can play the saxophone with the expression of jazz greats such as Lester Young and Charlie Parker. The Saxex program studies sheet music and compares it to a stored repertoire of performances by famous jazz players. When it has made the closest match it can, it plays the score with the tempo and tonal expression of that particular jazz player.

▶ Talking computer can sense the needs of the user

Vienna-based scientists at Philips Speech Processing are developing voice-recognition computers that can also sense non-verbal communications from the user. Routine enquiries regarding train and flight timetables can now be dealt with by the system which helps to put unsure and unfamiliar callers at their ease by responding empathetically. The system works by picking up on basic enquiry phrases and then assessing the caller's needs. However, if the caller is more experienced, the computer will adjust its responses accordingly. They are even learning to be polite. A sneeze, for example, will elicit a 'gesundheit' from the system. Ultimately, it is thought that such systems will be able to take on much more complex work like discussing and analysing a patient's symptoms in order to relieve the workload on doctors.

COMPUTING METHODS

▶ Computers which use light instead of wires

The need to build ever more powerful computers has led to research on the use of laser beams bouncing off mirrors, lenses and prisms to move information between microchips, rather than circuits of wires. Called free-space optics, this new kind of superfast computing will benefit from beams of light being able to pass through each other, and some scientists foresee that optics will even be used inside microchips. The challenge lies in making the lasers and lenses small, cheap and hardy enough. Free-space optics will be used in NASA's PetaFLOPS project which aims to build a computer by 2010 which can make a million billion calculations a second. @ *nanotechnology p154*

▶ The wormhole computer without a brain

The Defense Advanced Research Projects Administration (DARPA), USA, is funding research into a computer which operates without the central processing unit (CPU) – the brains of today's computers through which all information must pass. The wormhole computer bypasses commands, making the process faster and more energy-efficient.

▶ Circuits designed by natural selection

Dr Adrian Thompson at Sussex University Centre, Falmer, UK, and Hugo de Garis at the Advanced Telecommunications Research Laboratory in Kyoto, Japan, are exploiting the evolutionary process of natural selection – the theory by which only the best-adapted organisms survive to reproduce. Both scientists have set up breeding colonies of microchips which combine and mutate over many thousands of generations to create new and innovative circuit designs. @ *artificial life p152*

QUANTUM COMPUTERS

▶▶ Quantum computing with subatomic computers

US physicist and Nobel prize winner Richard Feynman, came up with the idea of quantum computing, a technique that follows the laws of quantum mechanics. Conventional computers store information as binary digits that can be either 0 or 1. Quantum bits, called qubits, equal both 0 and 1 and can therefore do two different calculations at the same time, making possible computers which may be able to work billions of times faster than the most powerful computers of today. However, quantum computing can only operate on a subatomic level, that is, smaller than atoms, making them extremely difficult to build with present technology.

Above
A demoralized world chess champion Gary Kasparov considering a move against IBM's chess playing supercomputer, Deep Blue, on Sunday May 11, 1997 in New York. Deep Blue was the first computer ever to beat a grandmaster.

▶▶ Biological computers make calculations using DNA

Prof. Leonard Adleman from the University of Southern California, Los Angeles, USA, put forward the idea of bio-computers in Nov 1994 after having used DNA molecules to help solve a mathematical puzzle. In theory, DNA computers could operate billions of times faster than conventional ones, but the problem is to find ways of reproducing DNA reactions in computer code. In 1996, researchers at the Mount Sinai School of Medicine, New York, USA, found a method of encoding DNA able to calculate one plus one.

♻ Back to the future

Thomas J. Watson

In 1947, Thomas J. Watson, the chairman of computer mainframe builders IBM, announced that, "I think there is a world market for about five computers."

ENIAC

In 1946, the first electronic computer to appear in the USA was ENIAC – Electronic Numeric Integrator and Calculator. Eniac had 19,000 vacuum tubes and weighed 60,000 lbs. It was slow, but could still perform calculations as fast as mechanical calculators.

π

In 1995, a supercomputer calculated π to 6.4 billion places in under five days.

Left
The world's longest fibre-optic cable, launched in 1998, spans 17,000 miles (27,000 km) and will lead to much faster communication across the globe.

COMMUNICATION

SATELLITES

Equatorial oil platform to launch satellites

Boeing Commercial Space Company and its European partners plan to launch their first satellite-carrying rocket from a former oil drilling plaform. The 30,480-tonne floating launch-pad, named Odyssey, will provide a reliable and cost-effective launch service from the Pacific equator. Launching from this location gives the satellite extra boost into orbit as this is where the speed of the Earth's rotation is greatest and the distance to the vital satellite orbit of 38,500 km (23,908 miles) is the shortest.
@ new media p34

Two-way satellite will make communication easier

Teledesic, a new telecommunications company backed by the Boeing Company and Microsoft, launched its first low-orbit test satellite in 1998. The company plans to launch 288 satellites 1,368 km (850 miles) above the earth to provide an advanced two-way broadband service across the globe by 2002. This will enable anyone in the world to transmit voice or computer data at a much faster rate than existing methods. Current one-way communications satellites are usually too high (35,880 km or 22,300 miles) for adequate two-way services. @ new media p34

Student satellite project blasts into orbit

Students from the Laboratory for Atmospheric and Space Physics at the University of Colorado at Boulder, USA, have designed and constructed a compact hexagonal satellite for measuring the effects of energy from the sun and the magnetosphere – the magnetic field which surrounds the earth – on the density of nitric oxide in the upper atmosphere. Little is known about the gas except that it destroys ozone. The *Student Nitric Oxide Explorer*, sponsored by NASA, went into orbit in Feb 1998 and could provide clues as to what causes variations in nitric oxide's atmospheric levels.

Satellites used to track endangered eagles

Satellite tracking by Spanish scientists is helping to save the country's endangered imperial eagle. A two-year project focusing on eight tagged eagles has shown what happens to the birds during their life cycle. The data showed that the eagles were not making it back to the nesting sites alive, most often getting tangled in Spanish electricity wires. Moving the wires out of the birds' flight path has

resulted in their mortality rate dropping from 60% to 10%.

Balloon transmission station to ease cell phone traffic

A US-designed 'transmission station in the sky' in the form of a balloon could help Japan's cellular phone users by lightening communication traffic. Launched some 20 km (12½ miles) above Tokyo in the early 21st century, the unmanned balloon will be solar powered and able to carry mobile phone and data transmissions. The current system used to

Right
The Microcom-M Global is the world's smallest and lightest Inmersat M satellite telephone. It is small enough to fit into a briefcase and can also be used to send faxes.

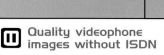
transmit and receive mobile phone calls – multiple black boxes mounted on telephone poles throughout the country – is proving inadequate as more and more people gain access to mobile telephone technology.

▶ New satellite will enable cost-effective video conferencing

An *Astra* satellite to be launched in 2000 will greatly reduce the cost of video conferencing in Europe with its high rate of data transmission. The satellite, being built by Aerospatiale of Toulouse, France, will transmit signals into space at a rate of 2 megabits per second, resulting in high quality pictures.

INFORMATION TECHNOLOGY

❚❚ Mapping cyberspace to view our world of information

New 'cartographers' like Greg Staple, who runs the US-based company Telegeography, and Martin Dodge of London, UK, who is compiling a Web-based Atlas of Cyberspace, are attempting to plot the current information flows in order to graphically represent our globe from a communication point of view. Using telecommunication statistics, the innovative data maps present the multitude of connections being made through the Internet, satellites and telephones.

▶ New fuel could make cellular calls last longer

One of the most frustrating problems with mobile phones is that most of them need to have their nickel-cadmium batteries recharged after only about 2 hours of conversation. However, Dr Robert Hockaday, formerly at New Mexico's Los Alamos National Laboratory, US, has invented a remarkable new form of fuel cell using methanol. Used in conjunction with mobile phones, it should allow much longer use, lasting up to four days before needing a recharge. Hockaday believes that his cells should be commercially available by the year 2000.

❚❚ Undersea fibre-optics for faster communication

Increased demand for Internet access and multimedia applications led to the launch of the world's longest undersea fibre-optic cable in early 1998. The Fibre-optic Link Around the Globe (Flag) can transmit 600,000 simultaneous conversations over the 27,000 km (17,000 miles) between the Middle East, UK and Japan and offers eight times the capacity of the other submarine cables linking Europe and Asia. Another mammoth fibre-optic communications project to be operational by 2000 is Project Oxygen, promoted by CTR Group, New Jersey, US. The 320,000-km (198,270-mile) integrated network will link 171 countries and carry 320 billion bits per second.

❚❚ Quality videophone images without ISDN

US company 8x8 has developed an affordable alternative to the pricey ISDN digital line. Suitable for home or office use, it is the first videophone with an integrated display to become available for less than US $1,000 (£625). ViaTV videophone is a basic camera which connects to an ordinary analogue phone line and a television set, while the telephone handset customizes the visual conversation by improving the screen's picture quality or frame rate. Using video compression techniques, the system delivers video at up to 20 frames per second, allowing for full-colour and motion phone calls.

▶ Holophones could project a 3-D image of the caller

Moving beyond videophones, the telephone of the future may enable you to interact with a 3-D representation of the person you are calling using holographic techniques. The technology to project a hologram already exists, but the holophone's introduction is being delayed by the problem of connecting people to a suitable bandwidth capable of transmitting real-time 3-D images and enabling two-way communication. This will probably be achieved by 2020 using 'smart' fibre-optic cables which could compress and reproduce holograms, eliminating the need for powerful computers at either end.

▶ Ants may ease the burden on massive telecom networks

In an attempt to avert a future telephone network crisis, designers at British Telecom, UK, and MCI, US, are considering moving away from centrally-controlled networks, which are fast out-growing their structures, and making networks self-sufficient by using artificial 'ants'. These miniature programs will be given free rein to roam around networks like their non-virtual counterparts, marking their tracks, and managing the flow of traffic, calculating phone bills and also replicating – creating smaller programs to achieve optimum solutions. There is a danger of the digital creatures getting out of control and colonizing networks, so it is unclear when these companies will feel brave enough to release the ants onto networks, a step they cannot reverse.

▶ Extranet systems could mean secure communication

Secure external communications between companies will in future probably be achieved through extranets. These systems will use net-based technology to link

Above
Technicians assemble an infrared astronomy satellite in a 'clean room'. The telescope contained in the satellite is cooled by liquid helium to a temperature of -271°C (32.5°F)

established internal company communications networks – known as Intranets. Networking company Novell, of Silicon Valley, California, USA, predicted that by 1999, nearly half of the world's large organizations will communicate with their business partners and clients via extranets which enable communication within the security of a firewall.

♺ Back to the future

The first fax

In 1907, a photograph was sent along telephone lines between Munich and Berlin, Germany, making it the first fax transmission.

Early telegraph network

Worldwide telecommunication was first made possible by the telegraph machine, which worked by exchanging information in the form of electrical code. By the 1920s, a global telegraph network was set up, but was later rendered obsolete by further developments.

Alien invasion

On 1 Nov 1938, panic broke out across America as millions of listeners tuned into Orson Welles broadcasting the H. G. Wells novel *The War of the Worlds*. The broadcast was so realistic that listeners were convinced an alien invasion was being reported, rather than the fictional dramatization.

1994	The most successful Internet search engine, Yahoo, is launched in the USA
2010	The world's largest library specializing in the Earth Sciences goes on-line

Left
The Internet offers a massive network of links between servers in the USA, meaning that information can be moved from point to point more quickly than ever before.

INFO POOLS

INFORMATION MINING

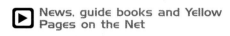 **News, guide books and Yellow Pages on the Net**

Since there are more and more Internet Search Services available on the Net, some of the leading brand names have begun to combine the search function with value-added services. They are integrating data provided by top news agencies, city and travel guides, book ordering services, Yellow Pages and even free e-mail.

Autonomous links when browsing on the Web

Researchers at the MIT (Massachusetts Institute of Technology) Media Laboratory, Massachusetts, USA, have created software that helps users browse the Net. As the user operates a conventional Web browser, such as Netscape, the program tracks user behaviour and attempts to anticipate items of interest. Because it autonomously explores links from the user's current position, the program proposes other relevant sites.

 **Digital footprints: communities of similar people**

New software called Footprints, created at the MIT Media Laboratory, makes use of the fact that in real life we often prefer to follow other people's paths. Footprints is a way to bring history to the Web by keeping track of the traces (digital footprints) people leave behind. The system gives you additional information, that helps you to contextualize where you are and where to go to next.

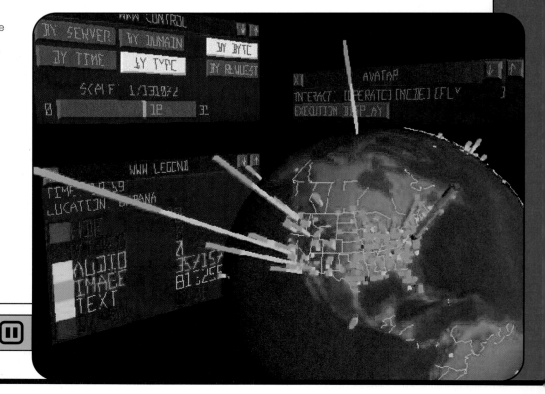

Right
Access to the Internet is largely controlled by Internet Service Providers, organizations offering users a range of services, from the use of simple e-mail to more complex facilities such as video transmission, audio play, image creation and the exchange of computer programs.

VR technology gives greater immersion

Research projects at the University of Virginia, USA, showed that people using VR (Virtual Reality) interfaces, like head-mounted display glasses, were able to complete information search tasks faster than users of traditional desktop interfaces. Immersion, the enhanced sense of 'being there' felt by VR users, allows for better orientation and avoids redundant searching.
@ *virtual reality p158*

NET SOURCES

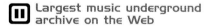

▶ Bodies donated to the Internet for medicine

The US National Library of Medicine is creating a digital atlas of the human anatomy, available through the Internet (www.crd.ge.com/esl/cgsp/projects/vm), to encourage medical researchers to develop new algorithms and to compare their work with others. The project started in 1991 when a murderer, who had received the death sentence, donated his body to science. The cadaver was frozen, then sliced from head to toe, and colour photos of the slices were taken. X-RAY Computed Tomography and Magnetic Resonance Imaging provided more visual data, resulting in an animated 3-D 'flight' through the body which is now available on the Net.

❙❙ Largest music underground archive on the Web

Founded by two students in 1993, the Internet Underground Music Archive is not only the earliest, but also the largest rock music resource on the Web (www.iuma.com). Based on the idea of bypassing record labels by marketing popular music on-line, the steadily expanding archive soon became an important resource for the music industry. Every day, hundreds of thousands of fans, radio station programmers, club promoters and music industry representatives browse the archive, downloading songs, contacting musicians directly, or simply just looking.

❙❙ Reviews of thousands of movies available

The Internet Movie Database (uk.imdb.com) was developed to become the ultimate free information source about movies. From the earliest cinema to the latest releases, the database covers hundreds of thousands of films, providing all you need to know about plot summaries, actors' names, distribution companies, filming locations, technical data, budgets, soundtrack info, special effect references and movie trivia. It also includes many relevant hyperlinks to scores of other useful sites.

▶ Largest library about the surface of the Earth

The Alexandria Digital Library Project (alexandria.sdc.ucsb.edu/) will become the largest library containing material about the

surface of the Earth. When fully operational it will incorporate resources such as graphics, scanned aerial photographs and seismic datasets, as well as reports and publications on the Earth Sciences downloaded from the Internet. The project is being jointly sponsored by the National Science Foundation and the Digital Library Initiative, in collaboration with NASA and the US Department of Defense.

❙❙ New French library offers 100,000 digitized volumes

Over 100,000 volumes have been digitized so that they can be accessed by computer at the Bibliothèque Nationale de France's new home in the Tolbiac Tower complex in Paris. The books, which mainly deal with French history and culture, can be downloaded in seconds, so that several people will be able to read the same book simultaneously. Rare and fragile originals, in the past only accessible to qualified scholars, can now be seen by all once they are digitally converted.

❙❙ Digital Encyclopædia Britannica released

The on-line version of the world's most recognized reference book has been designed to consist of an easily browsable, fully cross-referenced collection of authoritative entries – *Britannica*'s latest article database, *Merriam-Webster's Collegiate Dictionary* (10th Edition), the Britannica Book of the Year, hundreds of articles not found in the printed version of the encyclopaedia, and thousands of links to other useful and interesting World Wide Web sites selected by the *Encyclopædia Britannica*'s editors (www.eb.com/).

❙❙ US Library of Congress goes digital

The Library of Congress (LC) has backed up its vast collection of knowledge on a computer catalogue (lcweb.loc.gov/) that

Above
The Internet has the potential to change the way we communicate permanently. Already, it offers users the chance to send messages and even speak to each other anywhere in the world, and all for the cost of a local telephone call.

contains entries for all books in the English language catalogued since 1968, and for those in most of the other Western languages since 1973. In addition to book information, the system also contains bibliographic data for serials, maps, music, audiovisual materials, official government publications issued since 1976 on public policy subjects, copyright information files, magazine articles, and information on all public bills and resolutions introduced in the House and Senate since the 93rd Congress (1973). There are also a wide variety of enabling facilities for people with disabilities, which include auditory equipment, Braille manuscripts, and large print access to records in the Computer Catalog Center.

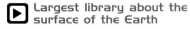 ♻ **Back to the future**

Web Indices invented

The most successful 'handmade' Internet Index to date is Yahoo!™ (www.yahoo.com). It was launched in April 1994 by David Filo and Jerry Yang, then Ph.D. candidates in Electrical Engineering at Stanford University. Tens of thousands of Web pages are made accessible through well-organized categories such as Business, Reference, Society and Culture. Each entry is then filtered by human browsing experts to allow searches to be as focused as possible. Once a subject is located, even more refined searches can be made by typing in keywords or characteristics relating to that subject. The service is so successful that it has been split into regional divisions, such as Yahoo!™ China, Yahoo!™ Japan and Yahoo!™ France, all in the local language. As Yahoo!™ has grown it has expanded into new areas and now offers on-line shopping, programming and even investment, so that by the beginning of 1998 its first quarter revenues stood at over $30 million (£17 million).

Left
Using 'artificial stupidity', 'Ghengis', a robot insect from MIT, USA, detects and chases anything that moves near it. It has pressure-sensitive whiskers and infrared sensors, and, in the future, will carry out on-the-spot machine repairs.

ROBOTS

TELEROBOTS

 Deep sea diving robot to check and maintain oil rigs

A research team at University College London, UK, are testing a hydraulic robot that can search for signs of decay and perform welding on oil rigs. The 2.5-m (8-ft 2½-in) long robot is 'flown' by humans on the surface who watch a virtual model of the robot on a computer screen. The robot has three legs with suction feet to latch onto a surface. @ *the sea p133*

 **Professor plans to control fish with electric shocks**

Prof. Jens Balchen from the Norwegian University of Science and Technology in Trondheim, Norway, is experimenting with controlling fish by attaching remote-controlled rucksacks to them. He hopes to control fish using ultrasound and direct their swimming by administering mild electric shocks to one side of their heads. Prof. Balchen aims to use his creatures to carry cameras and search for leaks in underwater gas and oil pipelines.

 **The Black Falcon robot can perform precision surgery**

Robotic assistance in surgery can enhance the skill of the surgeon by performing jobs with submillimetre precision. In Jan 1998, a research team at the Massachusetts Institute of Technology (MIT) developed a robot called the Black Falcon which is controlled by the surgeon on a television monitor. Attached to a mechanical arm, the Black Falcon reduces movements made by the surgeon from 5 mm to 1 mm, reducing the size of cuts and the loss of blood. MIT hopes that the instrument will be used in heart bypass surgery in which it will pass through the ribs in order to get to the heart, rather than the surgeon having to cut the ribs open.

The bionic cockroaches which could be used as spies

Research teams from the University of Tokyo and the University of Tsukuba in Science City, northeast of Tokyo, Japan,

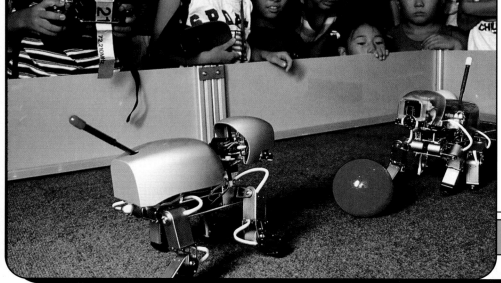

 Left
Sony robots playing football during Robocup '97 in Nagoya, Japan. Each four-legged robot has a camera, touch sensors, speakers and microphones, enabling them to communicate with team-mates.

have created bionic cockroaches whose wings have been replaced with electronic circuitry. The new 'wings' stimulate the cockroaches' nervous systems with minute electrodes, and the insects can already go forwards, or turn to the left or right. Future applications could include flying insect spy cameras, insect search teams sent into buildings destroyed by earthquakes, and bionic locusts, able to lead plagues away from crops. @ *sport p16*

SEMI-AUTONOMOUS

⏸ The robots which can decide which way to walk

Research into robots that perform their jobs unattended has already produced robotic lawnmowers and vacuum cleaners. Japanese company Honda is working with the Agency of Industrial Science and Technology in Japan to create a humanoid robot. The 1.82-m (6-ft) P2 is able to push trolleys, tighten bolts and climb stairs. P2 also uses its artificial intelligence to decide how to circumvent obstacles.

▶ Anthrobot design inspired by Leonardo da Vinci drawings

Mark Rosheim, president of Ross-Hime Designs from Minneapolis, USA, has designed a robot for NASA's Johnson Space Centre, which is studying different prototype cosmorobots that could service the International Space Centre. Inspired by drawings of a robot knight by Leonardo da Vinci, Rosheim's Robotic Surrogate has almost human flexibility leading its maker to call it an 'anthrobot'. @ *space stations p146*

⏸ Roving waiters automate the Yo Sushi restaurant

In Yo Sushi, a Japanese restaurant in London, UK, the menus are colour-coded and meals picked up by customers from a conveyer belt. Robotic trolleys with drinks rove the restaurant – human waiters attend to special requests and the final payment.

▶ Inspection robot that can crawl like a worm

Denso, a leading Japanese car parts manufacturer, has created a prototype inspection robot which, by expanding and contracting, can crawl like a worm through very small pipes. Eventually, the inspection robot will look for cracks in chemical and power plants.

⏩ Microscopic robots could perform surgery

Japanese company Olympus Optical Co. is developing catheters – or tiny tubes – and endoscopes which will one day snake through blood vessels and microscopic body cavities. Equipped with cameras and micro-scissors, they could be used in surgery without the doctor having to cut open the patient. @ *nanotechnology p154*

ROBOTIC SYSTEMS

▶ The robot nurses which can closely monitor patients

Scientists at the University of Tokyo are building a prototype 'nursing' room. Pressure sensors in the bed's mattress and a floor that relays information to a central computer tell a human nurse or carer whether a patient has fallen, or has not been moving enough in bed and risks getting bedsores. There are also cameras which can monitor the patient's breathing and raise the alert if necessary. The scientists are also working on a range of robots, that include a 'pet' robot, which can retrieve objects that the patient points to.

▶ The automated office can watch your every move

MIT's Media Lab is developing a smart room in which the microphones and cameras connected to computers are learning to recognise the movements and emotions of people who work in the room. The room has a video receptionist, that can suggest a cup of coffee if it notices you yawning. For entertainment, there is also Silas, a virtual dog, who sits and rolls over, or fetches a ball on command.

⏩ Robot football teams compete for the Robocup

The next step in creating robots that think for themselves lies in the study of insects such as bees and ants – creatures with little intelligence, but which can work together to perform complex tasks. Some researchers are investigating 'nerd herds', groups of robots working together to perform tasks such as detecting and destroying landmines. The ultimate test for nerd herds is Robocup, a robotic football contest, held for the first time in 1997 at an artificial intelligence conference in Nagoya, Japan. Forty teams from universities around the world brought their five-member teams to compete in various leagues, from the Small Robot League, which play on table-tennis size fields, to the Expert League. There are plans to include a humanoid league in the near future. @ *artificial life p152*

⏩ Robots of the future could rebuild themselves

Joe Michael of Robodyne Cybernetics in London, UK, envisions robots of the future being able to build themselves and change shape in order to perform different duties. Michael also sees future machines in space, where the adaptable robots could negotiate

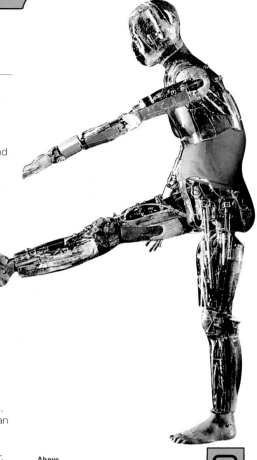

Above
'Manny', a sweating, breathing mannequin, is used by the US Department of Energy's research labs to test human reactions to space and fire-fighting clothing.

difficult terrain and help build space stations, and in the military too, where they could form the ultimate fighting unit.

♻ Back to the future

Factory of the Future

In 1986, at General Motors' 'Factories of the Future', in Michigan, USA, robots started to smash bodywork, seal windscreens into the wrong places and paint each other instead of the cars. This was due to software problems.

Rebel Robots

In 1987, the company Virgin installed a Compact Disc pressing plant in its Megastore in Oxford Street, London, UK, complete with monoline – a sealed room in which robots would assist in the production process. But in 1989, Virgin sold the line after human technicians had spent two years tending to independent-minded robots who preferred to throw away half-finished CDs.

Titanic found

A remotely operated vehicle – or ROV – called Argo helped Dr Robert Ballard and his US-French team to locate and explore the *Titanic* shipwreck in Sept 1985.

Left
Traders on the Australian Stock Exchange in Melbourne monitoring the shares indexes. The rise of new technology makes trading faster than ever.

MONEY

ELECTRONIC CASH

Computer code replaces money in a cashless society

David Chaum, the founder of Amsterdam-based DigiCash, is largely credited with inventing an electronic cash or e-cash system which transmits money as computer code over the Internet. Chaum's system ensures the safety of transactions through an encryption code he calls 'blind signatures', which authenticates payments without revealing the identity of the payer. This both protects the customers from cyber-thieves and acts as protection for the individual's civil liberties. E-cash is always pre-paid to banks which issue e-cash currency. Already there are a few banks in Europe, the USA and the Asia-Pacific region which offer e-cash accounts. Another leading e-cash handling company is the USA-based CyberCash. @ *digital crime p64*

Multi-purpose smart cards store ID as well as credit

It is estimated that by 2000 there will be one billion smart phone cards in use worldwide. New smart cards being developed by companies, such as the US-based Motorola Semiconductor and French computer firm Bull, will contain central processing units, which act as the brains of conventional computers, with short and long-term memory cells. Once the networks of smart card readers are set up, hybrid smart cards, which perform many different functions, will be used in banks, shops,

cellular and public telephones and to pay taxes. They could also store drivers' licences, health records and even passport information. Many smart card trials are being conducted, for example, in Swindon, Northampton and Dunfermline, UK. One trial in Guelph, Canada, even included parking meters in the smart card scheme.

Student smart cards used in the library and the canteen

Aston University, in Birmingham, UK, has been turned into a cash-free zone because students are now issued with smart cards which they use for student ID, in the library and for security checks. The cards can also be used to buy lunch at campus eateries and books from the university book shop. When the balance gets low, it can be replenished by inserting the smart card into a machine which will transfer money from an ordinary bank account.

New York tests the e-cash combined smart card

US banks Citibank and Chase Manhattan, together with credit card companies Visa and Mastercard, are testing a smart card scheme in New York City, USA. Around 50,000 cards with e-cash capabilities will be issued, and about 500 retail outlets and businesses in the city will accept them. The

cards also retain their magnetic strips for conventional banking requirements.

Fingerprints could be used instead of pin numbers

As smart cards begin to take on more functions, it is important that they are protected by identity systems. It is likely that the personal pin number system used for bank cards and cash point machines will be replaced by a more sophisticated system. First National Bank, in South Africa, is already using fingerprint recognition in

Right
Laili Begum, 27, in Patria, Bangladesh, calling to Dhaka, March 1997. Mohammad Yunus, who founded the Grameen Bank, now has a six year plan to connect the country by putting at least one cellular phone in all of the country's 65,000 villages.

paypoint systems, which are specialized systems usually housed within the bank and used for more complex banking functions. The bank is also investigating the introduction of more sophisticated systems, such as iris recognition, for their cashpoint machines in the streets. @ *policing p62*

EXPERT SYSTEMS

▶ The computer program that predicts the stock market

Pension fund specialists, Pareto Partners of London, UK, is in partnership with Los Angeles-based Hughes Electronics – a research contractor to the US military – to develop an expert artificial intelligence program which has specialist knowledge on how to play the stock market. The Hughes system, called Modular Knowledge Acquisition Toolkit (M-KAT), uses artificial intelligence modelled on the thinking of Pareto's bond market expert, Christine Downton. The researchers don't always understand how M-KAT arrives at its decisions as to which bonds are overvalued or undervalued, but every month it extracts about 800 items of information pertaining to the world economy which it thinks are relevant to the bonds markets. M-KAT then makes suggestions of what to buy and sell, which Downton can choose to take as advice or ignore.

❚❚ Electronic neural networking can aid the fiscal analyst

State Street Global Advisors, the third largest investment management firm in the USA, bought the international Florida-based company, Advanced Investment Technology (AIT), designers of electronic analyst systems, in 1997. AIT has a system which uses neural networking. Every week the system searches through about 24 million items of information and studies 3,000 stocks in order to conclude which stocks will rise or fall. The resulting information can then be used by dealers to assist them in making decisions. @ *artificial life p152*

ALTERNATIVE MONEY SYSTEMS

❚❚ Community spends HOURS instead of dollars

The town of Ithaca, New York State, USA, operates on its own currency system, the HOUR, instead of the US dollar. Started in 1991, the scheme uses the HOUR which is equal to $10, the average pay per hour for work in the county. Residents trade HOURS of work with each other so, for instance, a plumber might earn 5 HOURS for completing a job and go to a hairdresser and spend 1 HOUR on a haircut. That night the hairdresser might buy supper at a restaurant for 3 HOURS. Attracted by the community spirit and promotion of local business, more than 1,400 businesses and individuals are participating in the scheme.

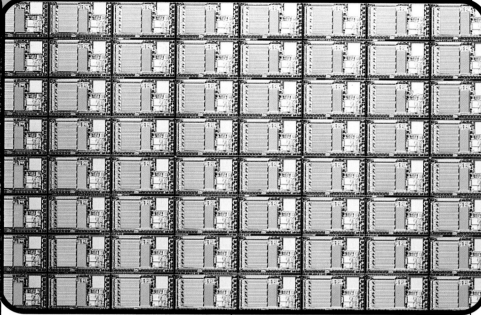

▶ Exchanging virtual skills across the Internet

A scheme whereby people trade virtual skills has been set up on the Internet by the Global Village Bank (GVB). For example, if someone is skilled in animation but has no knowledge of computer languages such as Java, they could advertise their animation skills in return for Java writing skills. The GVBs Nellapages uses a virtual currency, the Nella, to set a standard for exchange of work. It is not necessary to trade directly, as Nellas can be earned and exchanged for another product or service. GVB also has swap shop sites like Exchange and Recycler.com. @ *citizens' networks p42*

❚❚ Local support found in township credit system

Community saving schemes, called stokvels, popular in the townships of South Africa, are usually groups of women who pool a part of their monthly salary. Every month one member will receive the total amount pooled; this can be used to start a small business or for home improvements. The group can also act as a support network. For instance, if an unexpected death occurs in the family, that group member might jump the queue for the pooled cash in order to pay for the funeral. Some of the most successful stokvels use the money to hire a venue, a band, and purchase refreshments for a fundraising party, and then share the profits afterwards.

❚❚ Bangladesh microloans help the poorest villagers

In 1976, Bangladeshi economics Prof. Muhammad Yunus started a microloan system for Bangladeshi villagers which has grown into Grameen Bank, an institution which today has 2.2 million borrowers, 94%

Above
A macrophotograph of integrated circuits used in smart cards. The plastic cards' memory chips can be read and altered and can store personal medical data, providing a very portable and comprehensive medical history.

of whom are women. The bank makes small loans which are usually granted to groups of five women who use it to start small businesses. The loans are repaid with interest, but a written clause also allows clients to save money too, extending the role of the bank to a credit union. The loans have already helped one third of borrowers out of poverty, and the bank boasts a repayment rate of 98%.

♻ Back to the future

Automatic cashier

In Denver, in 1977, a US credit card processor introduced the first Automatic Teller Machine.

Folding plastic

In 1988, Australia successfully launched the first crossover currency, in the form of plastic folding money, a A$10 dollar bill, introduced to commemorate the Australian centenary.

Olympic cards

During the 1996 Olympic Games in Atlanta, USA, about one million stored-value cards were issued for use in Olympic venues. Stored value cards are really smart cards which register a money balance to which the card holder can add.

Telephone cards

In 1980s, France introduced telephone cards, the first 'smart cards', which were prepaid and disposed of after the balance had run out. Now there are over 20 million smart cards in use in France, including smart cards for kidney patients which store dialysis records.

The World Wide Web – WWW – doubles in size every six months

MEDIA

• **Interactive TVs will have built-in modems and ethernet connections**. The computer and the TV will become one and the same, resulting in a new medium, offering unlimited programmes and services. Touch-screen technology and voice-activated software should eliminate the need for the keyboard as we talk to and touch our boxes.

• **The actual shape of the TV set will change**. No longer rectangular boxes, TVs will come in all shapes and sizes, varying from wide-screen versions to ones that can be seen in 360°. The TV will no longer simply be known as the tube or the box, but as Web TV, or Digital TV, or Interactive TV. Radio, too, will become digital and be linked to the Internet and interactive services.

• **Advertising will appear everywhere**. Traditionally, advertising has been confined to the press, posters, television and cinema, but Ambient advertising will be found on bus tickets, inside golf holes and in other unexpected places. New technologies will allow creative directors the freedom to experiment with ads that rely on taste, smell and touch for their effectiveness. Already, aromatic bus tickets have been used effectively to promote brands of soap powder. Communication will be interactive, involving the customer directly. Posters will literally talk to us.

• **The Internet 2 will take over from the Internet**. It will be a high-speed network used by scientists and academics to transfer and observe scientific tests and experiments. Out of the Internet and Internet 2 new cultures will grow with new types of citizens, or Netizens, and their own code of behaviour, Netiquette. Whole communities will spring up, linked only by telephone lines and computer screens. And, after micronations, the next step will be Digital beings.

NEW MEDIA

TV AND RADIO

ADVERTISING

NET CULTURE

CITIZENS' NETWORKS

TECHNO-BABBLE

CAJ
Computer-Assisted-Journalism, a new breed of reporting that depends on the Internet and news wires for stories.

CINEMADS
A series of commercials that present an unfolding minidrama between its characters. The Gold Blend adverts are an example.

DUAL CHANNELER
One who gleams all their knowledge by flipping between MTV and CNN television stations.

GREY LITERATURE
Brochures, reports, research results, pamphlets, product data and other material that is produced by institutions who are not primarily publishers.

HAMMOCKING
Placing a new television programme between two popular established ones.

HYBRID CD
A CD-ROM which contains useful information which can be updated using hotlinks from a Website.

INTERMERCIAL
An interactive commercial, displayed between website pages.

IRRITAINMENT
Annoying media events that are compulsive viewing.

OUTERNET
Traditional media not on the Internet, such as TV and the press.

1931	Ikonophone – a two-way telephone with two-way television transmission – is invented
2005	Digital TV becomes the standard for the Western World

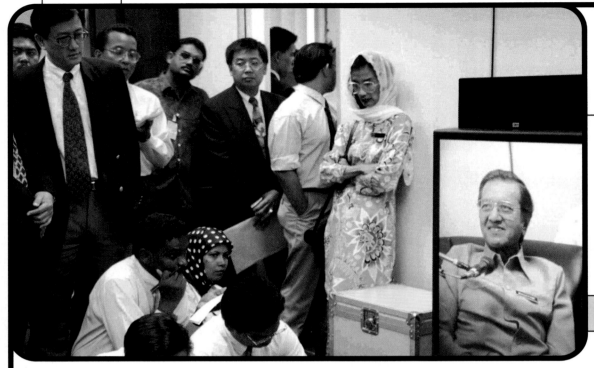

NEW MEDIA

COMMUNICATIONS

▶ New generation mobiles offer high information rate

The third generation of mobile telephony has now entered a trial phase and will be launched in 2001 in Japan, with advanced European and Asian operators following soon after. It offers wide area coverage with data rates of up to 384 kbps, rising to 2 mbps at a local level. This is a unique feature of third generation mobile phones and will be one of the fundamental technological components of the information society. Data rates above 100 kbps open up a new set of applications for business and personal use, including video-conferencing, using voice browsing to search for information and other highly advanced communication methods between man and machines.
@ *communication p24*

⏸ Mini communication base gets your life into shape

The Communicator fits in your pocket and contains all you need to communicate – a phone, a fax, e-mail, the World Wide Web, a calendar and a notepad, and it has been on the market in some countries since 1996. It is compliant to the global GSM standard for mobile telephones and can be used in almost every corner of the world to send and receive e-mail, store addresses, and even send pictures by fax.

⏸ Tying up global communications with Iridium

Iridium LLC has developed a global wireless communications network that combines the worldwide reach of 66 low-Earth-orbit satellites with land-based wireless systems to enable subscribers virtually anywhere in the world to communicate via pagers or telephones.

⏸ The dream of a virtual office comes true

'Unified Messaging' makes global telecommunication cheaper and more efficient. For a small sum of money you can rent a phone number in a city of your

choice. All incoming faxes and voice messages will be automatically transformed into attachments and forwarded to your e-mail address. Now you can get your mail at home and never miss a call wherever you might be. E-mail to fax gateways also works the other way round, so that the vision of a 'virtual office' on a tropical beach or buried deep in green countryside can become reality relatively cheaply.

NEWS AND ENTERTAINMENT

▶ Digital video transmissions open new horizons

New standards in digital video transmissions are opening up more digital possibilities. In 1998, a number of digital television services were launched worldwide. Compressing existing bandwidth allows it to be used much more efficiently, and enables hundreds of digital audio and video channels to be received via satellite, cable, and terrestrial antennae. @ *TV and radio p36*

▶ Digital audio broadcast is the future for radio

DAB provides multiplexes, or 'packages', of up to six stereo services at a time in digital format. Unlike the older car radio systems, it delivers a consistently high-quality reception on the move. Stations can transmit data along with the audio signal, so listeners could listen to continuous traffic, or alternatively be told which song is playing or hear tour dates or promotional information.

▶ Tomorrow's televisions will be network computers

'Set-Top Box' is a generic term for the devices that will be necessary to receive digital television signals. The 'Box' will combine the interactive features of a television tuner to choose between different channels, with a network computer that lets you browse text menus via a remote control and even establish a return channel. It also unscrambles pay-TV films and simplifies individually customized payment procedures.

⏸ Data-casting and surfing the Internet via satellite

Various European satellite operators including Astra, Eutelsat, and Hispasat have implemented data broadcasting via satellite. With more than 16 million PCs bought in Europe in 1996, and more than 30 million households with direct access to satellite transmissions, there is already wide acceptance of the technologies involved. A typical CD-ROM has potential bit rates of more than 30 mbps per transponder, which means it could be transmitted to a whole continent in less than three minutes.

⏸ Italian broadcaster first with a digital newsroom

RAI, the Italian national radio and television broadcast network, is one of the first major

broadcasters to implement a digital media catalogue within its audiovisual library. Throughout the television production cycle, the catalogue system analyzes, captures and synchronizes relevant information about the many audio and video elements that make up television programmes. Editors can then search television and radio programmes quickly and easily, using criteria such as type, title, participant, keyword or date, and can instantly re-use audiovisual material. A customized graphic interface and automated documentation system provides rapid access to a complete broadcast publishing system.

⏸ Direct real-time news service over the Internet

News agencies such as the Associated Press (AP), which is the world's oldest and largest newsgathering organization, now deliver real-time news services via the Internet to subscribing magazines, newspapers, radio and television stations. AP employs nearly 3,500 journalists and technical staff worldwide, and loads its database with more than 1,000 stories and 1,000 photographs every day. The web site's editorial staff collate the stories, images and other multimedia elements into 'packages' that are available for downloading by subscribers and are updated automatically as new content is loaded into the database.

⏸ Real-time financial and market information

Data Broadcasting Corporation (DBC) provides real-time financial and market information specially tailored to the individual investor. The company deploys

Above
3-D worlds can be used for interactive learning, and 3-D chat worlds enable people to communicate for entertainment, business or educational purposes. London-based Okupi already designs 3-D worlds for a wide range of situations.

a sophisticated network to deliver timely market intelligence, stock quotes and informative editorial matter to more than 37,000 subscribers throughout the US. The guiding premise behind the service is that "Real time is real money" for equities and options traders, brokers and other professionals. The company's nerve centre is a sophisticated network that delivers streams of real-time data to subscribers over FM wideband, the Internet and direct broadcast satellite as well as the cable TV vertical blanking interval (VBI).

♻ Back to the future

Vocal Telegraphy

In 500 BC, King Darius I of Persia used hilltops to shout his orders from. He also enlisted smoke signals, horns, trumpets, drums and reflecting mirrors in his efforts to communicate across large distances.

Jumbotron

In 1985, the largest high-definition television was unveiled. Called the 'Jumbotron', it was 40 m (131 ft) wide and 25 m (82 ft) high. It was demonstrated at Expo '85 in Japan.

Ikonophone

The 'Ikonophone' is a two-way telephone with two-way television transmission. It was invented in 1931, but to this day no company has ever managed to successfully mass market the video-phone.

1977	The first miniature TV is launched with a 5 cm screen
2000	Interactive TV is launched on a pay-per-view basis

Left
When digital television is introduced there will be a massive increase in the number of TV channels on offer. Some new channels will cater for niche and specialized markets, allowing for the development of off-beat programmes that should make currently controversial TV shows like *South Park* look tame.

TV AND RADIO

TV HARDWARE

▶ Wide-screen TV is naturally pleasing to the eye

Wide-screen television, based on the proportions of the cinema screen, could be the format of the future. Wide-screen technology is being developed with high-definition television (HDTV) and digital transmission in mind because it produces high-quality sound and pictures. Instead of the conventional TV width-to-height ratio of 4/3, wide-screen TVs have a ratio of 16/9, which is more pleasing to watch as it enhances the eye's natural preference to scan across horizontal spaces.

▶ LEP technology will result in thinner screens

Technology developed at the Cavendish Laboratory in Cambridge, UK, is being used to enhance the colour from TVs, resulting in thinner, lighter screens. Cambridge Display Technology has joined forces with Japan's Seiko-Epson Corporation to devise a new system which uses Light Emitting Plastic (LEP) technology, rather than the traditional bulky cathode ray tubes used in conventional TVs. Using light-emitting polymers – glowing plastic – the team has managed to produce a prototype black-and-white screen which is just 50 mm² (2 in²) and 2 mm (0.078 in) thick.

▶ 360° television is flat any way you want to look at it

California-based ESP Electronics has developed a 360° television which viewers see as a flat image wherever they sit. The television works by spinning the image around a drum at a speed which can be frozen by the human eye. It can display all television formats and can even be used as a computer monitor. Only 1,000 limited-edition sets have been produced, set in casing designed by Frank Gehry, the architect of the new Guggenheim Museum in Bilbao, Spain.

▶ Hands-free video recorders by 2002

According to Richard Ames of Philips, voice-controlled video recorders could be on the market within four years. Already video recorders are becoming more user-friendly. Manufacturers are developing machines which emit a warning if you forget to insert a tape and which switch to long-play mode if the tape is about to run out before the end of a programme. Thomson is marketing Commercial Advance VCRs, which purposely skip commercial breaks.

Right
While TV is usually seen as a conversation killer, ESP Electronics' 360° television is a sure-fire conversation piece. Viewers can sit around it and see and talk to each other as they watch TV – perhaps discussing its £24,000 price tag.

TV SYSTEMS

⏸ MED-TV broadcasting to the Kurdish people

MED-TV is the world's first and only Kurdish television station, delivering 18 hours of broadcasting to a potential audience of 30 million people daily. Using bases in

Europe and a satellite over Africa, MED-TV focuses on the plight of the stateless Kurds scattered across Iraq, Iran, Syria and particularly Turkey, where the government is waging a war against the Turkish Kurd organisation, PPK. @ *communication p24*

▶ Telemedicine and housecalls of the future

In a trial project in Kansas, USA, a few health clinics are using cable television 'telemedicine' consultations between elderly patients confined to their homes and nurses at the clinic. A two-minute bleep reminds the patient that the 'house-call' is about to proceed and a nurse appears on the screen. The nurse instructs the patient how to use diagnostic equipment and waits for the results. A small camera fitted to the patient's TV lets the nurse check readings. In Singapore, the government aims to connect at least 90% of homes by high-speed fibre-optic lines by 2005.

❚❚ CamNet offers a truly diverse news service

CamNet is the latest offering from a group which has its roots in a 1960s radical video group called Videofreex. Broadcast from Los Angeles, USA, it can be picked up on cable. CamNet is an offbeat news show, comprising amateur footage from around the world and covering subjects such as the everyday lives of New York's squatters.

▶ Digital TV is just waiting in the wings

Digital television is set to become a reality as satellite and terrestrial TV companies around the world race to provide attractive services. Digital systems transmit images as compressible computer code which allows space for more channels and wide-screen pictures. Digital TV will reach the public via land lines, satellite, or cable services which use high-speed fibre-optic cables.

❚❚ Web TV puts the Internet on your television

In a step towards digital television, WebTV Networks, acquired by Bill Gates's Microsoft Corporation in 1997, is the first on-line service to offer customers Internet access via conventional television sets. The low-cost and user-friendly system, housed in a set-top box, allows users to access entertainment and information on the Internet without a personal computer.

▶ Interactive TV is getting closer and closer

The television of the very near future will enable viewers to shop, do their banking, send e-mail, surf the Net and choose from hundreds of TV channels all at the click of a remote control. Digital television will hasten the arrival of interactive TV, including a pay-per-view system – paying for individual programmes as you watch them. Interactive TV will also mean you can take part in quiz shows from home, or choose which replays and camera angles you want to see while watching a football game.

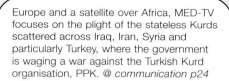

RADIO

▶ Bitcasting takes radio onto the Web

Bitcasters are radio stations which broadcast on the World Wide Web. They are fast becoming part of popular culture and are an effective way for small stations and new bands to gain wider recognition as the Internet reaches a global audience. Although they are infringing many laws, most bitcasters feel that copyright issues need to be redefined. A Massachusetts Institute of Technology web site lists over 500 bitcasters worldwide, such as the UK underground music station InterFACE, and AIIR.COM, a US-based station which broadcasts music, talk shows and news aimed at Indian emigrants worldwide. @ *music p46*

▶ Digital radio will find you wherever you are

Scientists are predicting that the advent of digital radio will revolutionize the radio industry by 2010. Digital radio transmits sound as computer code, which is of CD quality and which cuts out the interference common on FM and AM radio. Canada leads the field in research into digital radio, and, as early as 1992, proposed that a new bandwidth, the L-Band, be used for digital broadcasting. This was accepted by the World Administrative Radio Conference in Feb 1992. Besides perfect reception, digital radio also offers services such as text information on screens fitted to the new radio receivers which will display song lyrics and album names, weather details and stock market prices.

Above
The Internet has benefited pirate radio stations such as InterFACE, which not only transmits music across the Net but allows users to talk to each other, choose the music they want to hear and find information on upcoming gigs and club nights.

❚❚ Whale FM's song reverberates 24 hours a day

Whale FM provides round-the-clock access to whale sounds. The station was set up by John Ford, a zoologist at the Vancouver Aquarium, Canada, and is intended for scientists who are studying killer whales, although all are welcome to listen in.

♻ Back to the future

Highest viewing figures

In 1980, an episode of *Dallas*, an American soap opera about Texan oil tycoons, had 80 million viewers watching to find out who had shot JR Ewing – the highest viewing figure yet for any television broadcast.

Nixon makes TV a tool

Senator Richard Nixon was the first politician to use television as a political tool. In Sept 1952, Nixon refuted charges of corruption live on television, and it worked: later that year Nixon was elected vice-president.

No more free telly

In 1957, GPO detector vans hit the streets for the first time, making it difficult for people to dodge paying their TV licence fee.

TVs are getting cheaper

The first BBC TV broadcast went out in 1936. TV sets were then being sold for £110.

1957	First British product-placement TV programme launched
2015	Advertising messages are superimposed onto sporting events visible only to TV viewers

ADVERTISING

NEW MEDIA

'Ambient' advertising takes on the unexpected

In 1996, the British advertising industry devised numerous alternative media to the traditional vehicles of television, newspapers, magazines, radio and posters. Dubbed 'ambient media', an umbrella term coined for what is a diverse collection of small media, these ranged from the bottom of golf-holes, to lids on take-away meals, urinal walls, bibs on cows, tops of buses, shopping trolleys and holsters on petrol pump handles. Ambient media also embraced such new fringe media as destination boards at railway stations, beer mats in pubs, wheel hub-caps, headlights on buses and shop floors.

How to put your products into orbit

A UK advertising consultancy called the Mighty Big Idea Company created a method of projecting ads onto the Moon in 1997. It involved using a vast, reflective sheet of material that harnessed light from the Sun and bounced it onto the Moon. NASA confirmed that the technology would be extremely expensive but nevertheless feasible, particularly for projecting simple visual images such as the Nike tick or the McDonald's golden arches logo. However, the company was swamped by a deluge of calls from members of the public horrified at the idea of using the Moon as a billboard and, as yet, no advertiser has made use of the technology.

▶ Multinationals jump on the space wagon

The cash-strapped Russian Space Agency, which receives only 50% of its funds from the national budget, began to sell advertising for its space missions and related operations in 1996, in a bid to generate extra revenue. A Japanese journalist became the first human billboard in space when he was sent up to Mir in 1990. He was making a film for Japanese television about the Russian space programme, and his spacesuit and related space paraphernalia all bore clear Sony branding. The rocket itself also carried the Sony logo on its side.

▶ Advertisers step into the virtual market

In 1990, the UK beat the US in introducing advertising messages into computer games. At the beginning, advertisers were restricted to buying sites around perimeter fences within computerized football games, but the medium quickly became more sophisticated, and as a result it will soon be possible to get Lara Croft, the shapely star of the game Tomb Raider, to wear a certain brand of sunglasses or trainers. Already, advertisers are creating their own branded games, such as the Adidas Power Soccer game in which the computerized footballers sport Adidas Predator boots.

⏸ Ancient chalk carving tradition revived

Scottish Courage, the brewers, devised a massive advertising site for Becks in the UK which involved carving a huge image of a Becks bottle out of the side of a chalk cliff between Manchester and London. The idea was borrowed from the ancient tradition of carving horses and fertility symbols in chalk hillsides, such as the Giant at Cerne Abbas in Dorset and the White Horse in Wiltshire.

⏸ Jaguar takes its publicity into the air

The Irish airline Ryanair created a huge mobile advertising medium out of its planes in May 1997 when the car manufacturer Jaguar bought the rights to one of its craft. Although Southwest Airlines in the US had earlier carried a logo for the US cartoon *The Simpsons*, this was the first time a European plane had been used for advertising.

NEW TECHNOLOGIES

⏸ Freshly-scented bus tickets lure consumers

In 1997, Lever Brothers used the power of smell to promote its UK washing powder brand, Radion, by creating the first scented bus ticket. The soap giant wanted to promote Radion's new 'sunfresh' fragrance, and in conjunction with Image Promotions, a bus ticket manufacturer, it devised a way of scenting 50 million tickets nationwide with the fragrance. The base oil of the

scent was micro-encapsulated onto each scratch-and-sniff ticket so that the smell could be released on contact.

⏸ Missile technology used for selective commercials

Four companies in France, Israel and the US have developed the technology to superimpose advertising messages onto TV transmissions of live sporting events. The centre circle or the perimeter hoardings of football matches, for example, can bear images which only TV viewers can see and people attending the match are not aware of. This involves remodifying the TV signal, allowing different pictures to be inserted over the background via the TV feed and locked into position permanently. The process evolved from a combination of defence technology used for guided missiles and computer software used for TV weather reports.

⏸ Interactive posters keep eyes and ears entertained

Waterloo Station in London, UK, launched a revolutionary interactive poster site in 1997 to publicize Channel 4, the UK's fourth terrestrial TV station. Measuring 6 m x 3 m (20 ft x 10 ft), it consisted of four TV screens on the station forecourt, each displaying different images – one running trailers for that evening's TV viewing, another with trailers for future programmes, a third carrying advertising and the fourth an interactive game.

⏸ Condensed 'blipverts' keep viewers tuned in

In 1994, the British advertising agency Howell Henry devised a blipvert commercial for the Mazda 323, a sporty new hatchback.

Above
Commuters at Waterloo Station, London, UK, were presented with a bank of interactive TV screens by Channel 4. They could play a game via their mobile phones, allowing sound as well as vision to be incorporated on the advertising site.

The idea was that such a special car deserved 'special' advertising, and a 40-second TV commercial was made incorporating three one-second blipverts in which a full page of information about the car was blipped on screen. To read the text, viewers had to video the ad and freeze-frame it on playback. Screening times for the commercial were listed in TV listings publications so viewers could set their videos, and ratings for the surrounding programmes soared as thousands tuned in.

♻ Back to the future

Breakfast TV

The British population were reluctant to accept advertising with their cornflakes, and commercial breakfast television was a slow-starter.

Commercial radio

Convinced there was no real consumer demand, UK media pundits gave local commercial radio the thumbs-down in the early 1970s. However, by 1998, there were 195 local radio stations in operation and commercial radio generated £354 million.

Ad mags

In 1957, one of Britain's first advertiser-funded programmes was made. Called 'Jim's Inn' it incorporated heavy product placement and was hailed as the new form of programming for commercial TV. However, such 'advertising magazines' never had time to take off because they were banned in 1963 when new rulings governing product placement were introduced.

1930s	German playwright Bertolt Brecht predicts that every household will not only be a receiver, but also a transmitter for radio communications
1998	Musicians are able to digitally interact with music, enabling them to jam on-line

NET CULTURE

THE ON-LINE WORLD

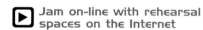 **Jam on-line with rehearsal spaces on the Internet**

On the Internet, geographically dispersed musicians can connect themselves and have a multi-user jam session together. Software programs by companies like RES Rocket Surfers (www.resrocket.com), or Sseyo (http://www.sseyo.com), support live jamming and composing on the Net. They create virtual rehearsal spaces where every participant can hear what everyone else is doing and contribute sounds of his own. What is now creative fun for the minority of users could soon, with improved bandwidths and file transmission rates, become a more common practice which might result in musical innovation as well. @ *music p46*

Performance on-line provides new expression for artists

Artists using the Internet are often taking the technology to its limits. Net art concentrates on group processes and performance-based events rather than the making of fixed objects for gallery spaces. One example is the Refresh Project, where artists from London, Riga, Moscow, Ljubljana and Berlin programmed their sites to hijack the users and take them on an uninterrupted default 'slide show' from one web site to the next in a long loop over pan-European virtual art territories.

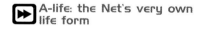 **A-life: the Net's very own life form**

What are computer scientists and Ph.D candidates in mathematics and biology

doing in their spare time? They are using programming methods like genetic algorithms in order to rear artificial life forms on the Net. These pieces of machine code can replicate themselves and mutate, making it possible for scientists to simulate digital life forms and study evolutionary processes under a virtual magnifying glass. One of the most ambitious projects of this kind is Tierra (www.hip.atr.co.jp/~ray/tierra/tierra.html) by Tom Ray. It will use more than 400 Internet hosts to study how these colonies of digital beings will behave when the shortening of resources puts migrative pressure on them.

▶ Millions of Netizens explore Mars live

The *Pathfinder* expedition in summer 1997 was a defining moment for the Net, when millions of Netizens watched live images of Mars. The images were transmitted to a web site (mpfwww.jpl.nasa.gov/default1.html) from cameras attached to a mobile vehicle exploring the planet's surface. A similar telerobotic vehicle is exploring the Andes (www.ri.cmu.edu/atacama-trek/). With NASA and other space agencies keen on fostering public support for their projects we can be sure of seeing further spectacular live image feeds from space expeditions or permanent stations like the Hubble Space Telescope.

❚❚ Earth Watch provides 3-D weather forecasts

With the help of video, the Earth Watch web site (www.earthwatch.com) creates a 3-D representation of the weather. The satellite and radar images are mostly of the US and are updated regularly with worldwide forecasts. Visitors can view cold and warm fronts, high and low pressure zones, soar through storms or zoom in and out of hurricanes. There is also a text explanation of weather patterns.

❚❚ Throw a digital message in a bottle into the Internet ocean

Yoshihito Nagai has created a piece of software which can be downloaded from the Net and used to create the digital version of a message in a bottle. Nagai's software enables users to create a message with graphics and then toss it into the ocean of the Internet. When they are downloaded, the Bottle Mail messages are washed up on the computer desktop to the sound of incoming waves.

NET VALUES

❚❚ Netiquette ensures good manners on-line

When the Internet opened to the public and millions of users surged into cyberspace, a basic set of rules for on-line behaviour evolved. Named after Virginia Shea's book *Netiquette* (derived from 'network etiquette'), anybody new to cyberculture is urged to learn Netiquette (www.in.on.ca/tutorial/netiquette.html) before taking part in chat groups on the Internet. Rules of Netiquette

include not spamming or starting flame wars, sharing knowledge and not wasting network bandwidth through unsophisticated web programming.

❚❚ gURL gets teenage girls on-line

gURL (www.gURL.com) is the largest on-line community of teenage girls. The website was started at the Interactive Telecommunications Program at New York University, USA, combining light-hearted exploration of Internet technologies with a virtual meeting and advice forum for teenage problems. The site offers free e-mail, chat worlds, interactive fashion and make-up rooms, animated cartoons and essays about favourite pets, first pimples and safe sex advice.

▶ Copyleft – Free Software for the masses

Network philosophy emphasizes the idea of free software and collaborative software development outside the commercial arena. Since the 1980s, programmers of the Free Software Foundation have released free 'copyleft' (a play on 'copyright') tools which are available for downloading on the Internet. Each one can download the kernel of the software, implement changes and improvements and play it back to a public site. Another impressive example of sharing on the Net is LINUX, a new operating system for computers, free of heavy licence charges.

❚❚ Information temple for the Web's lost information

Buddhist monk Shokyu Ishiko has set up a virtual temple for lost information on the

Above
gURL is a website devoted entirely to teenage girls and their interests, problems and worries, providing them with all the on-line advice and information they could require.

Web. Chief priest of the Daioh Temple in Kyoto, Japan, Ishiko's web site stores outdated software, business projects or proposals that have failed and files earmarked for 'trash' on computers. The site is dedicated to Manjusri, the Buddhist incarnation of wisdom. On 24 Oct 1997, Ishiko performed the first ever memorial service for lost information at his real temple in Kyoto.

♻ Back to the future

Radio Theory

In the 1930s, German playwright Bertolt Brecht foresaw the many-to-many communications model and the abolition of centralized broadcasting stations. In his *Radio Theory,* he speculated that every household could be not only a receiver but also a transmitter for AM and FM radio communications, making the world a more egalitarian and democratic place.

The Internet

The concept of an 'information superhighway' was born in 1957 when the US Department of Defense formed the Advanced Research Projects Agency (ARPA) in order to improve its technology. In 1969, the agency came up with a project to develop the world's first decentralized computer network, to be known as ARPAnet. It was essentially a military research project, aimed at enabling the network to re-route if the mainframe computer were to be bombed and the system go down.

| 1970s | Proposals were put forward for electronic voting systems that would allow citizens to vote on each single issue |
| 2100 | New micronations on the Net take the place of existing territorial nations |

CITIZENS' NETWORKS

SHAREWARE

Stop Thief! Sleuths solve crimes on-line

Organised by British Telecom (BT), Stop Thief! is an on-line detective game which was first run in the UK during summer 1998. Teams of school children and parents used the web site and the Internet in the race to solve a burglary which took place in the late 19th century at Charlecote Manor in Warwickshire, UK. On-line clues included detailed maps and original police statements.

Starbright World reaches hospitals across the USA

Starbright World (www.starbright.org/) is a virtual reality playspace on a high-speed network that links seriously ill children from their hospital beds across the USA. An 18-month trial linking seven hospitals showed that a virtual playground helps children feel less isolated in hospital conditions. Young patients can go on-line

and meet their peers either as cartoon-like avatars or via cameras connected to their computer terminal. The system seems to lessen pain and improve self-esteem, and will link an additional 100 hospitals by the end of 1998, offering expanded activities.

Micronations are model states in virtual territories

Cyberspace is seen by many as a new territory where traditional definitions of 'nations' do not apply. So-called

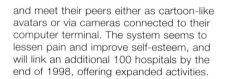

American Civil Liberties Union
Freedom Network

Students

Ask Sybil Liberty about your right to FREE EXPRESSION

Getting an education isn't just about books and grades – we're also learning ho hands!)

But in order to really participate, we need to know our rights – otherwise we may lose the amendments, known as the Bill of Rights. The Bill of Rights guarantees that the governm including the right to freedom of religion and to free speech and the due process of law. M

The Bill of Rights applies to young people as well as adults. And what I'm going to do ri

micronations are promising new virtual territories by setting up model states: self-governing and idealistic, they are mostly legally registered, non-territorial nations. The Refugee Republic (www.refugee.net), set up by Ingo Guenther, is one of over 80 micronations on the Net. It gives war refugees a virtual home, an identity and even economic weight. Another micronation project, set up by West Bank Industries (www.westbank.org), hopes to establish a virtual economy using E-cash.

The Well, America's anarchic on-line experiment

Whether in the form of discussion newsgroups, MUDs (Multi-user dungeons), or mailing lists, the Internet brought into existence a colourful range of on-line communities, where people sharing the same interests are communicating. So, if you cannot find anybody in town who shares your hobby, you will almost certainly find somebody on the Net. One such legendary virtual community is The Well (www.well.com), which hosts some 200 conferences divided into topics. Founded in the 1980s in San Francisco by tech freaks and hippies who had worked on the Whole Earth Catalogue and Whole Earth Review, The Well soon expanded to become an anarchic experiment in self-government joined by thousands of users.

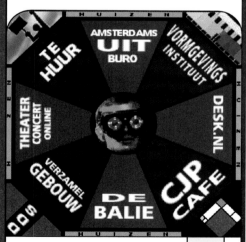

Above
DDS (www.dds.nl) is Amsterdam's freenet. The freenet encourages Netizens to actively participate by contributing their own pages as well as taking advantage of the information offered on politics and society.

Echo NYC, New York's historical on-line chat site

Echo (www.echonyc.com) was established in 1990, which makes it a relatively old virtual community in net terms. Based in New York City it is comparable only to The Well on the West Coast of the USA. Over 60 conferences can be attended through on-line chatting based on pre-World Wide Web bulletin board systems technology. Besides New York-centred topics such as the city's history, a range of broader subjects are discussed, from popular culture to lifestyles, politics and society. The administration behind Echo also organizes 'real' gatherings such as softball matches in Central Park.

Blackvoices offers community services and culture

Blackvoices (www.blackvoices.com) provides a community via chat worlds and e-mail discussions focusing on black culture. It also offers news, jobs and a members' photo gallery. Anybody can launch a debate about anything in the Black Wall chat groups.

Amsterdam-based DDS is a vibrant on-line city

The Amsterdam freenet DDS (www.dds.nl) is a grassroots and non-governmental organization. It was the first to apply the city metaphor to an on-line community structure. DDS provides easy access to information about government, social organizations and citizens' groups, and encourages netizens (Citizens of the Net) to become not only info consumers but also contributors by adding their own web pages. Communities on the DDS, which counted over 60,000 citizens in 1998, centre around forums such as chess cafés, art, cinema and metro users. One service indicates which locations, such as 'chat cafés', are crowded, where new information has been posted, and which information and places are the most popular.
@ techno utopias p176

Politicians battle it out on Minnesota e-Democracy

Minnesota e-Democracy (www.e-democracy.org) was the world's first election-oriented web site to host on-line debates by election candidates. By introducing a public forum on political processes, this non partisan, citizen-based project aims at improving participation in democracy by taking advantage of information networks. e-Democracy is built on voter information, mailing lists and direct e-mailing to candidates.

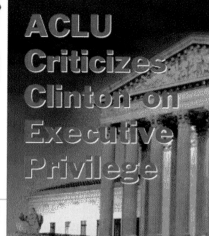

 In Congress

In the Courts

 Students

News and Events

About the ACLU

Join the ACLU

The Store

Library

 Act Now!

In the States

- Church and State
- Criminal Justice
- Cyber-Liberties
- Death Penalty
- Free Speech
- HIV/AIDS
- Immigrants' Rights
- Lesbian and Gay Rights
- National Security
- Racial Equality
- Reproductive Rights
- Students' Rights
- Voting Rights
- Women's Rights
- Workplace Rights

Above
ACLU Freedom Network (www.aclu.org) is maintained by the American Civil Liberties Network and it is intended to educate the public on matters of individual freedom. The site provides information about rights, litigation and legislation.

▶ Media Labs working to fuse art and science

With the growing influence of network technologies on our cultural and social life, new types of Internet Service Providers are continually emerging. Among the many already available are www.backspace.org and www.adaweb.com, which aim to supplement industrial and academic research, and provide platforms for interdisciplinary projects between artists, scientists and technicians. The grassroots and non-institutionalized character of such sites help in exploring the possibilities of the Net in new and critically challenging ways.

♻ Back to the future

Electronic Polls

In the 1970s, there were proposals for electronic voting systems, similar to the call-in poll systems used in television talk shows. The new system would have meant that representative democracy would have been replaced, with citizens deciding about each single issue rather than voting for Members of Parliament. Although the call for electronic polling devices has been heard frequently, no government has ever decided to use it.

Freedom of Information

The Public Record Office, UK, is committed to releasing records of public interest, in spite of strict laws governing official secrets. Buster Crabb went missing while diving in Portsmouth Harbour in 1956. At the time of Crabb's dive, Soviet leaders happened to be staying on a cruiser in the harbour. The official version of events leading up to his death will be kept secret until 2057.

By 2000 a game will go online that a million people can play simultaneously

ENTERTAINMENT

- **All video games will be set in a virtual environment**, where you see and experience everything in front, behind, above and below you. Games will be played without a joystick, using only head-movements to control the action on screen, while competitions will take place between people in different parts of the world all linked up to each other via the Net.

- **Amusement parks will be able to offer faster and more thrilling rides**, literally taking people to the limit of physical endurance. It will not be uncommon to be able to take a ride on a rollercoaster that lets you experience over 4 Gs. With cybertainment you will be able to experience a battle-field from a virtual point of view.

- **Virtual environments will take the place of the 'real' world** for many people. Already virtual dogs, cats, pop stars and even dolphins have been designed to keep people company. The Net is the perfect breeding ground for virtual characters: artists, cybergossip columnists, film critics and pop stars. There will be so many 'virtual relationships' going on that therapists will be kept busy with Net-caused diseases.

- **Cyber artists will use plastic surgery and metal prostheses** to transform their bodies for art's sake. The next step will be 3-D interactive installations and, perhaps, art in space. Listening to music will become more and more pleasurable with better quality sound-systems and we will all be able to record directly on to cds using our home stereos or simply download tracks from Internet jukeboxes that offer thousands of tracks.

- **Going to the cinema will be an unbelievable experience** thanks to digital special effects. It will be perfectly normal to go and see a film starring a simulacrum of a dead actor, his body having been apparently brought back to life using complete body scans, and to hear actors speak dialogue that was never used in the original film. One day, it will even be possible to go and see a film with oneself as the main star.

MUSIC

CYBER ART

GAMING

VIRTUAL WORLDS

VIRTUAL FRIENDS

FUN PARKS

SPECIAL EFFECTS

TECHNO-BABBLE

ADULESCENT
Old people enjoying youth culture.

AVATAR
A visual representation of a user in cyberspace.

HYPHENATES
Actors who also direct the movie, and thus get double billing as actor-directors.

INFOTAINMENT
Smuggling education across as entertainment.

THUMB CANDY
A computer game with little cerebral content.

PERFORMANCE CAPTURE
Using bodysuits to digitally capture human motion so that it can be used to generate realistic human motion in computer graphics. It is sometimes known as motion capture.

SCREENAGER
A streetwise, techno-wired youth, born and raised in the digital age. They were previously know as the MTV-generation.

SYNTHESPIAN
Entirely virtual actors and performers. Examples in the entertainment industries include Idorus, or virtual pop stars. Also known as vactors, cyberhumans, avatars, electronic puppets and cyberstars.

1961	Milton Babbitt creates first computer-generated piece of music
2004	CDs are abandoned as Internet customers download tracks from a digital jukebox to compile their own albums

Left
Brain synapses form the backdrop for *Brain Opera*, the largest-ever interactive project. Participants stand inside the structure and strike one of the suspended items causing reverberation throughout the system, creating music.

MUSIC

PERFORMANCE

⏸ Robot pop stars gig for the first time in Tokyo

Robots that can play musical instruments, or 'mubots', performed at the Tokyo Robot Exhibition in Oct 1997. A quartet of four mubots – one on violin, one on violoncello and two on the recorder – performed thirty pieces, from classical to popular music. There was also a guitar-playing mubot called Wamoeba-2 at the exhibition.

▶ Music that comes directly from the brain

Masahiro Kahata from Japan has developed a gadget which interfaces human thought with computers. Called the Interactive Brainwave Visual Analyser (IBVA), it consists of a box on a headband that holds electrodes which measure electrical activity in the brain. It can be used to control anything from games consoles to synthesizers. Kahata has sold the units to universities, governments and musicians, such as dance band The Shamen, who used it to create brainwave music.

⏸ The computer program which mimics the great composers

Mozart's 42nd symphony was performed in April 1997, at a concert at the University of California in Santa Cruz, USA – but Mozart only composed 41 symphonies while he was alive. The Santa Cruz performance was the creation of an artificial intelligence program called Emi (Experiments in Musical Intelligence) designed by composer David Cope. Under Cope's guidance, Emi studied the harmonies, instrumentation and rhythm in Mozart's symphonies in order to grasp the essence of the celebrated composer. "Without knowing Emi, there's no expert in the world who could say for sure that it's not Mozart," says Cope. Running on an ordinary Macintosh computer, Emi has also produced new works by Rachmaninov, Chopin and Scott Joplin.

⏸ Hyperinstruments play in the futuristic Brain Opera

Tod Machover from the Massachusetts Institute of Technology's (MIT) Media Lab has been designing and building 'hyperinstruments' – electronically enhanced musical instruments – since 1986. His clients have included British musician Peter Gabriel and classical cellist Yo-Yo Ma. He has also designed and composed The *Brain Opera*, an interactive composition which has been performed on the Internet and in various venues across the world. Each performance consists of two parts. The first is an introductory period in which the audience in the auditorium, or at home using the Internet, is allowed to explore and play Machover's hyperinstruments such as the Gesture Walls, which convert body movement into sound. Then follows the performance itself which is conducted by a human, but which incorporates the musical contributions from the audience's own experimentations.

⏸ Groove City goes on-line with Internet concerts

There are many sites on the Net which offer real-time audio and video links to music concerts. Canadian web site, Groove City, which offers the Internet user live links to clubs, concerts and street parties in Toronto, Canada, is planning to set up links

Right
Icelandic pop singer Björk is one of a number of musicians now using portable computerized songwriters to compose with. The small, versatile systems contain a vast array of sounds and are computer compatible too.

to events in Montreal, Canada and New York City, USA. Netizens were able to watch Radiohead, Blur, Alanis Morissette and the Beastie Boys when the Tibetan Freedom Concert 97, held on 7 and 8 June, was broadcast live from New York City, USA, to subscribers of the Internet music sites SonicNet and Rocktropolis. In 1997, avant garde musician Ryuichi Sakamoto gave a concert in Tokyo which was broadcast live on the Internet. The audience at home 'clapped' by pushing the 'f' key on their computers. Behind Sakamoto on stage was a screen which lit up with 'f's to show the digital applause. @ *new media p34*

MUSIC TECHNOLOGY

New music can be written with pocket-sized studios

German techno band Kraftwerk used portable synthesizers on stage as early as 1981. In the 1990s, musicians such as Björk and Tricky use portable songwriters. Usually about the same size as a personal organiser, the two leading models are Yamaha's QY70 and Roland's PMA-5. Both songwriters contain hundreds of sounds such as piano, drums, violins and effects such as reverb. They are also capable of multitrack sequencing – connecting programmed music to computers.

Compilation CDs could be recorded at home

Philips expected to sell about 5 million CD recorders in 1998. The first generation of CD recorders were CD-R, which permitted once-only recording onto a blank CD. But the second generation CD-ReWritable – or CD-RW – works like a tape cassette and can be recorded over more than once. CD-RWs rely on phase change technology. The discs are coated with a material which switches between crystalline and non-crystalline states when encountering a laser beam from the CD recorder. CD-RW models, released in Jan 1998, can also be used to make compilation CDs at home as they allow particular files containing tracks of music to be erased.

DIY music can be played with a joystick

Japanese company Denshai Media released software in 1998 for Sega games consoles, which act as music sequencers, allowing the DIY musician to make their own music. It is operated with a joystick and comes with 11,714 pre-recorded sounds ranging from dance music, ska and soul, to classical music.

On-line digital jukebox could herald the end of the CD

Some in the music industry are already predicting the death of the CD as a physical item for sale in shops. Already, there is an increase in the number of Internet users downloading CDs as digital files from on-

line CD stores. The Cerberus Digital Jukebox sells copyright-paid music by track from a selection which can be searched by artist or style. Customers can then manage tracks or entire albums as data files, and listen to the music through hi-fi speakers plugged into their computers – or they can take advantage of a new hi-fi system, the MDX8H from Sharp, which is designed to connect to PCs. @ *info pools p26*

Invisible loudspeakers create sound on a molecular level

First discovered by scientists at UK's Ministry of Defence, flat loudspeakers were launched in Britain by the Verity Group in April 1998. Although they are only 3 mm (1/8 in) thick, the speakers produce sound which is transmitted in every direction by vibrating on a molecular level. They can be painted and hung on walls as decorations, and could be built into panels in cars and aeroplanes.

Speakers use their incredible shape to enhance sound

Inspired by seashells, and the shape of the cochlea, or inner ear, the extraordinary B&W Nautilus speakers are also a marvel of sound engineering. The spiral horn is designed to send the sound from the back of the driver away to infinity, and the beautiful curves also negate the interference waves that distort sound inside an ordinary speaker cabinet.

Above
B&W's state of the art Nautilus speakers have supreme specifications and pioneer a new concept in audio sculpture. The marine-inspired design comprises four tapered drivers able to create a 3-D sound with a full spectrum of overtones.

Back to the future

Milton Babbitt

In 1961, US mathematician Milton Babbitt applied the theories of Austrian Arnold Schoenberg to create an electronic composition – the first music to be composed on a computer.

Walkman

In 1979, Sony launched a revolutionary portable cassette player, called the Walkman in Japan, the Soundabout in the USA and the Stowaway in the UK. The Walkman was originally devised by Sony's chairman, Akio Morita, for his children so that they could listen to music without disturbing him.

Koan

In 1994, British company SSEYO released Koan Plus V1.0, software which personalized music for the listener. Usually sold as CD-Rom, Koan provides music samples which the home user structures by specifying sound levels, which instruments to play and so on. In April 1996, British musician Brian Eno released Generative Music 1 which used Koan software to offer the listener 12 music pieces with which they could play – offering infinite varieties, but all with Eno's distinctive style.

1960s	Fluxus artist Nam June Paik created extreme forms of art – urinating on electric rails and tying up his audience
2005	The first choreographed zero-gravity dances are staged in outer space

Left
A voyager on the *Journey to the Knowbotic South*, where live scientific data from Antarctica is translated into a sensory experience via a 3-D installation and a light-data monitor worn on one eye.

CYBER ART

BODY-TECH

Australian has his internal organs filmed for art

The Australian techno-performance artist Stelarc transforms himself into a cyborg by re-engineering his body and connecting it to the Internet. Stelarc wants to show that the biological body is outdated and should be enhanced by technology in order to face the future. His previous work has used ECGs and he once filmed the inside of his stomach with an endoscopic camera. Since the 1970s, he has used the 'third arm', a prosthetic limb operated by nerve impulses.

Artist has her facelift filmed for sale

The French performance artist Orlan has altered her face and body through a series of plastic surgery operations guided by a computer-generated image to which her face is recut. Orlan sells the pictures and films of her bloody, surgical performances, as well as preserved body parts, complete with labels pointing out that, "This is my body, this is my software".

Right
Visitors at *A-Volve*, a cutting-edge computer installation where people can interact with 3-D lifeforms projected into a water tank. The viewer is able to influence the reactions of the virtual, fish-like lifeforms in real time.

Alluquere Rosanna Stone makes talking performance

Performance artist Alluquere Rosanna Stone, (www.actlab.utexas.edu./~sandy) is a cyber performance artist and academic specializing in exploring and contrasting the power of the spoken word – in whispers, screams and normal speech – with the effects of light, gestures and movement.

DIGITAL ART

A ride through a 3-D city on a virtual bike

Jeffrey Shaw invented 'inflatable sculptures' in the 1960s, and was a special effects stage designer for bands like Pink Floyd and Genesis in the early 1970s. By the end

of the decade, he began pioneering work in the field of art and virtual reality. Since then he has created ever-more complex, three-dimensional, interactive virtual reality works. His *Legible City*, designed in 1985, enables the user, sitting on a gym-bike and wearing 3-D glasses, to take a cycle ride through the streets of a virtual city consisting entirely of written sentences.

▶ Visitors interact with 3-D underwater projections

Together with her partner Laurent Mignonneau, the Austrian pioneer in the creative use of artificial intelligence, Christa Sommerer works with interactive computer installations in which the viewer influences the reaction of artificial lifeforms in real time. At *A-Volve*, visitors interact with virtual artificial lifeforms which swim in the form of 3-D projections in a water tank.
@ *artificial life p152*

▶ High-tech body-monitors used to make Breath

Ulrike Gabriel is a young German artist trained in complex computer programming languages like C and C++. Her skills enable her to create advanced artistic works which test the limits of conventional software. In *Breath*, a hi-tech belt, originally designed to detail the fitness levels of jet pilots during training flights, is used to monitor the breathing activity of the user.

▌▌ Science stations in Antarctica turned into installations

A group of Austrians and Germans based in Cologne are experimenting with contemporary scientific concepts of what they call 'nature'. In their *Journey to the Knowbotic South*, live technical data gathered by scientific instruments in Antarctica is fed into a 3-D installation and translated into sound, light and computer graphics. Users wearing a light-data monitor on one eye can then explore the artificial nature inside the installation space.

▌▌ Futuristic communications of the Global Interior Project

Masaki Fujihata from Japan is one of the world's most versatile digital artists. His Global Interior Project offers people a futuristic but easy-to-use communication system. Little booths containing a camera, microphone, speakers and a screen, placed in different cities and linked via high-speed ISDN lines, enable users to communicate live by voice and video image without the constraints of conventional, computer-based e-mail. @ *communication p24*

▌▌ Actors perform interactively using blue boxes

Since her late-1970s interactive art laser disk *Lorna*, Lynn Hershman Leeson has continued to develop digital technology for artistic projects. Her latest film, *Conceiving Ada*, uses a virtual setting in which actors, filmed in a bluebox, watch themselves simultaneously through monitors, allowing them to perform interactively.

photoshop background

alpha chann

quicktime fire

live actors

real bed

c.lynn hershman leeson 1997
"diagram of bedroom"

Above
A scene from *Conceiving Ada*, based on the story of Countess Lovelace, who wrote the first computer language. The actors were shot live against a blue digitized background which was simultaneously relayed back to them in real time.

SCIENCE AND ART

▌▌ Hackers and pirate djs use military technology

Slovenian artist Marco Peljhan, working together with a team of young hackers, hobby engineers and radio pirates, bases his work on the use of military technology. Their latest enterprise is *Makrolab*, an octagon-shaped, solar-powered capsule which functions as a living and working environment. *Makrolab* scans the sky for airwaves – whether radio waves, personal communication, weather patterns, satellite broadcasts or bird migration – and presents the collected information as art.

▶ Sculptures made out of deadly uranium

Artist Jim Acord has spent 10 years living on the Hanford Nuclear Reservation in Washington State, USA, in order to create his unique uranium-based sculptures. Acord is the only private citizen in the world licensed to handle uranium, but the US government refuses to grant him a licence to move the sculptures to a public gallery.

▶▶ French dancer performs in zero-gravity

The French choreographer Kitsu Dubois is the first dancer to perform in zero-gravity. Using a modified aircraft flying at very steep angles, she is able to experience zero gravity for up to 25 seconds as the plane reaches the top of its hyperbolic trajectory. Results of her work are used for astronaut training by the European Space Agency and may soon make her the first space dancer.

▶ Artists and scientists collaborate on new ideas

The Arts Catalyst is a British group set up to encourage projects between scientists and artists. The group has contributed to many collaborations such as *Navigators in the Playground of Possibility,* in which actors, directors and scientists explored theories of chaos in a workshop setting.

♻ Back to the future

Avant garde shock art

Korean artist Nam June Paik was a pivotal member of the 60s shock art movement, Fluxus. They tied audiences to their seats before shows, and urinated on electric rails to stop trains. More recently though, his videos *Buddha* and *TV Mantras* have blended Asian spiritual thinking with Western technology.

Charles Csuri, pioneer cyber artist

Since the 1960s, Charles Csuri has worked as a pioneer in the field of computer art. His work has been recognized to the extent that some of it, such as *Hummingbird* (1967), is held in New York's Museum of Modern Art.

Painting by numbers

'Algorithmic' fractal artist Ken Musgrave is a digital designer. He found that mathematical theory could produce great art while working with Benoit Mandelbrot, the pioneer of fractal geometry, at Yale University, USA.

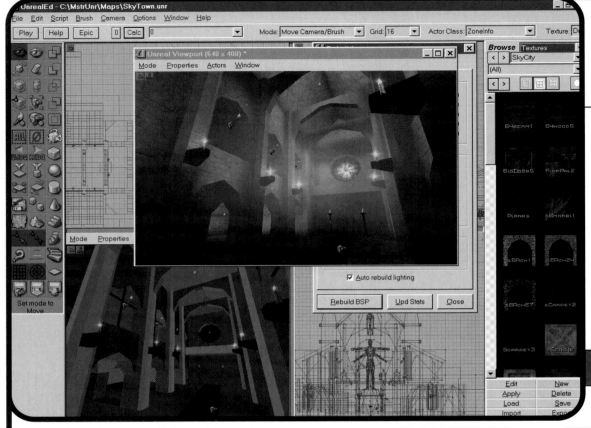

Left
Unreal is the most advanced 3-D game to date, and sets new standards for future games. It takes place on a mysterious planet where the water, sky and lighting are more realistic than ever before. Monsters and maps are impressively textured, and echoes and creaking floorboards add to the creepiness.

GAMING

GAMING DEVELOPMENT

⏸ British university offers gaming degree

Abertay University in Dundee, Scotland, is the first British University to offer a Bachelor of Science degree in video game design and virtual reality. An exchange programme has been set up with Japan's Gifu University, which has a £7.5 million virtual reality lab. In order to graduate, students will be expected to have created a fully interactive product by the end of their course. The university plans to introduce a Bachelor of Arts degree in Interactive Multimedia, focusing on more 'artistic' audio and graphics skills.

⏸ From military hardware to software

The aerospace and military hardware giant, Lockheed Martin, has its own games division, Real 3D, and has been developing arcade games with Sega. This military-entertainment collaboration seems logical in view of the fact that the Pentagon spends about $8 billion (£4.8 billion) on video games technology to refine its fighter aircraft, while the games industry has a $5 billion (£3 billion) market centred mostly on war-based games. Lockheed is liaising with software house Novalogic to produce flight simulator games based on its new fighter, the F-22 Raptor.

⏸ Arcade games not for the lazy

Some of the latest arcade games require a lot more physical exertion than mere button pressing. Namco's Final Furlong is a horse-racing simulator that requires players to straddle a plastic horse and bounce up and down to beat fellow jockeys to the finish. In their mountain-biking game, players find it harder to pedal than if they were riding up a steep hill. Konami UK produces other sports-themed games like hang-gliding and skiing arcade games.

⏸ The ultimate racing car game

Racing car fanatics will soon be able to test their skills on a super-sophisticated Formula One computer simulator. Players will sit in a full-sized racing-car replica, stationed on a

Below
Resident Evil is an interactive horror movie, set in a mansion filled with cannibalistic zombies. Its violence makes it unsuitable for children, but limited ammunition encourages players to use their brains before firing.

hydraulic motion system designed to reproduce all the bumps and bounces of a real racetrack. The driver's field of vision is filled with a widescreen video projection system powered by a 3-D graphics super-computer, like those found in Hollywood special effects studios.

Old movies become new games

Film studio giant, Metro Goldwyn Mayer, will be collaborating with entertainment software publisher Electronic Arts (EA) to turn some of their most famous films into interactive computer games. The first films chosen to be launched onto the small computer screen are *War Games*, the cold war thriller starring Matthew Broderick as a schoolboy hacker, and *Rollerball*, with James Caan as the first cyber sports star.

Hands-off games control helmet

A company called Union Reality has come up with a games controller that could spell the end for the traditional driving wheels, joysticks and gamepads. UR Gear is the world's first hands-free joystick, and allows players to control a character's movements

Above
Starship Titanic is the brainchild of *Hitchhiker's Guide to the Galaxy* author Douglas Adams. It cost £1.5 million to create, and includes more than 10 hours of dialogue so that the robots can reply to any question the player might ask.

with their own head movements. The open-fronted helmet contains stereo headphones and communicates with the PC via infrared. Weapon firing would still be controlled by a slider and a button on a handset.

ON-LINE GAMING

Gamesters subscribe to on-line games services

On-line games enthusiasts can choose to subscribe to one of dozens of competent

gaming networks, such as BT Wireplay, Thrustworld and Mplayer. Microsoft's Internet Gaming Zone has over 600,000 registered players, and claims to be the world's largest on-line games service. However, because it is located on the World Wide Web and sits on American servers it is agonizingly slow for users anywhere else in the world. On-line games services also supply a range of additional information which a gamester might find useful, such as gaming news, insider tips and strategies, contest results and player rankings.

Virtually killing strangers across the world

From now on, all PC games released can be played on-line against other players in a virtual, 3-D environment. Quake, and its successor Quake 2, both from id Software, have superseded Doom as the on-line warrior's game of choice. In fact, Quake fiends have developed into an on-line community, complete with their own newspapers, help sites, discussion groups and heroes. Local area networks (LANs) use super-wide bandwidths for fast access to the Internet, and hold regular knock-out contests between individuals or groups, known as 'clans', in cybercafes, which act as their headquarters.

Traditional games are popular on the Net

Surprisingly, the most popular game on Microsoft's Internet Gaming Zone is not a futuristic monster-slaughtering quest, but the age-old card game Spades. Virtual counterparts of other traditional games

Above
Resident Evil 2 reached sales of a staggering 1.8 million on the first day it was released in Japan. The plot is vastly improved as is the player's armoury, which includes a sub-machine gun, a flamethrower and a taser.

including Monopoly, chess, bridge and backgammon have also been developed which can all be played against other on-line enthusiasts. Most of the popular card and board games can be accessed directly from the World Wide Web on sites such as the Classic Games web site and do not require subscription to an on-line games service.

Back to the future

Old games become collectors items

Old circuit boards from 1982-85 are being sold for up to £500, with some classics such as Bionic Commando fetching even more. Original Spectrums with rubber keyboards have also become collectors items, fetching about £150 if in mint condition with games.

Ball games are a hit on screen

In 1972, the new Atari company unveiled Pong. Based on tennis, the aim was simply to keep a 'ball' in play for as long as possible using sliding rectangles. Together with variations including Tank and Double Pong, it ruled the market for nine years.

Games censors

In 1978, UK MP George Foulkes tried to ban Space Invaders, claiming it was creating nihilistic delinquents. The bill was defeated by just 20 votes. More recently, Carmageddon, in which pedestrians get run over, had to use zombies in its UK edition.

1993	Movie producer George Lucas develops Habitat, the technology behind the virtual world of Dreamscape
2020	Ancient Rome is reconstructed by computer scientists and archaeologists

WorldsAway
Gate to the Dreamscape

Left
By entering the Dreamscape world users can experience life in a virtual village. Dreamscape is part of WorldsAway, a virtual multi-site world that also offers journeys on the Starship Pride, holidays at the Hotel Silicon and even a matchmaking service at the Club Connect.

VIRTUAL WORLDS

CHAT SPACES

Children can meet each other and learn on the Net

Amy Bruckman is a pioneer in the use of virtual environments as educational sources for children. Her project, MOOSE-crossing (www.cc.gatech.edu/fac/Amy.Bruckman/moose-crossing/), is a place where children of 13 and under from all over the world can come and meet each other to chat, build places to hang out in and, last but not least, focus on their learning skills.

Dreamscape avatars that hold hands and kiss

Active since 1995, with approximately 100,000 members from over 16 countries, Dreamscape (www.worldsaway.com/) is probably the most successful avatar community ever created. It emphasizes personal presence rather than high-end, 3-D graphics. An avatar is the custom-built identity the user creates in order to visit a virtual world and can express non-verbal

forms of communication, such as facial expressions, gestures and different forms of movement. They can even hold hands and kiss. Users can also chat by typing on the keyboard, and visit a virtual shopping mall and buy products in Dreamscape's internal economy by using tokens.

▶ 3-D virtual complex allows a choice of new worlds

Worlds Inc (www.worlds.net) are pioneers in the creation of virtual environments. Their Worlds Chat, available on-line since late 1994, combines a 3-D complex and a

Right
Early in 1998, the BBC joined forces with Sony, BT Laboratories and Illuminations Television to create an experimental 3-D space on the Internet called The Mirror. The site created a number of fantasy worlds that users could enter and interact with.

futuristic building structure complete with hallways, corridors, teleports, secret rooms and a popular rooftop garden. In avatar galleries you can choose a virtual identity and use it to chat, walk and even fly.

▶ Cyberspace Pinball Machines and Virtual Theatres

Sony Community Place is a VRML (Virtual Reality Modelling Language – a 3-D version of HTML, the language that makes a text-based Web possible) browser and server software for building multi-user virtual worlds on the Internet. In addition to usual features such as chat rooms, walks, fly-throughs and 3-D visuals, Community Place offers the chance to make objects perform certain tasks; for example, there is a Cyberspace Pinball Machine, a Virtual Theatre and the Planets world, which features accurate planetary motions.

▶ Clubbers from around the world dance together

Oz, a company founded by software whizz-kids in Iceland, has developed a proprietary platform for VRML applications. Besides text-based chat, Oz World (www.oz.com/) offers a variety of voice communications and pre-programmed facial expressions. In March 1997, its associated company Oz Interactive took over a club in New York, USA, where a singer in a motion-capture suit was projected onto a web site, recreating the club in a virtual dimension. Perimeter computers allowed clubbers and web site visitors to interact, choose avatars and cyberdance. @ *virtual reality p158*

ON-LINE WORLDS

▶ Buy land and build a home in cyberspace

ActiveWorlds (www.activeworlds.com/) users can claim their own pieces of land in cyberspace and, choosing from a library of thousands of building models, use them to construct homes, palaces, fortresses, towers, or any other kind of building.

▶▶ Rome to be reconstructed in 3-D by 2020

Ancient Rome is going to be rebuilt in cyberspace. The Rome Reborn Project intends to show how Rome looked at different stages between 900 BC and AD 400. The team of computer scientists and archaeologists at the University of California, Los Angeles, USA, hopes to complete the construction of a 3-D Rome by 2020. The future city will allow visitors to move cinematically through streets and forums, led by a virtual guide speaking in Latin or English.

▶ The world shown as a 3-D virtual environment

The project Terravision (www.artcom.de) by ART+COM/Berlin is hoping to establish a representation of the whole earth as a 3-D virtual environment, combining satellite

Above
ART+COM's Virtual Berlin is part of the German organization's project to establish a fully-realized representation of the planet on the Net that allows users to swoop down from a global overview to visit individual city streets and buildings.

images, 3-D models and the constant input of databases with geographically- and ecologically-related data. Users can zoom continuously and seamlessly from an orbital satellite point of view down to street level.

⏸ Cities of Bonn and Berlin linked by virtual network

In Germany, the decision to move the seat of federal government from Bonn to Berlin has presented the POLITeam Project with the challenge of how to support the co-operation between two cities lying more than 600 km (373 miles) apart. POLITeam is developing an integrative groupware system to provide extensive support for government tasks, such as ministerial business procedures and co-operative editing of documents through shared workspaces. All components are integrated, making complex co-operation easier for all.

▶ Virtual starships built in real time on the Net

The Starship Construction Site (www.cube3.com/starbase.htm) is an adventure and entertainment site for science fiction fans. Containing 3-D VRML worlds and vehicles, multiple chat areas, Sci-Fi art galleries, news and links, it is planned to include a 3-D construction area that will allow people to log on, design, build and download their own starship in real-time on the Net.

⏸ Computer-generated responsive workbench

With a computer-generated responsive workbench, virtual objects and control tools are located on a real 'workbench', displayed as computer-generated images and projected onto the surface of a table. The user, wearing 3-D glasses, interacts with this virtual scenario, touching objects and manipulating them as if they were real. Connecting distant participants through networks such as broadband ISDN, the workbench offers a virtual but practical working tool for scientists.

♻ Back to the future

Howard Rheingold

In his book *The Virtual Community* (1993), Howard Rheingold writes about the "accidental history of the Net". Focusing on text-based features of the Net, such as mailing lists, he describes how they can be used for collaborative work over great distances between user groups of any size. This laid the ideological foundation for many later projects about virtual communities and multi-user environments.

Habitat

Habitat was developed by *Star Wars* director George Lucas's company Lucas Arts & Entertainment. After Fujitsu bought the rights in 1993, it was developed into a second-generation system with enhanced features. This software is now the technology behind some of the most successful virtual environments in the world: Dreamscape (USA), Habitat (Japan) and Glass City (South Korea).

1996	The first virtual pet, a tamagotchi, goes on the market
2020	Virtual pet cemeteries and bereavement support groups become commonplace

Left
Harry Knowles runs the Ain't It Cool News, a respected movie web site, from his house in Austin, Texas, USA, passing on film news, insider gossip and early reviews of films in production. The Internet is packed with DIY film, music and other entertainment sites, some more reliable than others.

VIRTUAL FRIENDS

VIRTUAL PETS

Digital pet craze replaces the furry faithfuls

The latest virtual pet is the touch-screen tamagotchi angel, winged creatures who need to do good deeds to increase their angel power. Tamagotchis can now be used on Gameboys, where you can cryogenically freeze your pet, and on PCs, which provide care centres for sick toys.

The heavy impact of losing a virtual pet

The attention tamagotchis command has led to schools in Japan, the Philippines, Australia, Hong Kong, New Zealand and the US banning the toy from their grounds, while in Canada a support group helps kids cope when their virtual pets go to hyper heaven. In Cornwall, UK, what is probably the world's first cyber pet cemetery has opened, allowing children to provide their virtual animals with a final resting place. The mail-order service costs £4.50 per pet.

Nothing cute-and-cuddly about the DigiMon

The Bandai second generation tamagotchi is aimed at boys, in the form of the Digital Monster, or DigiMon, which the owner raises to become a prize fighter. Within two days of its birth, the pet begins training. The 'battle connect' feature enables two DigiMons to meet for just a few seconds before battling it out. The victor increases in strength, while the loser goes back into training. DigiMons are big in Japan and new monsters are already in development.

Right
The My Lover toy has aroused some criticism from those who argue that it may teach its users that relationships are nothing more than games. Its manufacturers counter that it helps young people prepare for the rigours of romance.

⏸ Learning about love with a key-ring gadget

A new virtual pet for 1998 is the My Lover game from Solar Tune Electronics in Hong Kong, which is set to banish cyberpets to the doghouse. Owners of the electronic key-ring toy need to win the affections of their virtual lover (and points) by courting them correctly with flowers, chocolates, letters and even a session of karaoke. While the ultimate aim is marriage, failed lovers face rejection as the romance goes awry. Although the manufacturers claim the toy could help teenagers learn how to respect each other, others have argued that it may not help people handle human relationships in the real world.

▶ Overcoming shyness with digital girlfriends

In the same vein as My Lover comes the Toki Memorial, a virtual dating game. Manufactured by the Sony Corporation in Japan, it is already one of the giant company's 10 best-selling games. The game presents shy Japanese boys with a selection of digital girlfriends. Players score points for small talk and good behaviour and are awarded a kiss on the cheek if they conduct themselves correctly. Figurines based on the game's characters have also been selling well in shops.

Above
Lara Croft is the is the gun-toting, butt-kicking anthropologist heroine of the immensely successful Tomb Raider game, launched in 1997. With over 1.5 million copies sold, the virtual glamour girl looks set to give living pin-ups a run for their money.

▶ PC pets can amuse themselves on your desktop

Ganbare Morikawa-kun is a virtual pet for PCs. The makers, Sony, are working on an English version, called Pit, which lives for several hundred hours. Like Catz, released by US company PF.Magic last year, Pit is a proper pet and needs to be fed and played with regularly. It will amuse itself in its own environment, but becomes delinquent if ignored for too long. The digital kittens of Catz, which come with such enterprising diversions as balls, catnip and a mouse for them to chase, followed the earlier success of the Dogz program. To date one million copies of the pet programs have been sold.

VIRTUAL STARS

▶ Get the Drudge Report for the latest gossip

Matt Drudge's Drudge Report is making him arguably one of the world's most influential reporters. The report, originally available via his Internet site, is now sent to about 85,000 subscribers a few times a week – subscribers who in turn become his confidantes to inside political and star-studded gossip. Drudge, 31, who fashions himself on 1930s US columnist Walter Winchell, broke the Monica Lewinsky story.

⏸ Becoming a star on the World Wide Web

Austin-based virtual celebrity Harry Knowles is causing a stir in the movie industry by publishing embargoed information and juicy gossip about films, stars and directors on his web site, the Ain't It Cool News Page. The 26-year-old, who learnt his cyberscribe skills while working for Matt Drudge, has taken advantage of the immediacy and lack of enforcement on the World Wide Web to publish his well-informed insider gossip. The film industry itself takes his reviews seriously, as he has built up a reasonable amount of public clout, and Hollywood film posters have even been known to quote Knowles if they like what he says.

▶▶ Is he a figment of the art world's imagination?

Italian-German virtual artist Günter Solo lives between Bologna, Milan, London and New York. His amazing art events include parachuting over London while sketching the city below, and having a woman give birth at the opening of one of his shows in Rome. In Paris, he filled an art gallery with water and swam around in it for two hours at the opening.

Above
In the world of cyberpets, Norns are the digital equivalent of Gremlins: mischievous balls of fur that will invade your computer and play havoc with your desktop. Be warned: they are not easily trained but are an endless source of wild fun.

▶ There's nothing real about this virtual star

In 1996, 'cyperpunk' US writer William Gibson published *Idoru*, a novel predicting the rise of the computer-generated celebrity. Today, Japanese company Horipro have created Kyoko, the first completely virtual star – or Idoru – a girl based on the Japanese idea of teen perfection. It took computer designers six months to perfect her smile, and 10 graphic designers worked on her face alone. Every month, over 700,000 copies of her magazine *Famitsu* are bought and her life-story will soon be published. She even has her own radio show and you can write to her too.

♻ Back to the future

Tamagotchis

In 1996, Japanese pet lovers whose flats were too small to house cats and dogs rushed to buy a virtual pet known as a tamagotchi. Now, Japanese toymaker Bandai produces two million tamagotchis a month to meet the world-wide demand for the egg-shaped computer gadgets. The tamagotchi eats digital food, likes to be stroked and takes 10 days to mature from a chick into a fully-grown 'space bird'.

Max Headroom

In 1984, viewers in the UK witnessed the appearance of TV's first cyberpunk, the almost-virtual Max Headroom. Although played by an actor, the character's robot-like appearance was heavily altered by then state-of-the-art computer animation effects that influenced a generation of computer games animators and VR designers.

Left
Japan's Formula One Suzuka Circuitland allows visitors the chance to experience the thrills, but hopefully not the spills, of a new type of roller coaster, with the Pyrenees ride open in 1999. To add to the sense of danger, the ride will not incorporate seat belts, relying on gravity to keep customers in place.

FUN PARKS

THRILL RIDES

Highest roller coaster now takes you even higher

Perched on top of the 350-m-high (1,149-ft) Stratosphere Tower in Las Vegas, USA, is the world's highest roller coaster, the 277 m (909 ft) High Roller. Another thrill ride, the Big Shot, at 280 m (921 ft), is a vacuum-ejection seat into which you are strapped facing outwards and then shot up another 48 m (160 ft) in about 40 seconds, experiencing up to 4 Gs of pressure.

Rail flying on the Skytrack solocoaster

Set to open at Granada Studios in Manchester, UK, is the Skytrack solo-coaster, a first in the history of roller-coasters, as riders get a chance to 'fly' solo along a single rail track. Horizontally strapped into a flight pod and suspended below a single ride rail, thrill seekers plunge down the tightly-curved 15-m (50-ft) track, experiencing a variety of G-force pressures.

Euro-Mir ride where you can watch yourself go by

The Euro-Mir roller coaster, themed on the eponymous space station and based in Europa-Park, in the Strasbourg-Basel-Freiburg triangle in Germany, takes you on a 28-m (91-ft) trip up its high towers and through 610 m (2,000 ft) of blue tubular steel construction with glass-mirrored towers. @ holidays p18

Skycoaster is part skydiving, part hang gliding

Skycoaster rides are now common around the world from Cyprus to Canada, but the one with the biggest swing, measuring 91 m (300 ft), is in Kissimmee, Florida, USA, which opened in Nov 1997. It is described by the company that patented the thrill, Sky

Fun 1, as "part skydiving and part hang gliding". Fliers are attached to the structure by stainless steel aircraft cables and hoisted to a launch height at the top of the arch. They then release themselves with a ripcord and swoop through the arch at speeds of up to 112 km/h (70 mph).

Strapless passengers held in by G-force safety belts

Suzuka Circuitland, home of Japan's Formula One racing, is currently premiering a new roller coaster, called the Pyrenees, that does not use harnesses to strap you in. Instead, passengers will be kept in their seats by G-force (4.5 Gs) as they swing around a spaghetti-style track at a top speed of 96 km/h (60 mph). The ride will utilize Linear Inverted Motor (LIM) propulsion, which uses a powerful wave of electromagnetic energy, instead of hill lift, to increase the coaster's speed. This new technology will take thrill-riders from 0–96 km/h (0–60 mph) in just 3 seconds.

Travelling tornado fits inside a football field

Taz's Texas Tornado is a compact steel roller coaster that comes with four loops, impressive Gs and a hellacious reputation. It only has a top speed of about 96 km/h (60 mph) and the lift hill peaks at 34 m (112 ft), but what is astonishing about this ride is that it is completely portable and, once it is fully erected, its base fits inside a football field. It has to make some sharp curves and dives to fit into this relatively compact space and the first curving drop

 Left
The ultimate techno-thrill ride, Oblivion, at Alton Towers, Staffordshire, UK. Passengers fall 60 m into darkness at 110 km/h (68 mph) and experience G-forces of 4.5, which is 1.5 more than NASA astronauts feel at take-off.

falls away at 70°, making it one of the steepest in the world, where the body may experience pressures as high as 6.5 Gs.

⏸ Oblivion takes the mind and body to the absolute limits

Alton Towers in Staffordshire, UK, opened "the world's first vertical drop coaster" – Oblivion – in March 1998. The ride is just over three minutes of pure fear as it takes you on a thrilling 87°, 60-m (196-ft) plunge, headfirst into a dark, smoke-filled hole at up to 4.5 Gs of pressure.

▶ Unnatural disasters blowing through Florida

Universal Studios in Florida, USA, is set to unleash Twister – The Dark Side of Nature, a five-storey-tall cyclone based on the movie. The attraction whips up 57,000 m^3 (1.6 million ft^3) of circulating air per minute inside a 2,300 m^2 (25,000 ft^2) space. The special effects include a truck being flung through the air, enormous signs crumpling like tin foil and an exploding gas pump that turns the tornado into a fiery whirlwind.

▶▶ 3-D alien ride is coming to South Korea

Everland Park at Yong-In, South Korea, has a new attraction in 1999 – Aliens: 3-D, a movie ride based on the *Alien* movie saga, complete with powerful special effects, theatre stunts and 3-D movie technology. @ *special effects p58*

⏸ Florida Skyscraper will squeeze the life out of you

The Skyscraper is almost a bungee jump in reverse, and it's also the tallest and fastest portable ride ever built. First unleashed at the Florida State Fair in 1997 by Gravity Works, the ride features a 48-m (160-ft) propeller arm which launches you straight into the sky at 112 km/h (70 mph) before being turned face down and dropped from a great height. Seats are free to rotate once things get going, pulling 2 Gs at the top and 4 Gs at the bottom of each revolution.

THEME PARKS

⏸ 360° Futuroscope uses nine synchronized films

The European Park of the Moving Image at Futuroscope near Poitiers, France, boasts the first ever 360° cinema, using the latest in simulation technology and nine synchronized films to create the effect.

▶ Cyber-Space Mountain's DIY roller coasters

Disney plans to open the first of a chain of regional games centres in Orlando, Florida, USA, in 1998. One attraction called Cyber-Space Mountain will allow visitors to design their own roller coasters and then ride their creations in simulated motion. Another allows hand-to-hand combat with villains.

⏸ Cybertainment dogfights over virtual landscapes

Japanese games company Namco's Magic Edge centres in Tokyo, Japan, and Mountain View, California, USA, feature multi-player networks where users are strapped into seats to engage in dogfights over virtual landscapes. @ *gaming p50*

▶ Tomorrowland takes you beyond the planets

In 1998, Disneyland in California, USA, opened the revamped Tomorrowland. It includes the Astro Orbitor, which will allow visitors to fly their own spaceships through an animated whirl of planets.

▶▶ Islands of Adventure bring the film sets to you

A Universal Studios project, the Islands of Adventure, that is billed as "the most technologically advanced park ever", opens in mid-1999. The Islands, which cover 44 hectares (110 acres), include the Lost Continent and Jurassic Park.

⏸ Pleasure Dome simulator for the Sultan

At the Jerudong theme park in Brunei, a multi-million dollar Space Ship Simulator, housed under a 48-m (157-ft) domed steel roof, was constructed to coincide with the 50th birthday celebrations in 1997 of the world's richest man – the Sultan of Brunei.

⏸ Virtual rides inside Tutankhamen's tomb

The Luxor Hotel in Las Vegas, USA, which opened in 1996, combines a hotel, casino and theme park inside a glass replica of Tutankhamen's tomb. There are virtual

Above
Patrons of 'digital amusement parks' like Entros in Seattle, Washington, USA, can wear 3-D goggles to pick up clues used in solving mysteries in virtual reality games. Although only virtual, the experience reproduces the same physical sensations.

reality rides such as the R360 flight simulator, with a 10-storey obelisk, ancient temples, restaurants and shops, and a simulated trip down the River Nile.

⏸ Deep earth mine-shaft post-nuclear experience

Deep Earth Exploration, one of the big attractions at the MGM Grand Theme Park, Las Vegas, USA, uses a motion simulator and 'ridefilm' to blast passengers through a maze of post-nuclear environments and down into a deep, dark mineshaft.

♻ Back to the future

The Fun Palace

In 1970, Alvin Toffler wrote in his book *Future Shock* about The Fun Palace, aka the First Giant Space Mobile in the World, which was to be an entertainment environment of near-infinite versatility. The idea, put forward by the English theatrical producer Joan Littlewood, was for the Palace to be a multi-function environment where activities such as plays, wrestling matches and political rallies could be presented simultaneously.

In the beginning

On 17 July 1955, a $17 million (£10 million) Disneyland opened at Anaheim, California, USA. All the rides and attractions are based on Disney cartoons.

Khrushchev denied

A diplomatic storm blew up in 1959 when the USA would not allow the Premier of the USSR, Nikita Khrushchev, to visit Disneyland for security reasons.

1974	The film *Earthquake* is the first film to be enhanced by 'Sensurround', a deep sound felt as a vibration in cinema seats
2010	Synchronization technology allows it to become normal to see old movies reworked with new dialogue

Left.
The amazing set-pieces in the 1996 movie *Independence Day* were created by five different special effects teams using state-of-the-art digital techniques, computer-generated images, matte paintings, and traditional miniature models. With over 500 effects, the film won a best visual effects Oscar in 1996.

SPECIAL EFFECTS

PHOTOREALISM

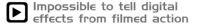

▌▌ Fake fur made to look like the real thing

The computer-generated puppies in *101 Dalmatians* (1996) looked strikingly realistic due to the new rendering software Fakefur Algorithm, developed by special effects company Industrial Light and Magic (ILM), California, USA. The individual hairs of furry objects are usually much smaller than a pixel and to recreate them realistically on screen requires massive amounts of computer memory. ILM's software has found a way around this problem, and this breakthrough in fur simulation will introduce lots of lively and realistic-looking animated animal characters into films.

▶ Animated figures given realistic facial expressions

A range of research projects concerned with the difficulties of facial animation will soon provide digital artists with useful new software. The facial expressions created by speech and emotion are all caused by the interaction of head and neck muscles, wrinkles, skin tension and light. Intelligent software will incorporate these factors and reproduce them in digitized form.

▶ Impossible to tell digital effects from filmed action

Hollywood-based special effects company, Pixar, has developed one of the leading rendering softwares, RenderMan. It produces high quality image synthesis, like the digitalized special effects in *Men in Black* and *The Lost World*. In fact, the effects can hardly be distinguished from film footage due to the high resolution rendering and accurate shading. @ *film p170*

▌▌ Non-Digital cheaper effects are increasingly used

Because of the high cost of digital visual effects, many special effects companies are

Right
Miralab, at the University of Geneva, Switzerland, is a leading research centre in the creation of virtual humans. It is currently developing software that not only reproduces human skin in a realistic way, but which shows it wrinkling and ageing too.

focusing on traditional methods. Improving robot technology, surface materials, use of chemicals, pyrotechnics and weather simulation methods all result in striking, and cheaper, special effects.

MOVEMENT

Transforming one image into another unnoticeably

In 1982, the technique of morphing, an effect for changing one digital image into another through subtle transformation, was introduced by Tom Brigham. The effect was also used to create 3-D morphs that could be viewed from different angles, and for the morphing of moving subjects to create the effects like those seen in Michael Jackson's video *Black and White,* and in movies such as *The Abyss* or *Terminator 2*. In the future, morphing software will offer much more accurate control, especially in selected parts of the image and not just the whole.

▶ Amazing new 3-D film sets, the look of the future

Keying, or Bluebox Effect, is familiar to film fans, especially when it is used to create the illusion of a moving landscape outside a studio-bound car's rear window. It is now possible to Key whole film sets, using virtual 3-D effects which react to whatever the camera is pointing at and create a virtual 'set' around it. The results can be seen in low-budget films such as *Conceiving Ada,* the first in a new era of movies made on fantasy film sets. @ *cyber art p48*

▶ Computers used to make natural looking cloth

One of the most challenging tasks in special effects is the computer animation of natural looking, moving cloth. A research group led by Nadia Thalmann at Miralab, Geneva University, Geneva, Switzerland, has now developed intelligent software for virtual cloth simulation. Recreating a famous scene from *The Seven Year Itch,* Miralab's virtual Marilyn Monroe stands over a subway grating while the wind below blows her skirt around her shoulders. This is not because a designer has animated the figure frame by frame, but because Miralab's new software can calculate the cloth's most likely pattern of movement and recreate it digitally.

⏸ Realistic Motion and Group Behaviour

The Computer Animation Lab at Georgia University, Georgia, USA, has invented new algorithms to reproduce the realistic motion of human bodies and group behaviour. In a virtual environment, simple behaviour, such as running, walking and biking, and more complicated movement, such as obstacle avoidance, grouping and rough terrain locomotion, can be all realistically recreated. The animator controls the behaviour of the group on a high level, while the details of the motion of each individual character are computed by the underlying simulation. @ *virtual worlds p52*

▶ Actors dress up in datasuits to improve animation

The new technology of Motion Capture Suits, originally developed by NASA, will help make animated characters look even more realistic. The suit records the positions of a moving actor's hips, back, shoulders, knees and so on, and transposes them instantly onto a 3-D model displayed on a computer screen. The movements are then analysed and applied to an animated figure. @ *materials science p160*

SIMULATION

▶ Actors speak new dialogue without realising

The Interval Research Corporation specializes in synchronization technologies between speech and lip motions and has developed Video Rewrite. By using existing footage, Video Rewrite can automatically create a new video of a person mouthing words that were not spoken in the original footage. It was used extensively, and to great effect, in the film *Forrest Gump*.

▶▶ Future movies to use scanned stars

Movies in the next millennium might feature a still-young Michelle Pfeiffer or an in-his-prime Arnold Schwarzenegger, so long as they grab the opportunity to produce a 3-D scan of their bodies right now. In just a few seconds, a cyberscanner, owned by Cyberware, California, USA, orbits through 360° and creates a complete body data set. With this handy option, future movie productions will have the chance to cast deceased stars in their films by merely animating their scan data. The technology could also serve as insurance in case the actor dies before the filming is finished.

Above
It took no fewer than three special effects companies – Industrial Light & Magic, Dream Quest Images and Cannom Creations – to produce the eye-popping morphing effects that helped make 1994s *The Mask* a smash hit.

▶ Reproducing the light from under the door

The simulation of light reflection is a must for realistic-looking computer special effects. The representation of indirect light sources, such as rays coming through a slightly open door, demand further software development. Recent solutions like Memory Coherent Ray Tracing from Stanford University, Palo Alto, USA, or Radiance Equation Rendering from the University of Kaiserlautern, Germany, based on complex algorithm programming, are just the very beginning of improvements which will one day create completely realistic artificial light.

♻ Back to the future

3-D specs

On 28 Nov 1952, Arch Obeler's much-publicized film *BuanaDevil* premiered in Hollywood, California, USA. Audiences were given specially-developed Polaroid spectacles so that they could watch certain sequences in the full 3-D effect.

Shaking seats

In 1974, shaking seats that moved at key moments in the film *Earthquake* were installed at certain American cinemas. It was also the first motion picture to use 'Sensurround', which enhanced scenes by producing very deep sounds inaudible to the audience which were felt as vibrations.

Toy Story

Released in 1995, *Toy Story* was the first completely computer-animated feature film. It took over 800,000 machine hours to create the blockbusting film.

Just one gram of sarin nerve toxin could kill over a thousand people

DEFENCE

- **Developments in biotechnology and genetics programmes** have introduced the idea of new weapons based on super-viruses or chemicals. Small, potentially devastating amounts of chemicals can be carried from country to country with frightening ease. Tighter controls will be needed over the production and proliferation of chemical and biological weapons.

- **In the future, warfare will take place in space**, where countries will have to fight each other to maintain or capture points of strategic importance for their satellites. The USA is already developing a number of space planes for this purpose.

- **Laser weapons will replace traditional types of gun**. Another ingenious new weapon will be one that uses acoustic power to make the enemy's internal organs vibrate, inducing nausea, vomiting and diarrhoea. However, fingerprint or iris-recognition technology may enable tailor-made guns to identify the proper user and thus stop deadly weapons falling into the wrong hands. One improvement might be non-lethal weapons, weapons that don't kill but just immobilise, but the long-term side-effects of such weapons are still unknown.

- **The police of the future will be kitted out with video helmets, smart guns and radars**. DNA fingerprinting, eye-recognition and 3-D facial-recognition scanners may make the identification of criminals easier. More sophisticated forms of tagging and monitoring systems – such as planting a microchip under the skin – should do away with the need for so many prisons, although the public may not react favourably to the idea of convicted criminals not being locked up.

- **Criminals will increasingly turn to digital technology** to carry out their crimes. The Internet has already been a medium for blackmail, stalking and hijacking so it is not surprising that there already exist cybersleuths whose job it is to track hackers and crackers. Cyberterrorism, attacking the civilian infrastructure of a country, may well become the greatest terrorist threat of the future.

POLICING

DIGITAL CRIME

HACKERS

WARFARE

GUNS

WAR MACHINES

TECHNO-BABBLE

ETHICAL HACKER
A hacker who breaks into systems purely to expose security flaws so they can be rectified.

HACTIVISM
Electronic civil disobedience in which activists take direct action by breaking into government or corporate computer systems.

LAPJACKING
Stealing laptop computers.

MILITARY ENTERTAINMENT COMPLEX
A venture combining technology from both military and entertainment industries.

SAMURAI
A hacker hired by a firm to legally hack its defences.

TELEPHONY
Telephone fraud, an evolution from phreaking.

WAR DIALING
Hacker slang for attempting to break into systems through random phone calling.

WATER WAR
A hypothetical war, which may occur when extreme water shortages combined with population increases force violent conflicts in an attempt to obtain enough water to survive.

1985	Dr Alec Jeffreys links genetic identity with DNA in body tissues
2008	Iris recognition replaces fingerprinting for personal identification

Left
Technicians checking DNA autoradiographs. DNA fragments are mixed in a gel with chemical markers that X-ray analysis can read, allowing samples to be compared and then identified.

POLICING

POLICE AIDS

▶ **The smart guns that can only be used by police officers**

Colt's Manufacturing Company in the USA is currently developing an automatic pistol that will only shoot if it is in the hands of a police officer. The gun will fire after it

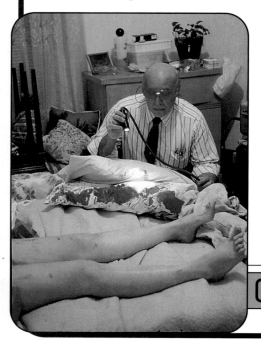

Left
A forensic scientist using a laser to search for semen traces at a murder scene. The area is sprayed with a marker that can bind to semen proteins and then glow under a laser beam, giving police vital DNA data.

receives a signal from a radar that can be housed in a ring, watch or button worn by a police officer.

▶ **The radar that can sense breathing through a wall**

A research team at Georgia Tech Research Institute in Atlanta, USA, has built a prototype radar torch which uses a signal processing chip to detect people through walls. To date, the torch can detect the subtle movement of a person breathing through a wall 20 cm (7 ¾ in) thick.

▶ **Two-way video helmets to assist British police**

Digital helmets, which can communicate with a central computer at the station, are being developed for British police officers. The aim is to fit the helmets with a camera which will film while on patrol and relay the video back to the station in real time – as well as being able to receive video footage of, for example, the architectural plans of a building or the street map of a suburb where a suspect might have fled. An eyepiece attached to the helmet will also enable officers to view data.

▶ **Remote vehicle disabler that uses an electromagnetic field**

A remote vehicle disabling device, patented in the USA by SAIC in 1994, fires an electromagnetic pulse from a police vehicle aerial at a fleeing car. The system, that can work up to 30 m (98 ft) away, surrounds the car with an electromagnetic field which disrupts the electronic devices, stopping the car temporarily or permanently. Another US company, Jaycor, is testing the Auto-Arrestor, a system which relies on a strip of vertical brushes in the road and discharges more than 100,000 volts of electricity through the car's bodywork when it passes over them. In trials, the system has stopped cars travelling at 105 km/h (65 mph) without harming the drivers.

FORENSICS

▶ **Goggles which make evidence glow for investigators**

Researchers at Sandia National Labs in New Mexico, USA, have come up with a time-saving and illuminating way for officers to pinpoint potential evidence at a crime scene: by making it glow. Exploiting the fact that most organic materials give off a natural fluorescence invisible to the human eye, the team have combined a flashing lamp and a modified pair of 3-D game goggles to make substances such as blood, semen, body tissue, drugs and explosives flash to the wearer of the goggles. The fluorescence given off by the objects in question can only be seen when the light and the goggles' shutter are synchronized, just a few times per second, making it appear as if it is flashing.

▶▶ Robot investigators could reconstruct the crime scene

The FBI forsees that the growth of identity databases will lead to forensic robots filming and combing crime scenes for evidence and then being able to analyse it on sight. The information could be used to reconstruct the crime scene in virtual reality which human investigators or even a jury could refer to at any time. @ *robots p28*

▶ DNA fingerprinting helped to identify Russian Tsar's bones

DNA evidence has featured in high profile court cases, most recently, that of O. J. Simpson. Courts prefer nuclear DNA evidence but this is not always available, and increasingly mitochondrial DNA is being used to link suspects to crimes. This type of DNA helped to identify human bones excavated in Yekaterinburg, Russia, in 1991 as those of Tsar Nicholas, who was shot with his family in 1918.

▶ Genetic evidence could be provided by a handshake

Forensic experts at the Victoria Forensic Science Centre, Australia, announced in 1997 that they could identify individual genetic profiles from fingerprints left on objects. A DNA profile is usually extracted from the analysis of blood, hair and bone, but this new method means that a handshake with a suspect could provide enough DNA for analysis.

▶ Microchip fastest so far at unravelling DNA code

Biotech company Nanogen, from San Diego, USA, is developing a way of radically speeding up DNA fingerprinting. Instead of painstaking separation of molecules by hand, a microchip uses electrodes to mimic DNA sequences in order to distinguish individual DNA types. After a DNA sample is added, a positive charge is applied to the electrodes, causing the negatively charged DNA molecules in the sample to pair with the corresponding sequences attached to the electrodes. Then the current is reversed so that the sample molecules which are not perfectly paired up are separated, leaving only the relevant DNA on the chip.

▶▶ DNA sample could give identikit profile

Advances in human genetics may lead to the construction of an identikit by using a DNA sample. A research team at University College, London, UK, is matching features passed down through families, such as dimples or a nose or jaw shape, with the corresponding genes. @ *genetics p112*

❚❚ Eyeprints may soon replace the fingerprint

Dr John Daugman of Cambridge University, UK, has created a blueprint by which a computer can be used to recognise the unique iris patterns in the human eye. Though more reliable than fingerprinting, iris recognition has proved too complex a task for most computers. However, IrisCode can represent an image of an iris in numerical code. A prototype database could search and cross-reference through 40,000 different iris identities per second.

▶ Fingerprint database could mean a quick match

The FBI is setting up a $500 million (£312 million) fingerprint database which aims to speed up fingerprint matching. The database of 32 million sets of prints will be searchable with handheld scanners.

❚❚ Jeans show unique wear-and-tear patterns

Criminologists have invented a very novel method of exposing criminals – they look at their jeans. Forensic scientists at the FBI have revealed that every pair of jeans that has been worn for some time exhibits its own unique pattern of wear, as individual as a fingerprint or a bar-code.

JAIL SYSTEMS

▶ UK id tags allow prisoners to be released early

In the UK, from 1999, some prisoners will be electronically tagged. Once fitted, a tag's electronic signal is monitored, allowing police to ascertain the offender's exact whereabouts so that many prisoners can be released early.

▶ Indestructible id tags in development

Philips Research in the Netherlands is developing flexible plastic id tags that defy being squashed or folded. The two-way radar circuitry is etched with ultraviolet light into foil within the tag.

▶ House-arrest offenders monitored by satellite

US company Pro-Tech Monitoring is testing a device called Smart (Satellite Monitoring and Remote Tracking system) which allows a central office to track the movements of an offender who is under house-arrest.

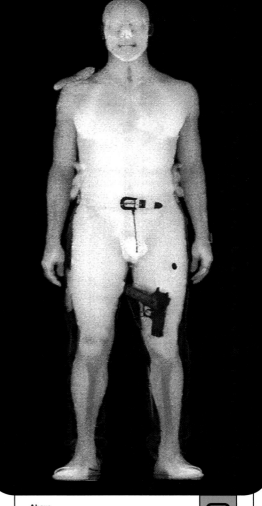

Above
A male suspect carrying bags of cocaine (shoulder, waist); scalpel blades (chest); plastic gun (back); metal gun and file (legs). The Bodysearch X-ray uses 1/7000th of the radiation normally used.

♻ Back to the future

Photofit

In 1971, 'Photofit' was introduced to the world's police systems. 'Photofit' is a face-making system which allows witnesses to build up detailed images of suspects. The modern kit can recreate millions of faces.

Interpol

In 1923, Interpol – International Police Organisation – was founded. Its headquarters in Paris has an international register of criminals and fingerprint file, and now more than 120 countries belong to Interpol.

Lie Detectors

The polygraph – or lie detector – was invented by Californian medical student John Larson. In Mar 1985, Dr Alec Jeffreys from Leicester University, UK, discovered that a human's unique genetic identity could be identified from DNA in blood, semen and saliva.

1983	The term 'computer virus' is coined to describe programs that can alter or erase data on a computer hard disk
2000	Cybercops become a branch of future policing, monitoring the Internet

Left
A scene from the film *Sneakers*, about an electronic device that can penetrate the government's most secure computer. New ways are constantly being sought to access computers and, equally, new ways are continually being tested to prevent access.

DIGITAL CRIME

CYBER CRIMINALS

The MOD and crime with just five keystrokes

In 1997, John Lee, founder of the Masters of Deception hacker group, which made headlines in the USA in 1989 when it crashed computers at a New York TV station, spelled out in an interview how he could "commit a crime with five keystrokes". Lee, who has served a prison term for hacking, said that in just a few minutes he could change credit card records and bank balances, arrange free limousines, aeroplane flights and hotel rooms and obtain inside stock exchange information. @ hackers p66

Vladimir Levin is a cyber Robin Hood

In Feb 1998, a hacker from St Petersburg, Russia, was given a three-year sentence by a New York court for attempting to steal from Citibank in the USA. Vladimir Levin and his accomplices transferred an estimated $12 million (£8 million) to bank accounts in the USA, Finland, Holland, Germany and Israel by hacking into accounts designed for corporate clients. Citibank noticed money was being stolen from customers' accounts in July 1994, after the first $400,000 (£250,000) was transferred, and contacted the FBI who tracked it to Levin. In March 1995, Levin visited the UK, where he was arrested and then extradited to the USA in 1997.

Blackmail on the Internet is on the increase

Legal experts in the UK warned in 1997 that there would be an increase in Internet blackmail, in particular a tendency toward targeting big companies, with blackmailers threatening to post defamatory statements about senior public officials on company web sites. The British newspaper *The Daily Telegraph* reported in June 1997 that the hamburger chain McDonald's had been threatened by a group demanding that the company change its position on a libel case which it had just won in the UK. In a separate incident, in Jan 1998, the German bank, Noris Verbraucherbank, appealed for information that would lead to the arrest of a blackmailer who had demanded DM1 million (£292,000) not to release clients' account numbers on the Net.

Cyberstalking can lead to actual stalking

Police in the USA have recently identified a new form of harassment: cyberstalking. It involves posting threatening messages to someone in an on-line discussion group, or to their homepages, and can lead to physical stalking. In March 1998, death threats to the Hollywood actress Jodie Foster were placed on a 'chat room' page.

Right
The lava-lamp is being used to generate encryption codes that protect computer data. Truly random numbers are difficult to produce, but as a lava-lamp heats up, its random generation of blobs is photographed and then converted into virtually unbreakable computer code.

Ex-employee blocks rivals

Steven Domagala of Gippsland, Victoria, Australia, was convicted in 1997 of setting up a business to rival his former employer and then conducting a secret hacking campaign against them. As soon as Domagala had set up a rival Internet service provider company, which offered a variety of e-mail addresses and Internet services, his former company coincidentally began experiencing problems such as their computers crashing and their customers being blocked from accessing their own e-mail or even just browsing on the Internet.

▶ Internet hijacker gets away without paying the bill

In Feb 1998, Mary Picken from Glasgow, UK, was fighting a $3,000 (£1,800) bill for on-line time from her Internet service provider. Picken claimed that her Internet account had been hijacked by a hacker in eastern Europe, who was identified as the source of the expensive telephone bill. However, the police could not investigate the case as it was outside Scotland.

❚❚ Cypherpunks, governments and cryptography

The Cypherpunks are a loose on-line network of people, mainly based in Silicon Valley, USA, who believe in distributing public key cryptography – computerized codes which protect the privacy of e-mail and business transactions on the Internet. This is a classic example of the clash between governments, who fear that public key cryptography will lead to an increase in digital crime, and Net users, who believe government control of cryptosystems will compromise the ethos of the Net as a free and anarchic information pool. The most popular freely-distributed cryptosystem is software called PGP (Pretty Good Privacy), but this is illegal in the USA, ironically leading to an increase in police wiretapping and raids on Net users' homes in order to criminalize the use of PGP.

CRIME FIGHTERS

▶ Cybersleuthing officers will patrol the Internet

The police forces of the future will have units of cybercops who patrol the Internet and computer networks. There are already companies in the USA that are hiring out consultant forensic accountants whose job it is to sift through companies' systems, investigating any allegations of fraud and embezzlement that they come across. In the US police force there is also a growing number of cybersleuthing officers who are posing as children and participating in on-line chat sites in order to successfully trap suspected paedophiles. @ *policing p62*

❚❚ High-speed computer used to catch US Defense hacker

In 1997, Julio Ardita from Buenos Aires, Argentina, was arrested and charged with hacking into US military computer systems after a US court granted the first ever wiretap of a computer network. In 1995, the US Defense Department detected intrusions into military and university computer networks containing sensitive information about government research on satellites, radiation and energy. After obtaining the wiretapping court order, a specially-configured computer was set up to monitor intrusions and conduct high-speed searches in order to track down Ardita in Argentina. In Dec 1997, Ardita agreed to be extradited to the US and plead guilty to computer crime felonies, and his co-operation has been acknowledged.

❚❚ DIBS takes photographs of hidden files

British computer forensic expert Jim Bates has invented a way of creating exact clones of computers belonging to suspected hackers. Called DIBS, it consists of an optical disc drive and special software which is plugged into a computer, taking a 'photograph' of it and seeking out hidden files. This means that the computer under investigation can be preserved just as the police found it, thus ensuring that evidence remains credible.

▶ Sex stalkers are being monitored on the Net

In Oct 1997, 40-year-old Michael Shipman from Chamblee, Georgia, USA, was charged with the rape of a 13-year-old girl he befriended during a chat session on the Internet. Posing as a 17-year-old boy, he got her address and allegedly attacked her later in her home. Meanwhile, a US group calling themselves Ethical Hackers Against Paedophilia have declared that they will watch out for paedophiles on the Internet and pass information on to the police.

❚❚ Lava-lamp system is based on unpredictable lava

Computer company Silicon Graphics, from Mountain View, California, USA, has developed Lavarand, a novel new way of generating encryption codes based on the hypnotic motions inside lava-lamps. Random numbers produce the most unbreakable encryption systems, but it is difficult for both humans and computers to generate truly random numbers. As lava-lamps heat up, turbulence is created and the blobs inside react chaotically. Lavarand uses a camera which photographs a lava-lamp every few minutes and converts the images into unpredictable computer code.

▶ International agreement does not compute with the courts

In Dec 1997, Russia, the USA, France, the UK, Germany, Italy, Japan, and Canada signed an agreement to pursue cyber criminals. The eight nations will share information and train police in Internet and computer skills. However, legal systems lag behind new trends in digital crime. In Feb 1998, the Supreme Court of Argentina ruled that software piracy, making illegal copies of computer programs, was not a crime. This came about after a high court discovered that 1993 copyright laws were not written to include software.

▶ Encryption keys divided into high and low security

Conservative groups in the US government are lobbying to have encryption keys

Above
Scott Harshbarger, the Massachusetts Attorney General, announcing plans to combat high-tech crimes at a news conference on 24 April 1997, in Boston, Massachusetts, USA. Digital crime advances in tandem with technology.

disclosed to law agencies such as the FBI. If the S.909 bill, introduced to the Senate in 1997, is made law it will give law agents access to almost all information travelling over networks, including the Internet. The UK and France wish to follow the USA's example, but the European Commission is proposing that encryption products be divided into high security software, which would be registered, and simpler encryption products used by ordinary Internet users, which some feel is a small step in the right direction, but would not do much to satisfy campaigners for privacy rights.

♻ Back to the future

Johnny Kyong

In 1990, southeast Asian crime boss Johnny Kyong was convicted of selling heroin to the New York mafia. His trial revealed his method of money laundering, a precursor to the digital crimes of today. Kyong sent his money made from drug deals through a Venezuelan company to bank accounts in Hong Kong. Then the money was sent through underground banking systems to Burma and Thailand to buy more heroin. Finally, Kyong's profits were moved through banks in central Europe where it arrived in Indian and Pakistani banks in Canada as perfectly legitimate funds.

Birth of a virus

In 1983, the term 'computer virus' was coined to describe computer programs that are able to alter or erase data on the hard disk of a computer. Viruses have the capability to cause enormous amounts of damage and can be used to sabotage sensitive material.

1989	Hacker Kevin Poulsen seizes control of a radio station's 25 phone lines during a call-in competition and, as the only caller, wins a car
1998	The US Government estimates that their computers are attacked at least a billion times a year

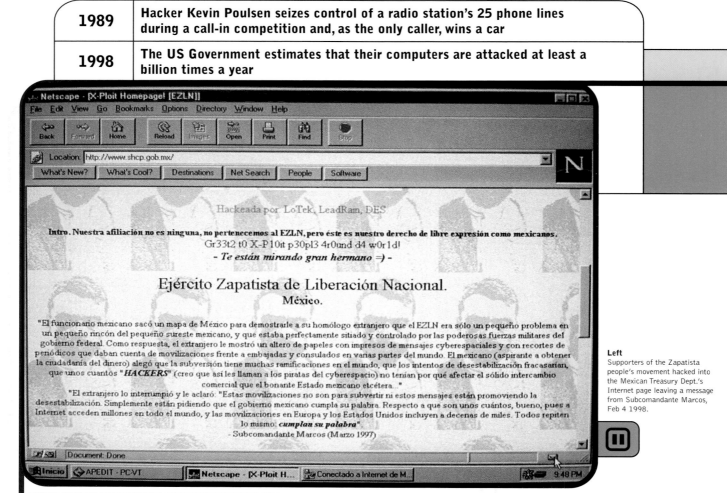

Hackeada por LoTek, LeadRam, DES

Intro. Nuestra afiliación no es ninguna, no pertenecemos al EZLN, pero éste es nuestro derecho de libre expresión como mexicanos.

Gr33t2 t0 X-P10it p30pl3 4r0und d4 w0r1d!

- Te están mirando gran hermano =) -

Ejército Zapatista de Liberación Nacional.
México.

"El funcionario mexicano sacó un mapa de México para demostrarle a su homólogo extranjero que el EZLN era sólo un pequeño problema en un pequeño rincón del pequeño sureste mexicano, y que estaba perfectamente sitiado y controlado por las poderosas fuerzas militares del gobierno federal. Como respuesta, el extranjero le mostró un altero de papeles con impresos de mensajes cyberespaciales y con recortes de periódicos que daban cuenta de movilizaciones frente a embajadas y consulados en varias partes del mundo. El mexicano (aspirante a obtener la ciudadanía del dinero) alegó que la subversión tiene muchas ramificaciones en el mundo, que los intentos de desestabilización fracasarían, que unos cuantos *"HACKERS"* (creo que así les llaman a los piratas del cyberespacio) no tenían por qué afectar el sólido intercambio comercial que el boyante Estado mexicano etcétera..."

"El extranjero lo interrumpió y le aclaró: "Estas movilizaciones no son para subvertir ni estos mensajes están promoviendo la desestabilización. Simplemente están pidiendo que el gobierno mexicano cumpla su palabra. Respecto a que son unos cuántos, bueno, pues a Internet acceden millones en todo el mundo, y las movilizaciones en Europa y los Estados Unidos incluyen a decenas de miles. Todos repiten lo mismo: *cumplan su palabra*".

- Subcomandante Marcos (Marzo 1997)

Left
Supporters of the Zapatista people's movement hacked into the Mexican Treasury Dept.'s Internet page leaving a message from Subcomandante Marcos, Feb 4 1998.

HACKERS

CYBER SUBCULTURE

Though police around the world refer to most crimes involving computers as hacking, hackers themselves draw a clear distinction between what they see as a quest to understand computer systems, and the crackers, those who break into computer systems by guessing passwords. Most hackers tend to be teenagers who

very often destroy or replace data. The essence of hacking is an ingenious foxing of the system and a belief that bureaucracies, whether they be governments, banks or companies, have no right to profit from concealing information from their citizens and customers. Often though, hackers break into a system to look around simply for fun or to prove that it can be done. Other sub-cultures in the hacking community include phreaks, who prefer to specialize in cheating the telephone system, and warez d00dz who get their thrills by pirating software and then beating other groups and manufacturers into releasing it either before or on the day of the software's commercial release.

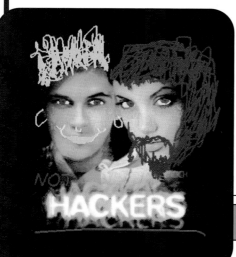

Left
The promotional picture for the 1995 MGM movie, 'Hackers' was defaced; the title of the movie changed to 'Not Hackers', and links to "real hackers sites", such as the magazines *2600* and *Phrack* were added as well as advice on how to make the site hack-proof.

⏸ Hacker's magazine which the authorities find very useful

2600: The Hacker's Quarterly, was started in the USA in 1984, by someone calling himself Emmanuel Goldstein and is a magazine championing hacking. Protected by the constitutional right to the freedom of the press, it has been tolerated by the authorities and it is rumoured that even the

police and security personnel subscribe in order to keep abreast of new hacking trends that their software and data may be subjected to.

⏸ The hacker's bible which promotes on-line mayhem

The US publication, *Phrack*, an on-line bible of phreaking and hacking, was started in 1985. It included features about bomb-making and general cyber anarchy for subscribers to digest. The publication was shut down briefly in 1990 after charges of fraud were brought against one of its co-editors. @ *citizens' networks p42*

HACKERS

▶ Kevin Mitnick: a hero among hackers is arrested

Legendary among hackers throughout the world, Kevin Mitnick was arrested in 1995 after a highly publicized cat-and-mouse cyberhunt led by security expert Tsumoto Shimomura. Armed with a laptop and cellular telephone, Mitnick went on a hacking spree throughout the USA and allegedly even managed to hack into Tsumoto's own computer system. @ *digital crime p64*

❚❚ Dark Dante takes control of radio station's telephones

A.k.a 'Dark Dante', Kevin Poulsen was sentenced by a US court in April 1995 to 51 months in prison. Well known in the USA for hacking government sites and military systems, Poulsen's most infamous exploit was while he was on the run in 1990, when he seized control of a radio station's 25 telephone lines during a call-in competition, making him the only caller and winner of a Porsche sports car.

▶ Gulf War crackers tried to hand over information to Iraq

In March 1997, Dr Eugene Schultz, former head of computer security at the US Department of Energy, revealed that Dutch crackers stole military information including troop movements and missile capabilities from US government computers before the Gulf War. The crackers gained access to a US military web site, and over a period of months hacked their way around 34 military sites. Schultz said that the Americans found out in Oct 1990 that the information had been offered to the Iraqis who turned it down thinking it was just a hoax.

❚❚ The Black Baron devastated data and hard drives

In 1995, 26-year-old Christopher Pile, a.k.a. 'The Black Baron', from Plymouth, Devon, UK, was given an 18-month jail sentence after being found guilty of writing and releasing two viruses, Pathogen and Queeg, both of which caused hundreds of thousands of pounds of damage. The viruses destroyed data on computer hard drives, leaving a joke from the British cult television series *Red Dwarf* on the screen: "Smoke me a kipper, I'll be back for breakfast … unfortunately some of your data won't." @ computers p22

❚❚ Datastream Cowboy rumbled by undercover agent

It took US security agents 13 months to track down 16-year-old Londoner Richard Pryce who hacked into systems belonging to the US Air Force and Lockheed Martin, missile and aircraft manufacturers. Using the log-on 'Datastream Cowboy', Pryce downloaded secret information on the research and development of ballistic missiles. He was found out after he told a military agent, posing as a fellow hacker on the Internet, that he was 16, English and interested in US military systems.

▶ FBI network hacked to make international phone calls

In Feb 1997, a French court fined 21-year-old Anthony Zboralski $9,000 (£5,625) after he was convicted of hacking into the FBI computer network and using it to make $250,000 (£156,000) worth of phone calls to friends around the world. Zboralski obtained the name of an FBI official working in Paris from the city's US embassy and then rang the FBI in Washington on their free international line and asked how to be connected to the FBI computer network.

HACKED WEB SITES

❚❚ UK politicians satirized on their own web sites

In Dec 1996, the British Labour Party web page was hacked, with Party leader Tony Blair's photograph replaced with an image of his puppet from satirical British television series *Spitting Image* and the election slogan changed from 'New Labour, New Britain' to 'Same Politicians, Same Lies' and also alluding to a 'road to nowhere'. Then on 27 Apr 1997, only three days before the General Election, a group calling themselves Circle of Deception hacked into the Conservative Party web site, and set a photograph of the party leader John Major against a Nazi swastika.

▶ Yahoo! homepage sabotaged for 10 minutes

A group called PANTS/HAGIS hacked into the Internet search engine Yahoo! on 9 Dec 1997, demanding the release of US hacker Kevin Mitnick from jail. Their message, which claimed that a virus to be activated on Christmas 1998 could be stopped, "but not by mortals", replaced the Yahoo! homepage for about 10 minutes. Yahoo! checked, but no such virus was ever found.

▶ East Timor protest on Indonesian web pages

Web pages of the Indonesian government have been under attack from a group of Portuguese hackers protesting at the

Above
New Corporation security analysts, 'AJ', right, and 'Def Veggie', discuss new ways to prevent hackers from entering company web sites at the Def Con 5 convention at the Aladdin Hotel and Casino, Las Vegas, USA, July 11, 1997.

oppressive administration of East Timor. The group hacked into the government's web site twice in Feb and again in Nov 1997. Various sites were changed to "honour and remember the 250 people killed in Dili on the 12 November 1991" – some sites were erased completely.

♻ Back to the future

Abbie Hoffman

Most hackers trace their ancestry to Abbie Hoffman, prominent member of the Yippies, an underground movement active in the 1970s who believed in challenging what they saw as a stupid and humourless 'system' of government and society. Hoffman, who regarded media as both a weapon and a playground, wrote a book titled: *Steal This Book,* which detailed how enterprising hippies could live off the system, cheating payphones and parking metres and not paying bills.

CIA caught out

In Nov 1996, the CIA's web page was hacked and changed to the Central Stupidity Agency with a link to 'Nude Girls'.

Masters of Deception

In Nov 1989, New York gang, the Masters of Deception led by master hacker, Mark Abene a.k.a. Phiber Optik, crashed computers at WNET, the city's television station, leaving the message: "Happy Thanksgiving you turkeys, from all of us at MOD."

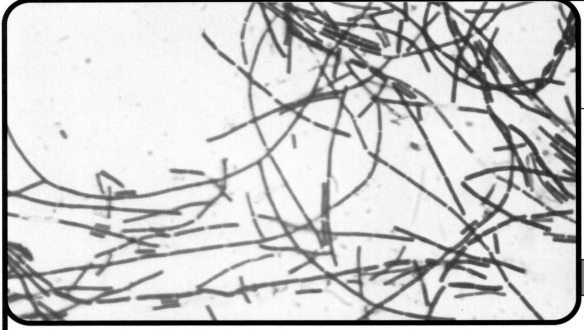

Left
The cause of anthrax, in animals and man, *Bacillus anthracis*. It attacks either the lungs or the skin, but is curable if treated with the right antibiotics. Nowadays, it is a standard part of chemical weapons arsenals.

WARFARE

CHEMICAL WARFARE

Chemical weapons are non-living toxins like the nerve agent sarin, used in the 1995 Tokyo subway attack by the Aum Shinrikyo cult, whereas biological weapons are living organisms such as bacteria and viruses that can be contagious and multiply. The 1972 Biological Weapons Convention included chemical toxins in the definition of biological agents, which the 139 treaty signatories are prohibited from developing or stockpiling.

⏸ UN inspectors dismantle Iraq's chemical arsenal

Iraq is suspected of using the chemical hydrogen cyanide, a form of which was used in Nazi gas chambers, during the Iran-Iraq war of 1980–88. Saddam Hussein's regime

acknowledged possessing Scud missiles with biological warheads during the 1991 Gulf War. Despite having dismantled more than 75 chemical warheads and 40,000 chemical weapons since the end of the Gulf War, UN weapons inspectors were believed to suspect that in 1998 Saddam had 20 secret bunkers and a secret hoard of the biological agents anthrax and botulinum.

⏸ Plague could be used as a biological weapon

It is believed that there was research in Russia in 1992 into using forms of plagues

as biological weapons. In 1995, the USA was known to have had nine chemical weapon stockpiles throughout the country and it was reported that in 1986 strains of anthrax and botulinum were secretly sold by the US government to the Iraqi military.

CONTROLLING BODIES

▶▶ Doctors may police viral outbreaks around the World

In 1993, an organization of US doctors proposed ProMED, a team of scientists that would travel to outbreaks of disease worldwide to identify possible foul play. One ubiquitous viral agent on their list is a pathogen which, when released into the environment, could either die out quickly or spread beyond its intended area. It is also easy and cheap to grow. A single bacterium can divide every 20 minutes, producing about one billion copies an hour.

▶ Weapons convention agrees to on-the-spot inspections

By Dec 1997, 106 countries had signed and ratified the Chemical Weapons Convention. This convention was put in

Left
With the threat of an Iraqi chemical attack ever-present, troops from the US Armored Division's 1st Brigade practise emergency field treatment in the Saudi desert, Feb 20, 1991.

place to bind nations to declare any chemicals in their possession and includes 'verification provisions' – short-notice inspections of suspected violating nations.

⏸ Sound waves used to identify chemical weapons

A team led by Dr Dipen Sinha at the Los Alamos National Laboratory New Mexico, USA, announced in Dec 1997 that they had patented a device which, using sound waves, can identify, through the walls of a container, more than 100 agents used in chemical warfare in less than 20 seconds.

▶▶ The gene therapy which could be used in warfare

In July 1997, the British Medical Association announced it had commissioned a report to investigate the threat of a new kind of biological warfare that utilizes advances in gene therapy. Dr Vivienne Nathanson said at a conference in Edinburgh, UK, that it was possible that in the future armies could develop agents able to target specific genes to induce illness or death or even certain ethnic genetic characteristics.

INFORMATION WARFARE

▶ The electronic battlefield without limits

The battlefield has become a 'battlespace', as militaries around the world become more technologically advanced. Not only will wars be fought on land, sea and air, but also in the electronic domain, where speed will mean having the upperhand. Spy satellites and unmanned reconnaissance drones that can speed up information between soldiers in the field and generals are being developed in the USA. @ *war machines p72*

⏸ Satellites used in war for exact military positioning

The Gulf War of 1991 is considered to be the first 'information war' because the Allied troops had a significant strategic advantage owing to the Global Positioning System (GPS). This is made up of a ring of US military satellites which gives a person holding a GPS sensor their location on the planet, accurate to within inches, making it easier and faster for troops to estimate enemy positions.

⏸ Australia's north coast protected by radar

In Australia, the Australian Defence Force's response to possible threats from a variety of aggressive smaller powers has been to develop the Joint Warrior Interoperability Demonstration, (JWID), which includes a radar network that monitors the whole of the north coast up to a total distance of 3,000 km (1,864 miles). This is connected to a computer network which both shares information and simulates defence exercises with the US military.

▶ 3-D spy maps could give a real-time picture of the World

A space shuttle mission planned for 1999 is being organized to gather data which will contribute towards a real-time supermap of the entire world being produced by US intelligence. The goal is to compress within 10 years the intelligence gathered from spy planes, satellites, missiles, and the shuttle into a single computer system which will produce detailed 3-D maps of geographical features, weather conditions as well as troop movements.

▶▶ Cyberterrorism could be the future for remote attacks

The Feb 1998 edition of the US computer magazine *Wired* carried an article in which author John Arquilla created the scenario of the 'Great CyberWar of 2002'. In this article, North Korea launches a hack-attack on the USA's computer-controlled dams, power and nuclear plants, telephone and transport systems. This hypothetical hack-attack escalated into full-scale war as the USA, believing the offensive came from China and Russia, retaliated by paralysing their financial systems with logic bombs, computer virus programs sent through networks that activate at their destinations. The US Defense Department has already taken the initiative and conducted 'simulated' cyberterrorism exercises in which they managed to cut off Californian

Above
An artist's impression of a Navstar Block 2R Global Positioning System (GPS) satellite, which will allow military organizations to pinpoint locations to within 30m (98.4 ft). In total 20–26 satellites are to be bought.

electricity supplies, penetrate the Bank of England in London, UK, and cause aeroplane crashes in Chicago.

♻ Back to the future

Anthrax leakage

In 1979, about 1g of the chemical anthrax was accidentally leaked from a Soviet biological weapons plant in Sverdlovsk, (now called Yekaterinburg), Russia. 64 people who were downwind of the plant were killed.

Gruinard Island

Gruinard Island, off the coast of Scotland, UK, remained infected with anthrax spores for some 40 years after biological weapons tests were conducted there by the British army during WWII.

Biological weapons stockpiles

In 1995, the US Office of Technology Assessment named 17 countries they suspected of secretly possessing biological weapons. The countries listed included Iran, Iraq, Libya, Syria, North and South Korea, Taiwan, Israel, Egypt, Vietnam, Laos, Cuba, Bulgaria, India, South Africa, China and Russia.

GUNS

MILITARY ISSUE

Smart bombs will revolutionize future wars

Current smart bombs are all laser-guided. As lasers cannot penetrate smoke or fog US designers are working on a weather-proof secret guidance system, code-named 'edge'. It will use global positioning signals from satellites to guide weapons. As the satellites talk via radio, the weather will not affect the weapons' efficacy.

South African mobile long-range gun

The G6 is a highly mobile and accurate long-range gun developed and produced by South African arms manufacturer, Denel. The fast reaction capability of the G6 self-propelled howitzer allows the gun to fire the first round within 60 seconds of the vehicle stopping, often the time difference between life and death. The 155 mm (6 in) main gun is equipped with a 45 calibre autofrettaged barrel and is fitted with telescopic sight giving it a firing range of 3 km (1³/₄ miles).

Gun that can see around corners

The Land Warrior, developed in 1996 by the US military, is an M16 rifle with a thermal camera, infrared laser rangefinder and a digital compass mounted on the rifle barrel. Instead of exposing himself to enemy fire, the soldier will be able to use the weapon to 'look' around corners for thermal images. A computer provides a topographic map of the area and the positions of the enemy and his own troops. This information is displayed on a small headset and can be communicated to fellow troops.

Tank guns to use electric energy

The US Army's Focused Technology Program is using electrical energy to increase the fire power in future land combat vehicles. Electrothermal-Chemical (ETC) guns offer the potential of significantly increasing the muzzle energy of tank gun systems with only minor modifications to the structure. The system works when a body of high-temperature, low-mass plasma ignites and controls the burning of the propellant, providing the transfer mechanism whereby electrical energy from a power supply is coupled to the release of chemical energy. The result, in layman's terms, is a very big bang.

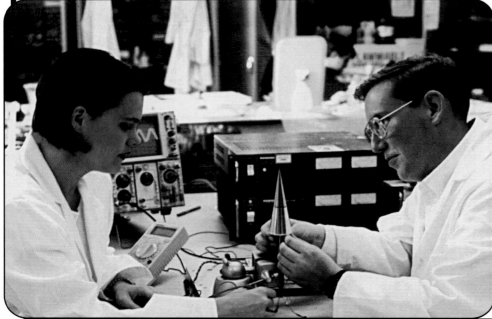

Left
Scientists at work developing 'smart' bullets at an Aerospace Engineering laboratory in Auburn University, Alabama, USA. Like smart bombs, the bullets will be able to track targets, and should be ready for military use within the next 15 years.

NON-LETHAL WEAPONS

⏸ Self-defence weapon which stuns attackers

The air taser stun weapon is a hand held, non-lethal self-protection system which uses compressed air to launch two small probes attached to a 5 m (15 ft) wire. When the probes make contact with an assailant, powerful electronic pulses are emitted through the wires, which enter the nervous system and disable the target. It causes incapacitation for one to 15 minutes, but no permanent injury. The technology was invented by the chief scientist from the Apollo Moon Landing Program and is already available in the US. After firing the probes, the taser can be used as a contact stun gun.

⏩ Electromagnetic weapons affect nervous system

Electromagnetic weapons emit radio frequencies that heat up a target like a microwave oven, with effects ranging from discomfort and fever to death, depending on the distance. Very low frequency electromagnetic radiation has been used to put test animals into a stupor or cause their brain cells to release histamine, a phenomenon that would cause flu-like, debilitating symptoms in a human. Successful prototypes have already been developed but are so sensitive that they have been classified as 'top secret'. However, it is believed that some of the more advanced systems in existence can be used to exert control over human minds and behaviour.

⏸ Blinding lasers are considered too dangerous

A fourth protocol added to the Geneva Convention in 1995 outlawed the use of blinding lasers in warfare. A short while before, the US Pentagon cancelled an outstanding order for a blinding laser, called a Dazer, that could be fitted to an M16 rifle. The Chinese military is believed to have withdrawn a similar laser weapon from service in compliance with the Geneva agreement. A non-lethal laser, which can disable an adversary with temporary blindness, has since been developed.

⏸ Acoustic weapons that vibrate your insides

Acoustic or sonic arms are classified as non-lethal weapons. They are set to resonate at certain very high or low frequencies which vibrate the internal organs of the targeted person. It stuns them and induces extreme forms of discomfort, nausea, or, according to the experts at the Pentagon, can even "liquefy their bowels and reduce them to quivering diarrhetic messes". The flexibility of use of acoustic weapons means that they can easily be mounted on helicopters or armoured cars, allowing for a wide array of delivery options for maximum effectiveness.

Above
The Hellfire is a laser-guided anti-tank missile. With over 11,000 already built, its makers are building an updated version that can evade electro-optic counter-attacks and which will have a digital autopilot and a more powerful warhead.

INVENTIONS

▶ Phaser gun is too big to move

Hans Eric Herr from San Diego, USA, has patented a laser gun (a 'phaser' in *Star Trek* terminology) which uses lasers to produce beams of ultra-violet light. The beams create a path of ionized air down which the desired amount of electric current can pass. It has a range of 100 m (320 ft) and can stun a victim painlessly, cause painful muscle spasms, or induce a heart attack. Presently, however, Herr's invention is too big to be hand-held or operated as a gun.

⏸ Combination of rifle and shotgun developed

M & R Machine and Tool shop owner, Richard Pitoniak, of South Hampton, USA, has built a prototype firearm, the first ever combination rifle-gun. Called the Crossfire Mark I, the gun offers the choice of firing shotgun ammunition, like buckshot, from an upper barrel, or, with the flick of a switch, calibre bullets from the lower rifle shaft. In a situation where less than lethal force is required, hunters can shoot up to 27.5 m (90 ft) using the shotgun, or 91.5 m (300 ft) with the rifle.

▶ Guns that can recognize their owners

Oxford Micro Devices in the USA has developed an electronic fingerprint verification device which ensures that a weapon can only be fired by its rightful owner. The FingerChip is a miniature sensor, built into the handle of the firearm, which captures a live image of the authorized user's fingerprint. The data is stored in non-volatile memory within the weapon, and the gun only responds once the user has been properly identified. The ingenious user-identification capability can be fitted in to existing weapons once fully developed.

♻ Back to the future

Super Gun

The final secret weapon Germany built in WWII was a huge super-gun, the *Hochdruckpumpe*, developed by Saar Rochling. It was built as a sectional 50 m (200 ft) tube with side-branches, aligned like ribs on a backbone. A succession of charges propelled a missile at 1,500 m per second (5,000 ft per second). Prototypes were built at Antwerp and Luxembourg, and the largest one of all was set-up at Calais to bomb London.

Babylon

The greatest secret gun in history was designed by Gerald Bull for use by Iraq against Israel. Code-named Babylon, it would have weighed 2,100 tonnes. The steel barrel, 30 cm (1 ft) thick at the breech, was to have measured 150 m (500 ft) in length. The gun's components were built in England under the guise of oil-refinery components. When the plan was revealed in 1990, Gerald Bull was shot dead by Israeli Secret Police.

WAR MACHINES

AIRCRAFT

Airborne-laser fighters to destroy missiles

The US Air Force, in conjunction with Boeing, LWR and Lockheed Martin, is testing laser-equipped aeroplanes capable of destroying enemy missiles from hundreds of kilometres away and expect to launch the first plane in 2002. Within seconds, airborne lasers will lock onto the threat and eliminate it using an on-board infrared system with 360° sensors. The Army is also developing a squadron of manned or unmanned space planes armed with lasers which are able to destroy both missiles and their connected satellites. The first of these space fighters could be launched by 2030.

Apache helicopter detects and identifies enemy targets

After the success of the Apache Longbow helicopter comes news of its successor, the AH-64 Apache. Containing advanced avionics, it can detect, identify and prioritize enemy targets in all-weather conditions. The Boeing Company of Arizona, USA, built six prototypes to test the computer systems. Meanwhile, Britain's Royal Navy is set to launch the new anti-submarine helicopter in 1998. Built by Lockheed Martin, the Merlin EH101 is fitted with advanced radar and Active Dipping Sonar which can be lowered into the sea to listen for enemy submarines. On detecting an enemy sub, it can attack using Stingray torpedoes and depth charges.

Stealth surveillance using robotic spy plane

The US Air Force has developed a robot spy plane for military surveillance which could be operational by 2000. The Dark Star, a plane developed to be invisible to radar due to its revolutionary flying saucer-like contours, will fly unmanned at 10,000 m (30,000 ft) relying on remote control from a Nevada airbase. The stealth aircraft's advanced camera and radar capabilities will

enable it to fly over enemy zones and pinpoint detail to 30 cm (1 ft), relaying these captured images to headquarters.

▶ Versatile fighter avoids detection using Spectra

The new smooth-bodied Rafale from Dassault of France is a highly versatile fighter which can avoid radar detection by using Spectra, an electronic warfare system which blocks enemy radar signals. The pilot's multi-function headgear combines a helmet, missile targeting display, oxygen mask and chemical-warfare protection. Although the Rafale has already been tested, the French air force is unlikely to fly the first squadron until 2005.

▶▶ Unmanned planes will enable attacks direct from HQ

The British Ministry of Defence is developing plans to replace the expensive Tornado offensive strike bombers with unmanned planes and precision-guided missiles by 2015. The missiles, which can be launched from land-based vehicles, submarines or ships, can be guided to within metres of the chosen target. Attacks could therefore be ordered and carried out from military headquarters, and fewer ground personnel would be needed.

Above
The long, thin shape of the Very Slender Vessel (VSV) allows it to cut through the seas at high speeds even in rough weather. Its almost semi-circular underwater shape increases its strength and means it can be built from lightweight materials.

SEACRAFT

▶▶ Scientists in the UK design a three-hulled warship

The world's first three-hulled warship is being planned by the Royal Navy. A standard 100-m (30-ft) frigate travels at 30 knots, but the new trimaran will travel at 45 knots and have more internal space. The revolutionary ship is being designed by scientists at University College, London, UK, who estimate that the cost of the vessel would be about £60 million ($95 million).

Right
The XM2002 ammunition resupply vehicle, a self-propelled Howitzer, equipped with a fully automated ammunition handling system, fulfils the increasing demand for unmanned vehicles.

▶ Sweden tests her new Stealth Warship

Designed by Captain Lars Salomonsson of Sweden, the Stealth Warship is based on a twin-hulled catamaran powered by water jets instead of easily-detectable and noisy engines. The ship's highly angular, smooth, flat-surfaced appearance is calculated to deflect enemy radar signals. The Stealth Warship prototype has undergone sea tests and could be in service by 2000.

❚❚ Royal Navy's twelve deck helicopter assault ship

The Royal Navy's largest ship in 40 years, the helicopter assault ship *Ocean* is the first ship of its kind to have been purpose-built as a helicopter platform ship. The 12-deck leviathan, launched in early 1998, will be used to transport a 500-man Marine commando unit and their equipment to the battlefield. In non-military situations, the ship could be used to dispatch up to 250 aid vehicles to a crisis zone.

VEHICLES

❚❚ Smart tanks work together to clear mines

A robotic tank called the Fieldable Explosive Target Clearer and Hunter (FETCH) has been developed by Massachusetts Institute of Technology (MIT) professor and IS Robotics founder Rodney Brooks and IS Robotics researcher Joe Jones to locate anti-tank cluster munitions. A number of these smart tanks, each equipped with Global Positioning System (GPS) navigation, magnetic grippers and sensors to detect terrain and munitions, work together to search an area. The developers hope to create a system that locates and digs up land mines. @ *robots p28*

❚❚ Tanks that can assemble bridges

Purpose-built tanks can aid troops in assembling bridges in minutes with a system devised by Vickers Bridging in Wolverhampton, UK. The BR90, bought by the British Army and three German Royal Engineer regiments, can span gaps from 9 to 60 m (27 to 180 ft) and withstand loads of up to 70 tonnes, including wheeled or tracked vehicles. The system is constructed from advanced aluminium alloy panels, and a two-man crew can assemble a bridge in under 10 minutes. A collaborative venture is under way with French tank manufacturers Giat to mount BR90 bridges on top of the Le Clerc tank.

♻ Back to the future

Caspian Monster

One of the most formidable military developments in cold-war Russia was the Caspian Monster, the ekranoplane (*ekrano* is Russian for 'surface'). Relying on ground effect, the build-up of pressure beneath aerofoils when the craft is near the surface, the vessel skims land or sea at 300 knots (550km/h). The prototype was also able to take off like a jet aircraft.

Spruce Goose

In 1947, the Spruce Goose flew for 900 m (2,700 ft). Commissioned by Howard Hughes, this wooden flying boat with a wingspan of 97.5 m (300 ft) was intended to carry supplies from America to Europe during WWII.

Frozen fleet

Pykrete was developed during WWII as an indestructible material with which to build boats. Made of a frozen mixture of water, wood and pulp, pykrete floated and did not melt very easily. The war was over before a pykrete fleet was built.

The car of the future will run on a fuel cell whose only by-product is water

TRANSPORT

- **The future car will be less polluting**. For many years, people have talked about the electric-powered car as being most likely to replace the petrol-run car. However, it is increasingly probable that cars will be run in future on a mixture of electric and petrol power. The car will run on battery power until that runs out before switching to an emergency petrol supply. Solar-powered cars are as yet far too impractical since they require a very large surface area in order to make them move. Perhaps the most exciting prospect for the future could be hydrogen-powered cars. Although still in its infancy the idea of using hydrogen fuel is particularly appealing because the main by-product is water.

- **Cars are bound to become safer and stronger**. NASA have developed many different types of new material for use on spacecraft that car manufacturers plan to adopt. This should mean lighter and stronger cars with better fuel consumption. Thanks to global positioning satellites (GPS) and automatic highways driving will become a thing of the past. Cars will simply be able to drive themselves.

- **International travel should get faster**. Supersonic planes should be able to carry more passengers and charge less. To fly from London to Australia may one day take only a couple of hours. It is hoped that laser technology can be used to create enough energy to power 'spaceplanes' which will make it possible to travel at Mach 2.4 (1,600 mph). No one is quite sure, however, how passengers will react to the massive amounts of G force experienced during their flight.

- **Ships will be able to sail both above and below sea level**. New ship technologies, such as magnetohydrodynamics and flipper technology, are already increasing the speeds at which ships can run. Massive cruise liners will cater for tax exiles as well as those bored with the traditional beach holiday. The next step in holidays will be underwater cruises.

CARS

CAR SYSTEMS

TRAINS

AIRCRAFT

SEACRAFT

TECHNO-BABBLE

GNOPTER
Aerial vehicles that do not require physical pilots on board, but which are remotely-controlled.

EKRANOPLANE
A cross between a plane, boat and hovercraft that uses 'ground effect' to fly a few feet over the sea. In the 1970s the Russian built military ekranoplanes.

MAGLEV
Electromagnetic system that uses magnetic attractions to levitate a train a few centimetres above a track.

MIDAIR PASSENGER EXCHANGE
A collision between two planes.

MOBILE AREA NETWORK
A car of the future with a host of features including GPS and multiple sensors.

VANITY PLATE
As well as being a pointless large web image that serves absolutely no function, this also refers to a private car registration plate.

1956	Jim Power of Ford, USA, builds a scale model of the flying car, the *Volante*
1997	Coventry University, UK, designs a concept car for the future which will no longer have a steering-wheel or engine

Left
The solar–powered car *Sunraycer* being followed by its support vehicle during a road test in the Simi valley, USA.

CARS

NEW FUEL CARS

 Honda Dream flies from Adelaide to Darwin

The 6-m (20-ft) long solar-powered Honda *Dream Car* won the 1996 World Solar Challenge which is held every three years. With the help of a sophisticated on-board computer, it travelled the 3,000 km (1,900 miles) from Darwin to Adelaide, Australia, in just four days with an average speed of 89 km/h (55 mph).

 Sunraycer and the World Solar Challenge

Sunraycer was General Motors' entry for the first World Solar Challenge race which was held in Australia in Nov 1987. Its efficiency impressed alternative fuel enthusiasts when it won the gruelling race at an average speed of 67 km/h (41.6 mph). @ *resources p124*

 Lotus Elise is not at all sluggish

Proving that electric cars do not have to be sluggish vehicles, Lotus has built the *Elise*, an electric sports car which can accelerate from 0–112 km/h (70 mph) in five seconds and boasts 20,000 rpm. Its two electric motors feature cooling ducts which, when combined with the light aluminium body, minimize air resistance.

 Mercedes' zinc-air battery goes three times further

France and Switzerland are encouraging the sale of electric cars by offering financial help and tax breaks to buyers. Germany's postal service, Deutsche Post, plans to replace its fleet of 15,000 Mercedes 410E vans with electric cars using a new zinc-air battery developed by Electric Fuels of Jerusalem, Israel. Trials conducted from 1996 indicate that the zinc-air battery is more efficient than conventional lead-acid batteries when used in electric cars, providing three times the driving distance and better capability on hills and in traffic jams.

 **Jersey is test ground for the Electric Toyota RAVA4**

Toyota is conducting a trial of five electric cars on the English Channel island of Jersey, UK. With a speed limit of 65 km/h (40 mph) and a land mass of only 45 miles^2 (11,650 hectares), the island is seen as a suitable test for electric cars. A Nickel Metal Hydride (NiMH) battery specially developed by Toyota and Panasonic gives the car a range of 200 km (124 miles). Regenerative brakes and special tyres with low rolling resistance help reduce energy consumption.

 Rover biodiesel and the fish and chip mystery

Scientists at British-based Rover have been experimenting with running cars on fuel from oilseed rape, the third largest crop in the UK. Rover has converted the plant into a fuel called biodiesel which can be used in conventional diesel vehicles. In 1997, in Reading, UK, Rover's researchers conducted tests on three buses running on biodiesel. The successful results showed

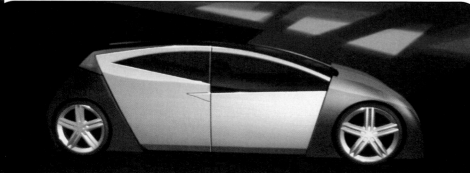

Left
The Ford P2000 whose lightweight design offers energy–efficient propulsion for the 21st century. The tiny 4-cylinder, 1.2 litre engine is made from aluminium but has 3-litre performance, and the promise of 160 km (100 miles) per hour.

that the buses produced fewer emissions than when using petrol, but there was a strange side-effect – the exhaust fumes smelt like fish and chips.

▶ Mercedes A-Class has a hydrogen-powered cell

Mercedes unveiled a prototype for the hydrogen-powered A-Class category at the 1997 Frankfurt Motor Show as well as plans to start mass production of the six-seater car in 2005. In Dec 1997, Ford and Daimler Benz contracted Canadian company Ballard Power Systems with a view to developing hydrogen-fuel systems. A hydrogen-powered fuel cell uses oxygen from the air and hydrogen gas to produce electricity, and helps to reduce harmful emissions.

❚❚ The Liquid Petroleum Gas network in the Netherlands

The Netherlands already has 45,000 vehicles running on Liquid Petroleum Gas (LPG) as well as an extensive LPG refuelling network. Producing lower emissions of harmful carbon dioxide and carbon monoxide, this alternative fuel was predicted to take off during the 1970s but was overtaken by diesel. However, it still remains one of the cheapest forms of conversion to cleaner fuel, taking only one day and involving fitting a larger petrol tank.

▶ Honda's Zero-Level emissions engine

In Oct 1997, at the Tokyo Motor Show, Japan, Honda unveiled its new Zero-Level Emission engine. The engine is designed to cut emissions to less than 10% of the minimum emissions level. At the heart of the engine is a combustion system that reduces hydrocarbons, and catalytic converters which remove excess pollutants.

▶ EV1 is fuelled by a variable alternating current

The two-seater General Motors electric EV1 car was first marketed in the USA in 1996. The car's System 110 incorporates an inverter which converts current (DC) from the battery pack into 110 kilowatts of variable alternating current (AC) which is used to drive the vehicle's motor.

CONCEPT CARS

❚❚ Chrysler's Composite Compact Vehicle

US company Chrysler's CCV (Composite Compact Vehicle) is made out of recyclable plastic similar to that used for fizzy drink bottles. The CCV can be made in only six and a half hours, has fewer parts and is therefore cheaper than its steel-bodied Chrysler counterparts. @ *waste p126*

▶ Ford Fiesta developed using hemp-based plastic

Ford has developed a new reinforced plastic using hemp, the plant which produces the

drug cannabis. They will be using the new plastic to make the spoilers which will reduce drag in the Fiesta model. Hemp is easy to grow and the plastic is cheaper than conventional plastic.

▶▶ Concept 2096 car has 'smart' colours and no driver

The *Concept 2096* car of the future was unveiled at the 1996 British Motor Show. Designed by the University of Coventry, UK, the car will be painted with 'smart' colours that allow the car to change colour with its environment and the glass will also be able to change from transparent to opaque. The interior has no steering-wheel or engine and, as the car is intended to be driverless, a computer navigation system will control the car leaving the driver simply to enter the destination. @ *car systems p78*

▶ Mercedes Benz F3000 is an 80 mph bubble car

This two-seater, three-wheeled bubble car, was launched at the Frankfurt Motor Fair in 1997. The car is capable of travelling at 130 km/h (80 mph). It uses technology similar to that used in tilting trains, meaning it can take corners at great speeds. Sensors in the car can analyze driving techniques and control the front axle, depending on whether the driver has a sporty or smooth style.

▶▶ Mini hovercraft which can fly over dry land

US vehicle designer Frank Didik has built a mini-hovercraft which can fly up to 20 cm (8 in) above the ground at 40 km/h (25 mph) over flat ground, 25 km/h (15 mph) over water and 74 km/h (45 mph) over ice. The body is made from styrofoam covered with a fibreglass shell.

▶▶ Lightcraft to travel 25 times speed of light

Leik Myrabo, an aerospace engineer at the Rensselaer Polytechnic Institute, New York State, USA, is developing a Lightcraft. The craft uses a propulsion system called magneto-hydrodynamics, a system based

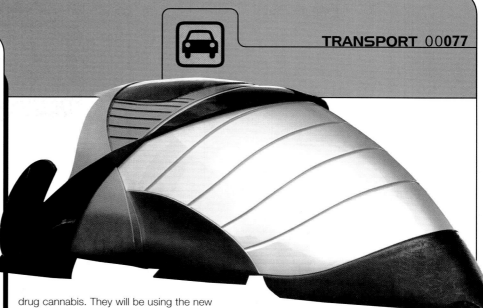

Above
The *Concept 2096* car was given an aerodynamic shape, and an adjustable aerofoil on the roof. Other features include windows that change from transparent to opaque, a computer-controlled navigation system, and no steering-wheel, converting the driver into a mere passsenger.

on power from microwaves directed at the craft from satellites in space.

▶ Hybrid Hypercar made from space-age materials

Rocky Mountain Institute's *Hypercar* is an ultra-light, hybrid-electric prototype which is three or more times as efficient and ten times cleaner than a conventional car. The car uses lightweight space-age materials, is rust-free, dent and scratch resistant, and capable of absorbing five times as much crash energy as steel. 'Smart' windows, though visually clear, reflect unwanted solar rays, and special paints, vented double-skinned roofs and solar-powered vent fans also contribute to interior comfort by repelling heat on hot days and retaining heat on cold days. @ *spacecraft p144*

♻ Back to the future

Volante

In 1956, Jim Powers at Ford, USA, built a scale model of the flying car, the *Volante*. In 1997, Dennis Bushnell, the chief scientist for NASA at Langely, Virginia, USA, predicted that the skycar would be the car of the future.

Ford Nucleon

The US government briefly sponsored a project to build an atomic-powered car in the 1950s but abandoned the project. In 1958, Ford designed a futuristic prototype car – low-slung and featuring large fins at the rear – for an atomic car called the Ford *Nucleon*.

C5

In Jan 1985, the British inventor Sir Clive Sinclair launched his electric vehicle, the C5, in the UK. The 3-wheeled vehicle was only 1.5 m (4 ft 8 in) long and a had a top speed of just 20 km/h (12.5 mph). The project was abandoned ten months later after the car was declared too dangerous for road use.

Left
The cockpit of the Mitsubishi HSR-V1 contains a concealed steering wheel available for when the driver wishes to steer the vehicle instead of relying on the in-car computer.

CAR SYSTEMS

SAFETY

 **Toyota's advanced safety vehicle systems**

Toyota has been developing a series of safety systems. Innovations include The Drowsy Driver Warning System, which prevents drivers falling asleep at the wheel, and the Automatic Collision Reduction Braking System, which uses a CCD camera and radar to measure the distance of an obstacle ahead and warn of impending collisions. @ cars p76

SAAB's crash responsive restraint technology

Saab is introducing a Saab Active Head Restraint (SAHR) system on its latest models to provide high-tech protection against rear-end collision whiplash. In a rear-end collision at over 8 km/h (5 mph), the mechanical system, activated by body weight and crash force, moves the headrest upwards in an arc motion to cradle the back of the head and absorb most of the kinetic energy. The latest Saab models also come with a pioneering electrostatic air filtration system which filters out airborne particles and atmospheric aerosols.

 **Walt Disney helps technicians design a new windscreen**

Pilkington of Lancashire, UK, is creating virtual views of a variety of new windscreen shapes and curves through computer simulation. The radical 3-D technology developed by Walt Disney for the film *Toy Story* gives researchers an idea of what drivers see through the glass, enabling them to design safe and comfortable windscreens. The simulation can also reveal whether or not a new design is technically possible and how it might be produced.

Sensors help with parking and sense the rain

ITT Automotive in Auburn Hills, Michigan, USA, is an innovative supplier of systems and components to the vehicle manufacturing industry. The company has developed Park Assist – a system devised

 Left
This Car Cosy is a state-of-the-art car protection system. It provides all-weather protection and security for your car as well as a guaranteed parking space.

to help drivers park their cars by warning of obstacles hidden from view via ultrasonic sensors. On detecting an obstacle, the system sounds a tone that becomes continuous as the distance narrows. The company has also devised a Rainsensor system that activates a single-arm extending wiper once moisture is detected on the windscreen. Wiping speed and delay time are also automatically set to the particular weather conditions.

GUIDANCE AND AUTOMATION

▶ Hands-free driving down the automated highway

Trials are set to begin in the USA on the Automatic Highway System (AHS) in 2002. Three basic concepts, hands-free technology, road tracking systems and vehicle automation, work together to form a fully functioning automated highway. At Demo '97, an event organized by the National Highway System Consortium (NAHSC), USA, several Buicks were equipped with computer-controlled steering, braking and throttle systems, a radar system, cockpit display, acceleration sensors and vehicle-to-roadside communication systems. Tests at Demo '97 included switching from computer to manual control, lane changes, speed control, lane tracking and rapid deceleration for obstacle avoidance.

Above
A network of 21 Navistar Global Positioning System (GPS) satellites provide the information for many in-car navigation systems. This hand-held device can be used by hikers, climbers and even private pilots as well as car drivers.

❚❚ New in-car navigation uses Global Positioning System

Philips has launched the CARiN interactive vehicle guidance system, the latest in electronic vehicle navigation, which directs drivers by connecting Global Positioning System (GPS) location with CD-ROM maps. The smart compact box system can provide directions through computerized voice instructions supplemented by on-screen diagrams. The system can also store addresses, re-plot routes when you stray off the path and warn of oncoming turns. Apart from navigational help, CARiN offers an on-board computer, TV reception, radio and telephone operation all via one screen.

❚❚ Mitsubishi HSR-VI concept car that drives itself

The HSR (Highly Sophisticated Research) V1 was Mitsubishi's concept car at the 1997 Tokyo Car Show. The car uses computer technology to drive itself, but should a human wish to drive, a steering wheel concealed in the dashboard slides out. Instead of an ignition key, the car will read a personal identity medallion.

❚❚ Automatic Petrol Station in use in USA

Shell has been operating a prototype robotic petrol station in Sacramento, California, USA, since Feb 1997. Called the Smart Pump, the automated system can tell which side of the car the fuel tank is on by reading an electronic tag on the windscreen and an in-built vision system allows the robotic arm to align itself precisely with the fuel tank door. The customer pays by swiping a credit card through a unit similar to an ATM. @ robots p28

MULTIMEDIA

▶ Chrysler's Edge Car includes a holographic display

The Edge Car was a prototype car built by Chrysler in 1996. It was equipped with a holographic display, a computer that displays data on journey time and fuel consumption as well as showing what is playing on the compact laser disc player.

▶ The multimedia dashboard centre

Citroën have developed a PC entertainment and information centre for the cars of the

Above
The Automatic Highway System (AHS) looks set to revolutionize driving in the next millennium. Researchers are looking at ways of combining computers, sensors and radars in their quest to create the ultimate hands-free drive.

future. The Xsara controls a car radio and television tuner, hands-free cellular telephone, surround-sound DVD-Rom unit and Internet access. The dashboard screen will automatically shut down when the car goes over 5 km/h (3 mph) so as not to distract the driver. Tourists can use the DVD-Rom, which is an advanced form of CD-Rom, to locate the nearest petrol stations and hotels.

♻ Back to the future

The Safety First campaign
In 1931, the British Government started a road safety campaign which advised pedestrians not to read or drop parcels whilst crossing a busy road.

Oil level indicator
The Lubimeter, a device which glowed red if the oil level in the car got dangerously low, was invented in 1908. The invention of the dipstick made the Lubimeter superfluous.

Manufacturers call brakes unsafe
During the 1920s, some of the major car manufacturers, horrified at the costs of having to refit cars with brakes, actually campaigned against brakes, claiming that they were a safety hazard.

The early answer to congestion
The Bubble Car went on display at the Motor show in London in 1958. One style of car sat the driver in front of his passenger and both had to climb out of the roof. This car was designed to counteract traffic congestion.

1920s	A suspended monorail that was driven along by a propellor similar to those used by aeroplanes was developed in Scotland
2000	Transrapid electromagnetic monorail travels at 500 km/h from Berlin to Hamburg in Germany

Left
Developed in Japan, the Bullet trains were the world's first high-speed train. The Asama bullet train, seen here crossing a bridge over the Chikuma River, links Tokyo to Nagano. When building the tracks, special care is taken to avoid bends, enabling the trains to reach and sustain maximum speeds.

TRAINS

HIGH-PERFORMANCE

Japan's bullet train spurs the quest for speed

The Shinkansen, or Bullet Train, was the fastest in the world when services started in 1964 between Tokyo and Osaka, Japan. It can clock 211 km/h (131 mph), and many countries, including the USA, still have no trains which run as fast, even though its success sparked global interest in making trains go faster. The trains are able to achieve such high speeds because tight curves and steep grades were avoided when building the tracks. The bullet train which runs between between Hiroshima and Kokura, Japan, is the world's fastest scheduled train service, with an average speed of 264 km/h (164 mph).

High speed line to race across Taiwan

The island of Taiwan is to have its own high speed rail network, which could be in operation by 2000. It is the largest transport construction scheme underway anywhere in the world, and will run from Taipei to Kaohsiung, relieving traffic congestion. This four hour car journey, which can take up to 12 hours in heavy traffic, will be cut to 90 minutes by train. The capacity of each train

ranges from 800 to 1,400 for the double decker variety, and one will run in each direction every three minutes. They are expected to operate at speeds in the region of 250 km/h to 300 km/h (156 to 186 mph), although the tracks will be able to sustain speeds of 350 km/h (220 mph).

Rapid monorail being tested in Germany

The German engineering giant, Thyssen, has been investing billions of Deutschmarks in a test track for Europe's first electromagnetic monorail, the Transrapid. The train is designed to travel at speeds of up to 500 km/h (310 mph) and by 2000 the Transrapid will be racing high above the fields between Berlin and Hamburg, soon after going as far as Amsterdam, Holland.

The many generations of France's TGVs

Train de Grande Vitesse (TGV) is French for high speed train. The TGV project began in the 1960s and many generations of TGVs have since been manufactured. The TGV Duplex is a double-decker train introduced when TGV services reached saturation point

with up to one train running every three minutes. At the cost of only 4% more drag, the Duplex has a capacity 45% greater than its predecessors. Long-term plans are in place to upgrade trains and tracks for the Nouvelle Génération TGVs, which will be able to run at speeds of up to 362 km/h (225 mph) in commercial use.

ICE trains speed through Germany

The InterCity Express (ICE) trains operate on high-speed lines between major German cities. Siemens Transportation Systems have developed four models, including a divisible train and a tilting model. Tunnels are required in order to keep roadbeds straight for high speed travel, but like jet airplanes, ICE cars are

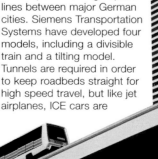

Right
Miami in Florida, USA, already has an established monorail network. German engineering company Thyssen is developing Europe's first electromagnetic monorail, which it plans to run from Germany as far as Holland.

pressurized, and so passengers are spared any discomfort to their ears. The cars are also equipped with stereo headsets, fax machines, telephones and even video screens in first class. The sleek white trains have a top speed of 330 km/h (205 mph).

❚❚ New brakes to stop high speed trains

High speed trains must be equipped with suitable braking technology: they must be able to stop efficiently at high speed without derailing or jolting the passengers. New generation trains are fitted with disc brakes which employ state-of-the-art dynamic braking systems. These work by converting mechanical energy from the traction motors back into electricity which can then be recycled. The dynamic braking system is responsible for more than 90% of the train's deceleration. In Sweden, tilting trains are each fitted with three independent braking systems: electric brakes, air-operated brake discs, and magnetic track brakes for emergency use.

❚❚ Design advances enhance stability and performance

As train speeds rise, so does the risk of increased vibrations causing the train to jump the track. To enhance stability, the designers of the French TGVs have altered the placement of bogies so that adjacent cars share a bogie, linking them semi-permanently and preventing them from pivoting away from each other on curves. As bogies get heavier, the risk of derailment increases so new materials such as aluminium alloys and carbon fibres are being tested to reduce their weight. The conventional steel-spring suspension has also been replaced by pneumatic suspension systems, providing better insulation from vibrations.

RIDES OF THE FUTURE

▶▶ Traffic jams avoided on the Beam

Futrex, based in South Carolina, USA, is currently testing a tunnel-free, non-collision alternative to the tube. The Beam will run two ways along a rail at around 60 km/h (37 mph) just over 5 m (16 ft) above the traffic jams at street level. This mode of public transport promises to be cheaper than any existing system, and, in addition, the Beam will be able to function in earthquakes and even 150 km/h (93 mph) hurricanes without being derailed.

▶ Magnetic levitation trains hover above the track

Magnetic levitation technology has been developed in Japan and also in Germany, where it is closest to commercialization. On the simplest level, the German electromagnetic system uses magnetic attraction, whereas the Japanese superconducting model is propelled by a

repulsive force created by repeated reversals of polarity in the two elements. The train relies on direct-current electromagnets to levitate a few centimetres above the track, and speed is controlled by varying the voltage and frequency of the current supplied. Maglev trains could be running by the end of 1999 and it is envisaged that they could be used on both intra-urban and intercity services.

▶ Tilting trains pull back into Britain

Tilting trains will be pulling into the UK in 2001. Virgin is paying £1 billion for 50 Pendolino trains, capable of 225 km/h (140 mph). The hydraulically-activated tilt of 8° allows the train to hit top speed around the bends without catapulting passengers and carriages. The technology was developed in the UK in the early 1980s but, when passengers aboard British Rail's Advanced Passenger Train prototype complained of feeling sick during high-profile demonstrations, the scheme was axed. In Sweden, however, tilting train technology was eagerly taken up when it was realized the country could never build straight enough tracks for Japanese- and French-style high speed trains. Four-hour journeys have already been cut by an hour, and there are plans to upgrade the current network to enable trains to travel at 300 km/h (186 mph). The trains are mounted on 'soft' bogies, which automatically adjust on curves and protect the track from extra stress. The amount of tilt required is calculated by on-board computers.

▶ Computerized carriages for cities and theme parks

Cybertran is a new method of mass transit and high speed rail, developed at the Idaho National Engineering Laboratory in Idaho, USA. The Cybertran system is based on using large numbers of small vehicles, as opposed to the conventional concept of small numbers of large vehicles. The carriages are controlled entirely by computer and operate on elevated guideways. It is estimated that speeds will range from 48 km/h (30 mph) to 241 km/h (150 mph) depending on the application. Two test series have been completed and a vehicle has now been constructed for further engineering tests. It is thought that the carriages could be used on the high speed inter-city market as well as on the metro systems, in theme parks and in congested tourist areas.

▶ Satellite system helps tackle a slippery problem

Thames Trains of London, UK, are running tests on a special train that has been

Above
This magnetic levitating linear railroad car was developed by Japanese company Miyazaki. German companies are working on similar 'Maglev' technology, and these trains could be in operation in cities across the world before 2000.

equipped with a Global Positioning System (GPS) receiver which is capable of detecting leaves on the track, a common excuse for delays in the rail service. These 'low adhesion zones' are picked up by the GPS which relays the information to a central control room, where a map pinpointing slippery areas is compiled. In the future, drivers may be able to receive this information on screens in train cabs.

♻ Back to the future

Bullet trains

On 1 Nov 1965, bullet trains began running in Japan between Tokyo and Osaka. The trains had an average speed of 161 km/h (100 mph) and were the first in the world to do so.

Tilting trains

In the early 1980s, the UK built the APT-E system. However, the tilting trains made passengers feel sick when they went round corners and the prototype was eventually consigned to a railway museum.

Sail plane

In the 1920s, George Bernie developed the sail plane. A suspended monorail that was driven along by a propellor similar to those used by aeroplanes was tried out on a line near Glasgow, Scotland. Despite all the sail plane's benefits, it never progressed beyond the experimental stage.

Left
The experimental National Aerospace Plane (NASP) is a space launch vehicle which may replace the space shuttle in the future. Fuelled by hydrogen, the NASP will be able to take off and land on conventional runways and fly at supersonic speeds to launch itself into orbit.

AIRCRAFT

ALTERNATIVE MODES OF FLIGHT

Boomerang planes solve twin-engine problems

Aviation designer Burt Rutan has developed a safer alternative to the twin-engined aircraft with an engine on each wing, which can be problematic if there is a slight discrepancy in power between the engines. The new Boomerang five-seater composite plane has a 210 hp engine mounted in the nose of the main fuselage with a smaller 200 hp engine mounted in a secondary fuselage set back 1.5 m (5ft) and connected to the tail boom and left wing. Navigation is via a Global Positioning System while other data is provided by a Macintosh computer.

New craft combines benefits of helicopters and aeroplanes

The tiltrotor, a combination of a helicopter and an aeroplane, could take to the sky by 1999, nearly 60 years after the craft was

first conceived in Britain. The V-22 Osprey tiltrotor, initially to be bought by the US Marine Corps, is being developed by Bell Helicopter Textron and Boeing and will take off like a helicopter and then continue to fly by tilting its rotors forward 90° like a conventional turboprop. The V-22 has the benefits of both its predecessors – it can land and take off in confined spaces, reach top speeds of up to 560 km/h (348 mph), is quieter than a conventional helicopter and

does not need to refuel quite as often. The military version can carry up to 24 marines, and a civilian nine-seater version, the Bell-Boeing 609, is also being developed. @ *war machines p72*

Cross the world in less than two hours in the Skylon

Constructed by Reaction Engines, UK, the Skylon spaceplane could make commercial

Right
Pathfinder is powered by solar cells located on the upper surface of the wing, and is supplemented by batteries. The unmanned aircraft has a wing span of 30 m, weighs just 190 kg, and will be able to reach altitudes of up to 20 km.

flights into space a realistic possibility. Taking off from a runway, the 747-sized craft is powered by an airbreathing rocket until it reaches the edge of the atmosphere, where it switches to conventional rocket technology. The skyplane is based on the horizontal take-off and landing (HOTOL) concept. It could be used to transport a maximum of 12 tonnes into space or fly people across to the other side of the world in less than two hours.

PASSENGER PLANES

▶▶ Second-generation Concord under development for 2010

European, American, Japanese and Russian aviation engineers are currently drawing up plans for cheaper-fare versions of the Concord Mach 2 which could be available by 2010. During supersonic flight the nose of the current generation Concords can reach temperatures of 127°C (260°F). As a result, the fuselage expands. To exceed Mach 2.4, very expensive materials would be required to cope with the extreme effects. It is likely that the second generation SST programme will utilize folding 'canard' fore-wings and, instead of the drooping nose which provides pilots with a forward view during landing and take-off, cameras will be mounted on the landing gear, cutting the plane's weight by 4,500 kg (4½ tons).

Above
A technician checks a model of an aircraft inside a Kolner Kryo Kanal (KKK) cryogenic wind tunnel. Liquid nitrogen prevents the air inside from heating, chilling it as it passes over the model, resulting in air densities that model the aerodynamics of full-size aircraft much more closely.

FLIGHT SYSTEMS

❚❚ Realistic flight simulation for air, land and sea craft

The Simona Research Simulator has been described as the most advanced flight simulator in the world. The simulator is mounted on six hydraulic legs, which provides a much more realistic experience than can be achieved in any other existing systems. The Simona system, developed by a research group at Delft University in Holland, incorporates a 180° by 40° view display, which can be remodelled to recreate the interiors of planes and helicopters as well as cars and boats.

❚❚ Stick-on patch to cover-up holes in aeroplanes

Scandia National Airlines has developed stick-on tape that can be used to repair aeroplanes. The tape, made of flexible, boron-fibre-reinforced composite materials, a mere 0.14 mm thick, can become three times stronger than a regular aluminium patch once laminated. The material, called a bonded composite doubler, was first tested on a Delta Airlines L-1011 jetliner to reinforce a corner of one of the doors. It will also be used to fix fuselage joints and landing gear bays.

▶▶ Air traffic to be controlled by Global Positioning System

As the skies become increasingly crowded with aircraft, the current Air Traffic Control (ATC) system, which relies on radar technology and strict flight path rules, will be superseded in the 21st century by the 'Free Flight' system. Using the US Global Positioning System (GPS) and the Russian Glonass satellite network for navigation, Free Flight should result in fewer delays and accidents as aeroplanes are directed along the quickest and most direct route. The more flexible system is currently being tested and could be reliable enough to land aircraft in zero-visibility by 2015. @ car systems p78

▶▶ Pilots of the future could be able to fly with a smile

A system that enables pilots and engineers to operate a computer using only their facial expressions is being developed by the US Air Force. Using technology called

Above
The Bell Boeing 609 is a new civilian tiltrotor plane, which will be able to carry up to nine passengers. The craft is being developed by Boeing and Bell Textron, who are capitalizing on technology initially formulated for military use.

Cyberlink, which has been developed with disabled computer-users in mind, the system enables up to 10 pre-programmed commands (a raise of the right eyebrow, for example) via 'smart' glasses or visors. The wearable computer system is particularly effective in areas where high levels of noise would make speech recognition systems superfluous. @ computers p22

♻ Back to the future

Avrocar

The VZ-9V Avrocar was developed first by Canada and then by the USA in the 1950s as an answer to vertical take-off aircraft. It was circular, about 6 m (20 ft) in diameter, and used a central fan powered by three turbo-jet engines to make a vertical take-off. Once in the air, the turbo-jet exhaust could be shifted to the rear to propel the vehicle forward. However, the vehicle only managed to fly at the low altitude of 1.8 m (6 ft) after which it became unstable. In 1961, the US Air Force dropped the project having spent a total of $10 million (£6 million) on it.

Concord

Concord, the supersonic airliner, was unveiled in 1967. From the start, there was diplomatic wrangling about whether or not the name should carry the French 'e'. After months of consultation it was decided that the English aircraft would be named 'Concord' and the French, 'Concorde'.

Left
Vessels of the 21st century may be designed to move through the water like a fish. The Robotuna forms part of a project to understand the physics of swimming and to develop better propulsion systems for submarines.

SEACRAFT

NEW FUELS

 Penguin-inspired technology used to propel a ship

A ship with flippers instead of a propeller is being developed at the Massachusetts Institute of Technology (MIT), USA. The prototype, a 4-m (12-ft) long boat named *Proteus*, was designed to imitate the way penguins swim. The flippers on a full-sized ship would flap about 30 times a minute, propelling the ship forward at a speed of 30 knots. Tests show that the flippers would offer nearly 90% efficiency, whereas a conventional ship has an efficiency of only 70%.

 Magnetohydrodynamics reduces noise and vibration

Researchers at the Argonne National Laboratory in Illinois, USA, are considering the benefits of using magnetohydrodynamic

(MHD) propulsion to propel ships and submarines. MHD uses a magnetic field and ionized particles to propel sea water, which in turn enables ocean-going vessels to move forward. The advantages of this concept over mechanical propellers include reduced vibration and noise in the vessel.

Furthermore, physical limitations would not restrict the top speed of MHD seawater vessels. Large and powerful magnets (8–20 tesla) will be required in order to achieve propulsion efficiencies comparable to those of conventional propellers.
@ *war machines p72*

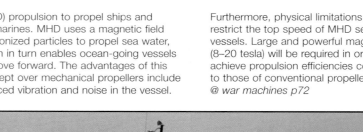

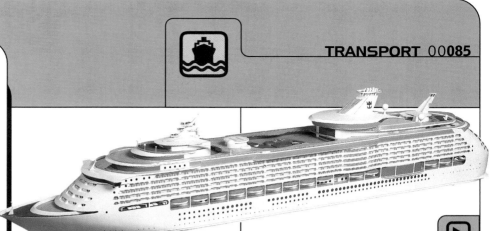

▶▶ The ship with wings designed for speed and economy

Wingship, a company based in Florida, USA, is to build the first Hoverplane incorporating elements of catamaran, hovercraft and wing-in-surface effect (WISE) technology in its design. The WISE design takes advantage of ground effect (or surface effect) in which a stable cushion of air is generated by a wing flying close to the ground or water. Reduced drag and increased lift make such a vehicle highly fuel efficient. The 10-m (33-ft) long Hoverplane, powered by a 300 hp engine and constructed from light-weight composite materials, will have a wingspan of 8 m (26 ft) and a passenger capacity of seven. The ship will travel at a height of 1 to 1.5 m (3 to 5 ft) above the water at a speed of about 100 km/h (62 mph).

Above
The interior of the cruise liner *Elation* shows how designers of passenger liners are creating bigger and more luxurious interiors to entertain and amaze their passengers.

PASSENGER SHIPS

▶ Eagle Class cruiser could include an ice rink

Plans to build the largest passenger ship in the world are now well underway and already more than 4,000 would-be passengers have booked to secure their places for a New Year cruise on 31 Dec 1999. The 311-m (990-ft) long by 48-m (144-ft) wide *Eagle Class* cruiser is to be built by Caribbean Cruises of Miami, USA, for a total $500 million (£300 million). It will rise 63 m (189 ft) above the water-line, with a gross weight of approximately 136,000 tonnes. Features on-board the massive vessel are to include an ice rink, a rock climbing wall, TV studio, wedding chapel and a multi-storey theatre.

▶ Escape for four months on the World of ResidenSea

Designed by Norwegians Knut Kloster Jr., Petter Yran and Bjørn Storbraaten, the World of ResidenSea will offer the rich and famous a tax haven and luxury home, cruising the world for four months of the year. With 15 decks and a crew of 500, the 333-m (1,000-ft) long liner will have all the facilities you could desire, from theatres and casinos to a supermarket and helicopter launching pad. With its maiden voyage only in mid-2000, more than a fifth of the 250 apartments have already been sold.

⏸ The first sailing liners with computer controlled sails

The *Wind Star* and her sister ship *Wind Song* are the first-ever sailing liners. They were commissioned by Windstar Sail Cruises and built by Ateliers et Chantiers du Havre (ACH), France. The ship's computer programmed sails have a total area of 2,000 m² (21,528 ft²) and the four masts are 58 m (190 ft) tall. The ship is able to carry as many as 180 passengers and a crew of 75.

SUBMERSIBLES

▶ The Nomad 100 can travel overwater or underwater

At first sight, the Nomad 100 looks like a conventional luxury cruiser, but this 70-m (210-ft) vessel can also travel beneath the ocean surface when it gets too choppy. Developed by a team in the US, the Nomad 100 can travel at 10 knots, powered by twin Cummins diesel engines, each generating 250 hp which switch to a 110 electric motor driven by a bank of accumulators if bad weather supervenes.

⏸ The new advanced Atmospheric Diving Suit

A heavy-duty underwater suit has been developed to enable engineers to repair sunken submarines at depths of 300 m (900 ft). Described as the world's most advanced Atmospheric Diving Suit (ADS), it is manufactured by International Hard Suits, Vancouver, Canada. The 300 kg

Above
Tickets have already been sold for the 1999 New Year's Eve party aboard the Eagle Class cruiser, which is set to become the world's largest passenger ship once it is complete.

(661 lb) Newtsuit is made of aluminium and has four engines for vertical and horizontal movement. The suit's engines and 200-watt headlights are powered by a cable connected to surface points and the pilot has 48 hours of continuous breathing supply. Surface pressure is maintained within the suit so post-dive decompression is not necessary.

▶ Deep Flight II to explore the world's deepest sea trench

British-born engineer Graham Hawkes is developing a mini-submarine with which he hopes to explore the deepest sea trench in the world – the 11 km (7 mile) deep Mariana trench in the western Pacific. *Deep Flight II*, a Fixed Wing Submersible which should be ready by 2000, will be constructed from lightweight, high-strength ceramic materials which have been developed by the US Navy and are designed to withstand phenomenal pressures. Unlike other submersibles, which use weights or ballast tanks to sink or float, *Deep Flight II* will use the new technology of thrusters and wings to ascend and descend. The 7-km (4½-mile) trip to the bottom of the ocean will take two hours. @ *the sea p132*

♻ Back to the future

Kon-Tiki sailing

In 1948, Thor Heyerdahl and his crew sailed the *Kon-Tiki*, an exact copy of an old Indian raft built of balsa wood, from South America to Polynesia. Lasting three months, the trip proved that the Polynesians originally came from South America.

WWII U-boat defeat

Germany conceded defeat and withdrew all submarines from the North Atlantic in May 1943. The development of radar enabled the Allies to destroy U-boats (German submarines) faster than they could be replaced.

Breathing appliance sinks sub

The faulty 'snort' breathing tube on British submarines was withdrawn in 1951, after the *HMS Affray* was found full of water at the bottom of the ocean.

ARCHITECTURE

FUTURESCOPE

- **Towers more than 2 miles high will be built**. In the past the limits of lift technology prevented enormous tower designs from being realised. Now magnetic levitation technology allows lifts to go at much faster speeds and there is no longer any need to stop and change lifts, which was the case with the old cable lifts. With less and less urban space to use and increasing pressure on planners not to touch the green belt it is inevitable that the tower will make a comeback.

- **In the technopark of the future every citizen would have a smart card** they could use in schools, banks and offices to access anything from blood type to library files. Though still some way off, the city of the future is destined to become totally electronic and automated.

- **Houses of the future will have to take into account changes in the environment** and the continuing shortage of basic resources such as electricity and water. The eco-houses of the future will use recycled materials for their walls, doors and windows, get their electricity from solar-panels on the roof and recycle bathroom and kitchen water for use in the garden. In extreme climates, deserts for example, natural materials – mud and sand – will be used to build cheap, well-insulated houses.

- **Automatic systems will revolutionize the home**. As you move from room to room in your own house the temperature will change, the lights will adjust and music will come on to suit your particular tastes. Housecleaning robots with inbuilt navigation systems will be left to get on with the cleaning and intelligent toilets will be able to analyse your bodily waste before sending the results to a doctor. It will even be possible to leave your house without worrying about the cooker, the alarm or the dog. The house will check all those things for you.

HOUSES

CITIES

TRAVEL PORTS

TOWERS

CONSTRUCTION

NEW MATERIALS

TECHNO-BABBLE

AUTONOMOUS HOUSE
House that generates its own electricity through solar power and other alternative methods.

EARTHSHIPS
Buildings made out of recycled tyres. Most of these houses are to be found in Taos, USA.

MEGAMALL
Enormous shopping and entertainment centre.

ECOCITY
Cities designed to be self-sustaining.

SMART BUILDINGS
Buildings than can measure the level of structural stress. Especially useful for bridges.

STRAW-BALE HOUSES
Homes in Nebraska, USA, that use straw bales instead of bricks for their walls.

1946	US inventor and physicist Richard Buckminster Fuller designs a long-lasting, recyclable house for the same price as a good quality car
2001	US project begins to build houses out of the 200 million tonnes of straw that is wasted or burned every year

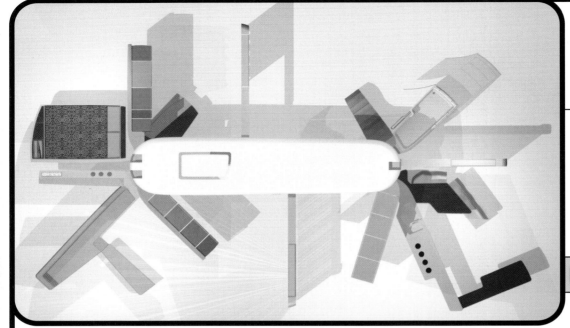

Left
Computer-generated plans of 'Maison Canif', a portable pod designed to fit into any rectangular space. The pod includes a bath, a kitchen, an enormous TV and dining room, all of which swing out from the centre.

HOUSES

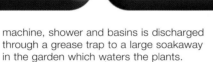

ECO HOUSES

⏸ Autonomous house uses the minimum then recycles it

The Autonomous House in Southwell, UK, was designed by two lecturers in Green Architecture at the University of Nottingham, UK. The house derives its space heating from 'passive solar gain', its electricity from photovoltaics, its water from rain, and turns most of its wastes into useful garden fertilizer, the rest being re-used or re-cycled. Waste water from the sink, washing machine, shower and basins is discharged through a grease trap to a large soakaway in the garden which waters the plants.

⏸ Future houses could be made from mud in under a week

At the California Institute of Earth Art and Architecture, or Cal-Earth, California, USA, Iranian architect Nader Khalili has started to build homes – some igloo-shaped, some barrel-vaulted, some in strange dragon-like forms – using traditional Iranian mud-building techniques. The houses are cheap to build, avoid the use of timber and are a possible solution for homeless people. The United Nations has been using Khalili's dome prototype since 1975 as a model for structures that can be built by two unskilled workers in a week.

⏸ Earthships built from tyres, earth and aluminium cans

Mike Reynolds is the owner of Solar Survival Architecture in Taos, USA, which builds Earthships. Earthships are home-made houses that use recycled tyres, aluminium cans and earth for construction materials. The houses are designed to be self-sufficient, getting power from the sun, water from rain, and recycling grey water and sewage. The tyres, packed with earth, are used as building blocks and more earth and cans are then packed round them. Cans overlaid with concrete make up the interior walls. @ *resources p124*

▶ Straw-bale homes could house 4 million annually

Increasingly popular in the USA, 'Nebraska' style homes use straw bales like bricks and have the roof load bearing down directly on the straw-bale walls. The US Department of Agriculture says that straw from the harvest of US major grains could help build 4 million 185-m^2 (2,000-ft^2) homes every year.

 Left
A model of the Amiga house designed by UK architect Ron Arad. The futuristic design was commissioned by a private client for a house in North London, UK. However, it is doubtful if it will ever get built because of planning difficulties.

ALTERNATIVE HOUSES

⏸ The house built almost entirely from glass

Designed by British architects Future Systems, the Hauer-King house in London, UK, is made almost entirely of glass. It includes a metal kitchen unit and bathrooms that are housed in coloured 'pods'. Remote-controlled white electronic blinds and special glass bricks prevent the house from overheating in the summer.

▶ DIY mail-order housing pack comes with free hammer

The French designer Philippe Starck has designed a mail-order house which costs only $1,000 (£650). Customers are sent a wooden box in the post which contains everything you need to build your own house: blueprints and interior drawings, a videotape guide, a hammer and a small French flag to fly over the site.

⏭ Portable pods that will fit inside a living room

A London-based design team, Softroom, has come up with the idea of a portable pod that fits into any reasonable sized rectangular space. The central elements of the 'Maison Canif' swing out from four pivotal points. Cooking and dining facilities can be arranged by swinging out combinations of preparation surfaces, appliances, cabinets and booth seats, and a diagnostic touch-screen displays current furniture positions and room temperature.

▶ Ski Haus is halfway between a tent and a mountain hut

The Ski Haus is a British mobile mountain hut for the 21st century built by Richard Horden Associates Ltd, London, UK, in collaboration with Yacht and Aerospace Industries. The Ski Haus is a kind of 'hard tent' whose lightweight construction allows a degree of mobility but is solid enough to allow electronics and equipment to be properly insulated and protected. It can house four people and is transportable by helicopter as a flat pack.

⏸ Web can provide solution to Tokyo housing crisis

Masaharu Takasaki has designed a housing complex intended to address Tokyo's cramped housing and rising property prices. The four-storey complex for 15 families is an intricate web of angular shapes, tubes, staircases and pillars. @ *cities p90*

▶ Oval cave rooms are more inviting for children

British artist, Roger Dean, believes many of the houses of the future will be oval shaped. Dean designed three cave-like rooms for the Tomorrow's World Live exhibition in Birmingham, UK, in Feb 1998. They were also a hit with children who found the oval rooms unthreatening and inviting.

Above
The Ski Haus on a mountainside. The house is both lightweight and strong. It can be transported easily by helicopter anywhere in the world and offers good protection from extreme climates.

AUTOMATED HOUSES

⏸ Bill Gates' electronic mansion knows you are there

Bill Gates' $50 million (£30 million), 45-room mansion fronting on Lake Washington in Seattle, USA, was completed in 1997 after seven years of construction. It is the world's largest and most sophisticated automated house – a central computer room controls everything from the security and the climate to the temperature of the jacuzzi. There is a 20-seat movie theatre, a games arcade and high-definition screens on the walls and ceilings. Guests wear small radio-transmitting pins so that heating, lighting, TV programmes and music can follow them throughout the house.

⏸ Japanese sanitary technology house removes the fuss

Belgian architect Frank Belien has designed a house in Brussels, Belgium, with the help of Siemens Nixdorf, Microsoft and Digital. Bar codes on used packaging are scanned to make new shopping lists, the lavatory is an advanced 'paper free' model which only uses hot air and water and the windows become opaque at the touch of a switch. The house is available for only $4 million (£2.5 million).

▶ Smart green house that can water the plants

British research group, The Intelligent & Green Housing Project, or Integer, is studying housing that is both green and smart. The house will automatically check that doors and windows are closed, the oven and iron are switched off and the burglar alarm is armed. Even more usefully, the house could look after itself, watering gardens at night and watching for fires, intruders and leaks. It can also call for assistance if it cannot manage on its own.

🔲 Back to the future

Dymaxion House

In 1946, the American physicist and inventor Richard Buckminster Fuller designed the 4D Dymaxion House. A hexagonal or round aluminium house, it could be produced for the same money per pound as a good quality car and weighed only 2,720 kg (6,000 lb). Partitions were movable and the cupboards featured electric 'O-Volving' shelves, which were hung off a conveyor belt mechanism. The house needed no paint or maintenance, was built from a common element, would last indefinitely and was recyclable.

Drop City, USA

In the late 1960s, a commune built a series of houses out of old vehicle parts. The small community in Trinidad, Colorado, USA, was abandoned in 1972.

Living Pod, UK

In 1966, British architect David Green designed a living pod which was made of synthetic material with integrated power and waste disposal systems. The structure was not unlike a moon vehicle and stood on telescopic feet. Features included automatic climate control, washing, cooking, and a machine that acted as a school teacher.

Left
The world's tallest building, the Petronas Towers, Kuala Lumpur, Malaysia, is lit up at dusk. The country plans to build two new cities in the next century outside the capital Kuala Lumpur, Cyberjaya and Putrajaya, investing $20 billion (£12.5 billion).

CITIES

URBAN RENEWAL

▶ Berlin Wall to become new entertainment centre

The former wasteland that divided East and West Berlin, Germany, is being completely rebuilt as a commercial and entertainment centre. The Reichstag is being revamped, the largest part of the Potsdammer Platz is being replanned and an entertainment and office complex is planned for Sony.

❚❚ Acclaimed architects design a Eurolille complex

The first phase of building at Lille, France, was recently finished. The vast urban complex includes conference and concert halls, an office tower, a mall and a hotel. Acclaimed architects Jean Novel, Claude Vasconi and Christian de Portzamparc have all contributed to the designs.

❚❚ The megamall that lights up at night

A megamall that is situated on the French side of the Channel Tunnel becomes a sculpture by night thanks to artist Yann Kersalé who created a design work of lights which shine from the structure, giving it a new form.

▶ The largest urban complex

The Pudong New Area which faces Shanghai, China, across the Huangpu River is the largest urban complex being built at the moment. It covers an area of 520 km² (201 miles²) and

Left
The Crédit Lyonnais building, at Eurolille, Lille, France. Known as 'The Boot', it forms part of Rem Koolhaas' masterplan for the new urban district.

consists of five zones: export-processing, free trade, hi-tech, a new port and a finance and trade zone which will include the world's tallest building.

▶ Inner city site could become 'mutual aid' neighbourhood

Lord Young of Dartington is planning on turning a derelict inner city site in Bradford, UK, into a new housing project modelled on the working class communities of pre-war Britain. With plans for 100 new homes for sale or rent, leases will contain 'mutual aid' obligations such as babysitting, garden tending and shopping for the elderly in order to help form a neighbourhood 'family'.

▶ Osaka island is designed to be an oasis of relaxation

In Feb 1998, Colombian architect Adriana Guttiérrez won the chance to design Osaka's new Central Business District in Japan. Plans include the construction of an easily accessible relaxation island space lined with lanterns, pergolas and benches.

ECO CITIES

❚❚ Curitiba, Brazil, is one of the world's sustainable cities

Curitiba, Brazil, is one of the world's best examples of a sustainable city. Every day, buses carry 900,000 passengers, about two-thirds of the city's population. Recycling is encouraged through residents being able to trade every six bags of refuse for one bag of food. In addition, about 1,000 'cart people' go from door to door picking up rubbish which can be sold at recycling centres. @ *resources p124*

The Australian ecocity with underground malls

The PEOPL Group has planned an environmental city of the future in New South Wales, Australia. A collection of ecovillages will be built on the Pacific coast within easy reach of each other and a Central Business District (CBD) accessible by bicycle. Private amphibious vehicles will be able to get to underground malls via traffic conduits and a street-canal system. Electricity will be generated from a hydro-dam.

Sir Richard Rogers' plans for Parc Bit, Mallorca, Spain

UK architect, Sir Richard Rogers, has plans for Parc Bit, Mallorca, Spain, which include three sustainable communities small enough to allow residents to walk instead of using transport. Renewable energy sources will be used to generate power.

The self-sufficient city that is built on arcology

Arcosanti is a new city in the Arizona Desert, USA, started in the 1970s, and built according to Italian architect Paulo Soleri's philosophy of arcology, a compound of architecture and ecology. The aim is to create a compact, largely self-sustaining city with multi-use buildings to minimize urban sprawl and destruction of the environment.

The Mirage City project by the South China seas

Off the Southern coast of China lies a 400 hectare (988 acres) island created by Japanese architect Arata Isozaki that will host Haisha, the Mirage City. Designed to incorporate innovative technologies, it is due to be completed before 2010.

VISIONARY CITIES

Japan's Aerial City is linked by colossal curves

Japanese architect Shei Yoh has designed plans for the Daikoku Pier at Aerial City in Yokohama, Japan, which include a road 5 m (16 ft) above the ground with colossal curves linking the four buildings themselves, in the shape of a cube, a cylinder, an upside-down pyramid and a tripod, while elevated transport grids will eliminate the need for roads so that the natural environment can re-emerge at ground level.

Putrajaya and Cyberjaya are the lights of the East

Up until the 1998 crash Malaysia had been planning to build two new cities between the capital, Kuala Lumpur, and the

International Airport which lies some 48 km (30 miles) to the south. This huge chunk of land will, it is hoped, become a massive technopark by 2005 known as the 'Multimedia Super Corridor' (MSC), home to two new cities, Putrajaya, 'city of the people', and the infotech city, Cyberjaya. The MSC includes far-reaching plans for smart schools and national smartcards which can be used to access everything from blood type to library fines, a paperless electronic government and a new multimedia university. @ *communication p24*

Singapore is set to win the Asian info-race

The race between Singapore, Kuala Lumpur, Malaysia, and, to a lesser extent, Bangalore, India, to create the new info-hub of Asia looks as if it will be won by Singapore which is luring many new technology and information companies with its Singapore One Project. Aiming to be the world's first intelligent island by 2000, the government plans to connect every home and business to a high-speed network which will provide home banking, legal and telemedicine services. Already fibre-optic lines are being laid, all of Singapore's 21,000 teachers are receiving computer training and primary schools are set to receive as many as 100 computers each.

170-storey Millennium Tower rises out of Tokyo Bay

British architects Foster and Partners have proposed a 170-storey off-shore tower for Obayashi Corporation, Tokyo, Japan. The Millennium Tower will be four times the height of the average Manhattan skyscraper – the idea being to create a 'vertical township' 2 km off shore. The building is conceived as a huge needle, bound in a helical steel cage, rising out of Tokyo Bay. It will be linked to the mainland by road and rail and the primary transport route will be via a vertical 'metro' of giant lift cars, capable of carrying 160 people which will stop at sky centres every 30 floors. Visitors will complete their journeys by high-speed lifts. @ *towers p94*

3-D model will help to rebuild Berlin's city centre

Following decades of separation by the Berlin Wall, the city's historical centre had become an urban wasteland. After reunification, a 3-D model was built to help to imagine the rebuilding of the city centre. It has since become an impressive piece of Virtual Reality, with photorealistic building façades and dynamically adapting perspectives. The model is to be combined with teleservices and databases and will be

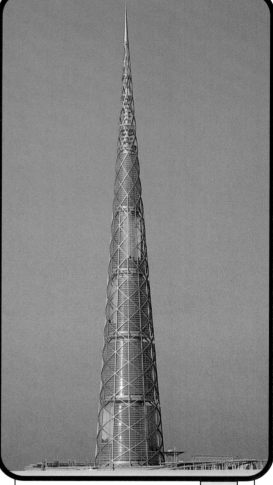

Above
A model of the proposed off-shore Millennium Tower for Tokyo, Japan, designed by Foster and Partners. The Tower will be a 870 m (2,855 ft) high, containing hotels, shops and apartments. Giant 'metros' will carry people and vehicles up and down.

made available on the World Wide Web. So, while strolling around the city, users will be able to do some teleshopping, gallery visits, or hotel room booking.

Back to the future

Arctic Town

In 1971, Atelier Warmbroom designed an inflatable, transparent dome to cover an area of 3,000 m² (32,500 ft²) in the Arctic. The idea was to create a central European climate to accommodate 15,000 to 30,000 people.

Broadacre City

In 1935, Frank Lloyd Wright designed a city plan for Broadacre City. Every household was to have an acre of land and the plans included a helicopter for every family.

Central Station

Le Corbusier's vision of a future city in 1929 was of an urban centre totally dominated by the need for transportation, represented by the car, train and the plane.

1893	The escalator was first introduced – as a novelty ride – on Coney Island Pier, New York, USA
2050	Kuala Lumpur International Airport becomes one of the world's largest airports

Left
Passengers at Dortmund's railway station will be forgiven for thinking the aliens have landed. The station's new covering is actually known as the UFO (Unlimited Fun Object) and will house shops, restaurants and entertainment centres for up to 8 million visitors a year.

TRAVEL PORTS

AIRPORTS

▶▶ Malaysian airport designed for continual expansion

The new Kuala Lumpur International Airport in Malaysia began operation in 1998, but it is still very much under construction and will be continually expanded so that by 2050 the project will have doubled in size. The airport site is the largest in the world – 10 km² (4 miles²). Architect Kisho Kurokawa has designed the roof of the main terminal building to incorporate a series of modules made up of hyperbolic paraboloid shells, representing the dynamics of flight. The enormous inner courtyards through which all passengers must pass on their way to and from the planes contain native Malaysian rainforest plants and trees.

⏸ Japanese airport on an artificial island

To protect the coastal environment, Japan's Kansai International Airport was constructed on an artificial island a little more than 5 km (3 miles) out into Osaka Bay. The design competition for this unique project was won by the Italian architect Renzo Piano, who is also engaged on the renovation of the Pompidou Centre in Paris, France. The terminal building's distinctive fluid form was created with the help of a sophisticated computer-assisted analysis of airflow dynamics, designed to move customers through the building in comfort and safety. Inside the airport, much of the interior space and embarkation piers is designed for maximum transparency. Two tree-planted valleys separate the terminal building from the runway and elevated roadways leading to the town.

Left
Bordeaux airport needs a new control tower and French architects Odile Decq and Benoit Cornelle have submitted this design for the 58-million-franc (£5.8 million) project which will create a new tower and adjacent terminal building.

⏸ Chek Lap Kok airport boasts record-breaking features

Hong Kong's new airport is an architectural wonder. Chek Lap Kok was built on an island off Hong Kong, which was planted with explosives and flattened. Sir Norman Foster designed the airport buildings which boast a 5 km-long (3 miles) glass wall in the passenger terminal, a great, curving Big Roof, hotels and a 28,000 m² (300,000 ft²) shopping centre. The suspension bridge between the airport and central Hong Kong 24 km (15 miles) away is the world's largest combined road and rail bridge. The airport, built at a cost of $19.9 billion (£12.4 billion), will be able to handle 87 million people per year and replaces Kai Tak airport, famously situated in the middle of Hong Kong Island with its hair-raising approach path.

▶ Heathrow's fifth terminal means more traffic

The congested roads around London's Heathrow Airport could get more clogged if proposals for a fifth terminal go ahead. One third of air passengers currently use public transport to travel to and from Heathrow, with forecasts showing that by 2016 about 38% would use public transport to travel to the proposed new terminal. In this light, the British Airports Authority (BAA) and London Underground want to extend the Piccadilly Line to Terminal 5 and are also looking at the viability of new rail links. The Heathrow Express would also be extended to carry 10 million passengers a year.

RAILWAYS

▶ German railway station gets a new look

Renovation soon starts on Stuttgart's 1930s Bonatz station, and commuters will be able to take underground high-speed trains into the city centre. The extensive project will see large tracts of railway land currently bisecting the city covered with a vast glass roof and the grounds of the palace gardens extended over the new station. Architects Ingenhoven Overdiek Kahlen & Partner have built three levels of shops and restaurants into the design, so you can still spend money even as the train leaves the station.

▶ Underground extension to the Millennium Dome

London's new £2.6 billion Jubilee Line extension promises to be one of the city's architectural wonders. One of the highlights of the project to extend the capital's newest tube line will be the station at North Greenwich, next to the Millennium Dome. Designed by the firm of Alsop, Lyall & Störmer it will be one of the biggest underground stations in the world at 405 m (1,328 ft) long, and decorated in stunning blue mosaic and blue glass walls to resemble a hi-tech undersea world. The station is already being talked about as a tourist attraction to rival the Millennium Dome itself, and much the same could be said of all the new stations in the project, which have been hailed as "the most exciting new architectural spaces in London". The project is being overseen by Roland Paoletti, who has assembled a team of experienced and relatively young architects – including Sir Norman Foster and the award-winning Chris Wilkinson – to construct a set of visually-dazzling and beautifully-engineered buildings.

❚❚ Spanish metro stations are glass grottos

The metro stations in Bilbao, Spain, celebrate rather than disguise their cavernous form. The street-level entrances to the city's stations consist of curved glass enclosures, which allow natural light in during the day and are illuminated at night. Once inside, commuters take underground lifts to the 16-m (52-ft) wide station caverns. The designers have copied the cavernous forms of underground rock structures to make their feats of engineering echo the forms of nature.

▶ Shopping in a giant intergalactic station

People go shopping-mad in airports, so why not in stations? By 2002, travellers in Dortmund, Germany, will be able to shop while they wait for their train in a giant entertainment centre being built over the city's central station. The centre, called UFO (Unlimited Fun Object), because it looks like a giant UFO hovering over the station, will include megastores and restaurants aimed at attracting 8 million visitors a year – and not just train passengers but ordinary shoppers too. @ shopping p12

CREATIVE DESIGN

❚❚ Evocative bicycle shelters become Japanese landmark

One upon a time, the only people you would find lurking behind the bike sheds were furtive teenage lovers or illicit smokers. But now, in the sleepy Japanese town of Sakai, you are just as likely to find design buffs or architecture students doing just that. This is because architect Shuhei Endo has brought architectural fame to Sakai with his cleverly designed bicycle sheds. The corrugated iron shelters at Sakai railway station are shaped like steel waves, bringing grace and fluidity to a normally mundane structure. The material has been shaped through careful cutting and joining to create an aesthetically alluring landmark.

▶ Germans design better bus shelter

Given the amount of time passengers spend waiting for the bus, it seems strange that most bus shelters are often little more than wind tunnels offering little protection from the elements. German architects and engineers IPL have designed a new type of bus shelter which made its debut in the southern German town of Offenburg. The structure is made from PVC, glass and steel, with an elaborate multi-canopied roof to shelter waiting commuters. The design is now being adapted for other cities, but it is not clear if a super rain-resistant model has been proposed to take on the rigours of the UK's waterlogged streets.

▶▶ Nagasaki's new ferry terminal

A new ferry terminal is the key element of Nagasaki Urban Renaissance 2001.

Above
The inviting entrances to Bilbao's metro stations take passengers down into a cave-like underworld deliberately designed to reproduce the ambience of a natural subterranean landscape – albeit one with hi-tech tube trains running through the middle of it.

This is a major urban redevelopment scheme, aimed at continuing the restructuring of the Japanese city largely destroyed when it was one of the two sites devastated by atomic bombs at the end of WWII. The building, designed by Shin Takamatsu, is built on a tract of reclaimed land, making it a focal point in the shorefront landscape. The architect is taking full advantage of the space, utilising bold, interlocking geometric forms and contrasting textures. The cigar-shaped terminal is crowned at one end by a sharply truncated cylinder which houses the circular entrance hall.

▓ Back to the future

Up, up and away

The escalator was first introduced in 1893 on Coney Island Pier, New York, USA, as a novelty ride. Before long, escalators had been installed in department stores and railway stations all over the country.

Air-conditioning

Air-conditioning in railway carriages was first installed in 1930 in American B & O Railway Co.'s dining car 'Martha Washington', when it was tested on *The Columbian* train from Baltimore to Cumberland, USA.

Rise of the railway centre

In the later part of the 19th century, railheads became major cities. For example, by 1860 Chicago had 109,000 inhabitants – three times the number in 1830 – with 70 trains running in and out of the city each day.

1956	Frank Lloyd Wright designs the Mile High Tower – it was to be 1,609 m tall
2010	Obayashi Corporation in Japan completes its 800-m Millennium Tower

Left
Sky City 1000 is planned to cover an area of 800 hectares. It has been estimated that the city would cost approximately 600,000 Yen per m² ($4,000/m²) to construct.

TOWERS

NEW TOWERS

Cesar Pelli's skybridge towers above Kuala Lumpur

Designed by US-based Argentine architect Cesar Pelli, the 452-m (1,482-ft) Petronas Twin Towers in Kuala Lumpur, Malaysia, was completed in 1997. Pelli's design called for a passageway or "skybridge" run beween the towers. There was concern that the skybridge would snap if strong gusts of winds were to strike the towers from different directions – both towers are designed to sway up to one metre in high winds. To overcome this problem, four steel legs were fitted to the base of the bridge and run at an angle down to the sides of the two towers. Each leg is attached to a rotating plate which can move up to 45° to absorb the sway of the towers.

World's tallest building will shape new look Shanghai

Work on the World Financial Centre (WFC) in Shanghai began in Aug 1997 and when it is complete early in the next century it will be the world's tallest building at 454 m (1,489 ft) high. The 95-floor skyscraper is part of a massive makeover of Shanghai – it was estimated in Jan 1998 that there were 22,000 building projects on the go in the city using 25% of the world's cranes. The World Financial Centre is being built by the Mori Consortium of Japan. The design, which includes a circular hole at the top, was almost scrapped when the Chinese authorities became suspicious that it resembled the Japanese flag. However, when it was pointed out that it was meant to represent a Chinese moon gate, the design was passed.
@ *construction p96*

JR Central Towers go up in record time

Scheduled for completion for 1999, the JR Central Towers in Nagoya, Japan, are being built at a record three floors a week – most construction teams manage one floor a week. The estimated cost of the structure is ¥1 billion per day. Architect John Koga has included light, strong ceramic materials in the outer walls to withstand an earthquake of eight on the Richter Scale. There are two towers in the structure, the tallest of which rises 53 floors above a station in Nagoya.
@ *new materials p98*

Kingdom Centre, the tallest building in the Middle East

Work on the 300-m (984-ft) high Kingdom Centre tower in Riyadh, Saudi Arabia, began in late 1997. The building, which is being funded by Prince Al-Walid bin Talal tapers to two points and will be topped by a horizontal bar. This creates a space like the eye of a needle through which the prince intends to fly his private Boeing 727 jet. The building will be the tallest in the Middle East, though the top 120 m (394 ft) will be empty, since Saudi town planning laws restrict buildings to 30 occupied floors. It will also include a women-only floor so that female customers can shop without their veils.

2,000 layers of glass glimmer in Birmingham

Sutherland Hussey won a competition in 1997 for the best design for a 30-m (100-ft) monument that will stand in front of the National Exhibition Centre in Birmingham, UK. Hussey's tower will be assembled out of 2,000 layers of glass to create a tapering helical spike. The towers will stand on a concrete cone filled with water which will be drawn up through the structure and then cascade down over the glass. Another short-listed entry was a design from AEM Studio for a monument which resembled an enormous lava lamp.

Left
Turbine Tower was designed by a UK firm to stand on a hill-top site high above Tokyo, Japan. The tower would be able to generate all the electricity it required itself, thanks to a number of carefully positioned turbines.

Germany's energy-efficient Commerzbank tower

The Commerzbank headquarters in Frankfurt was completed in May 1997 and is Europe's tallest building at 258 m (846 ft), excluding the antenna. Designed by British architect Sir Norman Foster, the Commerzbank building is a triangular tower with an energy-preserving water and waste system in which the cooling towers on the top of the building are used to flush lavatories. Windows can be opened and there is also a spiralling series of nine gardens for use by the office workers.

International Finance Centre, Hong Kong

While plans by Hong Kong property tycoon Nina Wang to build the 468-m (1,535-ft) Nina Tower have come to a halt, Sun Hung Kai property firm has started construction on a complex which will feature an 88-storey tower. The International Finance Centre is scheduled for completion in 2003 and features two towers and a station, all designed by Petronas Towers' architect Cesar Pelli. The station will receive trains from the city's new airport.
@ travel ports p92

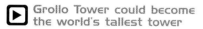

Above
Sutherland Hussey's winning design for a tower for the National Exhibiton Centre, UK. The 30-m (100-ft) tower will be made of 2,000 glass discs.

MASTERPLANS

Grollo Tower could become the world's tallest tower

Melbourne architectural firm Denton Corker Marshall has been contracted to design a new tower for the city which will be even taller than the WFC in Shanghai. The firm is proposing a 680-m (2,231-ft) high structure which will contain 137 floors. Tapering towards the top, the structure hovers 35 m (115 ft) over parkland and rests on four sets of twin-corner columns. There are also plans for viewing areas and restaurants at the top and glass lifts which will run up the corners of the silver-blue building.

Millennium Tower, Japan: taller still

The Obayashi Corporation hopes to build its planned 800-m (2,625-ft) Millennium Tower in Tokyo Bay early in the next century. The estimated cost of this massive project is $12 billion. While funding is being sought Obayashi is researching hi-tech fire detection and computer systems for the structure. They are also looking into a new type of lift using electromagnets which could be twice as fast as conventional lifts.

Most of the research is being channelled into developing new materials and making steel stronger and ductile to withstand earthquakes.

Eco-friendly towers will be more self-sufficient

Kuala Lumpur-based architect Ken Yeang's proposal for a 36-storey Armoury Tower in Shanghai is an expression of his bioclimatic ideas of design which aim to create more eco-friendly towers. Instead of relying solely on an air-conditioning system, Yeang has included features such as oxygen-producing garden areas, solar panels on the roof and moveable horizontal slats, known as louvres, between layers of wall. The louvres can be removed in the summer, so that windows may be opened to let fresh air in, and replaced in the winter to retain warmth.

Tornado Tower set to spin across the horizon

US architect Robert Hogenmiller Jr. is proposing a 186-m (610-ft) high structure called the Tornado Tower made out of stainless steel for Omaha, East Nebraska, USA. The tower, which widens as it rises to create the impression of a spinning top, would include a restaurant, a tornado museum and a 3-D cinema which recreates tornadoes in virtual reality.

An entire community inside Sky City 1000, Japan

Sky City 1000 is a concept city created by Takenaka Corporation for a 1,000-m (3,281-ft) high tower capable of housing an entire community. The plans include open areas in the tower which allow fresh air and natural light to filter into vast atriums and a monorail which spirals up through the structure. Takenaka Corporation estimates that Sky City 1000 will take 14 years to complete, but the city could be inhabited during construction because each level will be built with its energy and transportation systems completed as work progresses.

Turbine Tower, Tokyo, would provide its own electricity

Turbine Tower was designed by UK architectural firm Richard Rogers and Partners. The massive tower was proposed for a site in Tokyo, Japan, where it would stand as a landmark on the horizon, set high on a hill overlooking a huge park and a shrine. The design includes a number of turbines, which will provide the tower with all its electricity. This unique system was tested in a wind-tunnel, using a prototype of the tower to position the turbines so they would catch the most wind possible.

Above
The observation decks on top of the Tornado Tower would command 25-mile views across the US city of Omaha and its surrounding landscape. It has been estimated that the tower will cost about £22 million ($35 million) to build.

Back to the future

Mile High Tower

In 1956, US architect Frank Lloyd Wright designed the Mile High Tower, proposed for Chicago's water-front. It was to have 528 floors and be 1,609 m (5,279 ft) high.

WJJY-TV Tower

In 1978, the 491-m (1,611-ft) WJJY-TV Tower in Illinois, USA, collapsed during a violent winter storm.

X-Seed 4000

In the 1980s, the Japanese Taisei Corporation envisioned building X-Seed 4000, a 4-km tall skyscraper which was to take 30 years to build and would house 700,000 people.

Left
Canary Wharf station, part of the Jubilee Line Extension to London's tube network, will cope with 40,000 passengers per hour at peak times. The 280-m (919-ft) long structure reaches down to a depth of 24 m (78 ft) and will house 20 escalators and two lifts as well as two ticket areas and a parade of shops.

CONSTRUCTION

MAJOR PROJECTS

▶ Controversy surrounds the building of China's dam

Work on China's £16 billion Three Gorges Dam, the world's biggest hydro-electric power project, began in November 1997 and will take 15 years to complete. The dam wall, blocking the course of the Yangtze, the world's third longest river, will be 175 m (574 ft) high and 2.3 km (1½ miles) wide and it will have a generating capacity of twelve nuclear power stations. However, the creation of the 632-km (393-mile) long reservoir will submerge about 1,500 towns and villages, forcing over a million people to move and flooding hundreds of ancient archaeological sites. In addition, the land around the Yangtze river produces 40% of China's food crops, and such a major project may seriously affect agricultural output.

▶▶ New technology for floating platforms

Several countries are looking towards new technologies for floating platforms which could be used for airports, hotels and even troop carriers. In Japan, where little land is left for reclamation, a mile-long prototype,

called megafloat, is being tested in the sea off Yokosuka. The US navy is conducting a $6 million (£3.75 million) feasibility study for a mobile military base, which would be the largest marine structure ever built. A US company, Float, is developing technology for pneumatically stabilized platforms, consisting of 6 m (20 ft) concrete cylinders.

▶▶ Promotion of rail link between Canada and Russia

The Bering Strait Tunnel and Railroad Group is a non-profit organization whose main goal is to promote the construction of a rail and tunnel line connecting the Eastern and Western hemispheres. This would be accomplished by connecting the North American rail system with that of Russia through the construction of a 6,350-km (4,000-mile) long rail link. It would also require the building of a tunnel underneath the Bering Strait between Wales, Alaska, and Uelen, Russia. The project would re-join the two continents, thought to have been linked together in prehistoric times.

Right
This pipe is one of four under construction in Egypt to irrigate the Sinai Desert with water from the River Nile. When the project is ready, Egypt's government will use it to promote settlement in areas away from the Nile's cramped hinterland.

⏸ Chinese bridge the longest of its kind

The Tsing Ma Bridge is a spectacular suspension bridge that links urban Hong Kong with its new airport, built on reclaimed land north of Lantau Island. The bridge was

designed by structural engineer Mott MacDonald to withstand typhoon-strength winds, and built by an Anglo-Japanese consortium at a cost of £570 million. With an overall length of 2 km (1⅓ miles), it is the world's longest combined road and rail suspension bridge. An upper deck consists of a six-lane motorway, while the lower, enclosed deck contains a dual carriageway and an express rail link.

▶ Unusual design for French viaduct

French architect Jacques Hondelatte has been chosen to design a road crossing over the Tarn Valley, linking the Causse Rouge with the Larzac plateau in France. His design for the project is a simple, regular construction with uniform spans and beam lengths. What makes it different is that instead of placing the traffic lanes side-by-side, he has placed them one above the other, and will encase them in a thick hollow beam made of either concrete or steel. Because of the substantial winds that will buffet the 2.6 km (1½ mile) viaduct, it is supported by circular piers on simple foundations resembling giant bottles.

URBAN INNOVATIONS

❚❚ Upmarket pedestrian bridges in Moscow

The Moscow City Bridge is the Russian capital's first traffic-free bridge, joining the area west of the Kremlin, known locally as Moscow Manhattan, with the residential south side of the capital. Designed by the Russian architect Boris Tkhor, the blue glass 'living bridge' transports citizens along travelators to upmarket shops and cafés. A similar landmark, which will have entertainment and conference facilities, is being built a mile further down the river, a significant symbol of the city's regeneration.

❚❚ Floating bridge across the River Thames

A new floating bridge connects London's Canary Wharf commercial development with the Victorian warehouses on West India Quay in Docklands. Designed by Future Systems and Anthony Hunt & Associates, the bridge's foam-filled pontoons lie low in the water without imposing on the waterfront. Splayed tubular steel legs, connected to the pontoons, support a spine beam under the bridge's deck.

▶ New Tyne bridge to be an eye-opener

The competition-winning design to build a new footbridge across the River Tyne at Newcastle, UK, copies the way the human eye opens and closes. The £7.5 million bridge, designed by Gifford Partners and Chris Wilkinson Architects, allows ships to pass by pivoting the 600-tonne structure on concrete pillars. With a 121 m (400 ft)

span, supported by a 38-m (125-ft) high main arch, it will link the £35 million arts centre at Gateshead with the quay at Newcastle-upon-Tyne.

▶ New London bridge includes commercial property

Two designs have been chosen as joint winners in a competition for a new traffic-free, inhabitable bridge over the Thames in the heart of London. Without any government funding, the new bridge will be wider and taller than other crossings, since 13,656 m² (147,000 ft²) of commercial development is needed to make the project self-financing. British architect Zaha Hadid has designed a cantilevered glass and steel construction, while Frenchman Antoine Grumbac has proposed a suspension bridge with a 152 m (500 ft) commercial tower disguised as a hanging garden.

▶ Cable-car planned for Millennium Dome

London company Meridian Skyway has been given planning permission to run a cable-car service across the Thames to the site of the Millennium Dome in Greenwich, London, UK. The project will cost £7 million and soar up to 79 m (260 ft) over the river. The 23 gondola-style cable-cars will each carry 15 people from the East India Dockland Light Railway station to Greenwich. From October 1999, up to 2,500 people per hour are expected to enjoy the panoramic views during the 3-minute-long journey.

▶ Irrigation project aims to help settlement outside Nile Valley

Construction began in the Nile Valley in 1997 on a major building project that could

Above
Fireworks celebrate the opening of the Tsing Ma Bridge on 27 April 1997, linking mainland Hong Kong to the city's new airport on the islet of Chek Lap Kok. The 2.2 km (1⅓ mile) construction is the world's longest rail and road bridge.

see the largest exodus of humanity from the region since Moses led the Israelites out of Egypt and into the promised land. The Egyptian government is building four vast irrigation tunnels in an ambitious plan to take fresh water from the Nile under the Suez Canal and out into the Sinai Desert. The aim of the project is to make the desert bloom into life, thus attracting settlers into what is a sparsely settled area: at present 98% of Egypt's 62 million people are crammed into just 5% of the country's land, mostly along the banks of the Nile, an area prone to flooding and overcultivation.

♻ Back to the future

Chrysler Building

The spire at the top of New York's Chrysler Building, the first skyscraper over 305 m (1,000 ft), was added late in construction to make it the world's tallest building. This record only lasted a few months, until the Empire State Building was constructed.

Aswan High Dam

To build the Aswan High Dam, which was completed in 1969, the temples of Abu Simbel in Egypt, which were built by the Pharaoh Rameses II, were cut into over 1,000 pieces and reassembled on higher ground.

Tower Bridge

From 1909 to 1982, the walkways over Tower Bridge, London, UK, were closed because the bridge was becoming a popular suicide spot. Safety grills were fitted in the 1980s and the walkways now house a museum.

| 100 BC | The Romans discover that by adding volcanic ash to concrete they can produce a much stronger and waterproof material |
| 1999 | Ecorock factory in Japan begins producing synthetic stone from waste sludge |

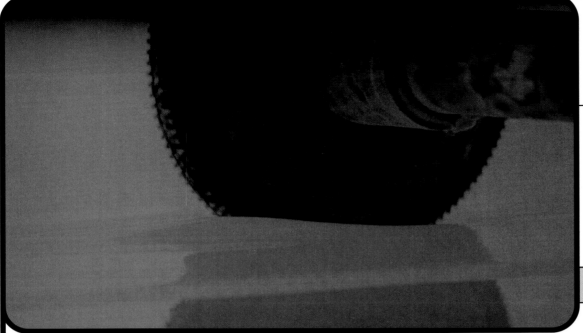

Left
Glass-making has always been a complicated business. The float method of production, shown here, involves a process whereby the glass floats on a bed of molten tin in a chamber heated to 815°C (1,500°F) while a wheel cuts the glass to the required thickness.

NEW MATERIALS

INNOVATIVE INVENTIONS

 **Germ-killing paint cleans up buildings**

US researchers have developed a paint that could keep buildings germ-free for years. The Southwest Research Institute in San Antonio, Texas, has devised a formulation that kills any fungus, bacterium, virus or alga that lands on the painted surface. The key ingredient is calcium hydroxide, or slaked lime, which can kill most organisms within 15 minutes and can remain active for at least four years. The paint would be suitable for sterilizing surfaces in hospitals, planes and offices.

Japanese method makes steel stronger

Japan's National Research Institute for Metals has developed a method of making steel 40% stronger than normal. When ordinary steel is hardened by rapid cooling, small grains are produced in the metal. The Japanese researchers found that by applying pressure to the heated steel just before cooling, the grain sizes could be reduced to around two micrometres, a tenth of the normal size.

Japanese have invented a self-cleaning coating

We may soon have self-cleaning toilets thanks to the Japanese company Toto, which has invented a coating for tiles, toilets and washbasins that becomes active when exposed to ultraviolet light. Used under fluorescent light, it kills over 99% of some bacteria in an hour. It is also effective against *E. coli* and *Pseudomonas aeroginosa*. The coating's active ingredient is titanium dioxide and the light-prompted reaction is called photocatalysis.

New alloy allows for magnetic fridge

American space scientists have developed a magnetic fridge that has no need for gases in the cooling mechanism and combines high efficiency with low cost. The advance was made possible by the discovery of a new metal alloy, called gadolinium-silicon-germanium. It exploits the magnocaloric effect, the ability of some alloys to become hot when magnetized and cool when demagnetized. The advance makes the cheaper production of liquid hydrogen possible, an environmentally safe and potentially endless fuel.

Magnets detect weaknesses in steel

Scientists have developed a method of detecting metal fatigue in the steel beams used in construction. Physicists at the

Illinois Institute of Technology, USA, noted that atoms in steel bars point in roughly the same direction, but if they are crushed or bent, their magnetic domains shift position with a pronounced flutter in the magnetic field, which indicates a defect. The discovery could be used to measure

Right
A problem with many older buildings, like this one in San Francisco, USA, is that they are not earthquake-proof. New ways to detect fatigue in steel, like that developed at Illinois' Institute of Technology, may make sights like this less common.

the integrity of critical steel parts in bridge struts, supports in nuclear power plants and aircraft engines.

Anti-static steel keeps buildings clean

The retention of dust and dirt through static electricity build-up is a common problem in office buildings with a controlled environment. Now, a new type of steel which can minimize the build-up of dirt has been developed in the UK. The unique anti-static surface coating reduces the risk of dust and dirt retention which, when airborne, can result in contamination in food and pharmaceutical products. In composite-panel form, the steel provides a suitable solution for most controlled environment wall and roof panels.

Smart buildings that can think for themselves

Soon, you will not be able to say someone is 'as thick as a brick'. Developments in buildings science have created smart materials – bricks and mortar that can 'think' for themselves. By placing sensors inside concrete, wood or plastic, it is possible to monitor the levels of stress and decay within them and program them to adjust themselves accordingly. Researchers at the State University of New York, USA, carried out an experiment whereby they mixed carbon fibres in with liquid concrete used to construct a bridge. By placing electrodes at strategic points on the bridge they could measure the stress levels bearing down on the structure and identify the areas of weakness within it.

Be at home in your very own Monolithic Dome

Monolithic Domes could be the future of low-cost housing. Plugged by their makers, Future Homes Now, as practically indestructible and fire- and earthquake-proof, they are simple concrete domes that you build yourself. To do this, first create a base, then cover it with an inflatable vinyl fabric. Using a high powered fan, you inflate the vinyl shell into a dome shape and then spray-coat it with a layer of urethane foam 10 cm (4 in) thick. Reinforce the frame with steel rods and, finally, spray the whole structure with concrete. One important tip: when spraying the walls inside, leave a hole for the front door.

RECYCLED MATERIALS

New factory turns sewage to stone

The Tsukikishima Kikai Co. of Tokyo, Japan, is building a $25 million (£15.6 million) plant to manufacture synthetic stone made from the ash of incinerated sewage sludge. Ecorock is a new building material that can withstand up to five times as much bending force as granite or marble. The sewage ash is blended with up to 20% silica, alumina

and lime and degassed at 1,300°C to produce glass-like stones. Finally, the product is reheated to produce Ecorock.

Recycling gives us rubbish buildings

A US company has developed a product which will enable us to construct buildings from rubbish. Scrap polystyrene, industrial waste and fly ash – a by-product from power stations – are being recycled and combined in a material called Polylite. Building blocks from the new material are stronger, lighter and have a greater insulating capacity than conventional materials. Polylite can also be used to manufacture roof tiles, house bricks and, ironically, rubbish bins.

Plastic is recycled to make lumber

US company Earth Care has developed a building lumber made from recycled plastic waste material. The material is made from 100% recycled high-density polythene plastic – a plastics by-product that would normally end up in a landfill site. The plastic lumber has a wood-like matte texture and can especially be used in applications where it is exposed to the outside elements, such as for fencing, decks and outdoor furnishings. It comes in eight colours and is guaranteed against damage by insects, rot, corrosion or fungal decay. An environmental bonus is that this new 'plastic wood' should reduce the demand for real wood products. @ waste p126

Building panels from recycled paper

A US company, Gridcore Systems International (GSI), has developed light-

Above
As steel is such a vital resource, new ways to make it more efficient are constantly being sought. Japan's National Research Institute for Metals has developed a way to make steel 40% stronger by compacting its atoms as they cool.

weight, high-strength building panels made entirely from recycled fibres. Old corrugated boxes and other paper waste are recast into panels by pouring a slurry of cellulose or other fibres onto a rubber mould which is then heat-pressed into shape. Two panels are glued together and, by filling the cavities with cellulose insulation, a lightweight insulated wall, ideal for low-cost home building, is created. This technique makes the resulting structures more heat efficient than previous low-cost buildings, such as post-war prefabs. GSI is also testing the use of recycled fibreglass for reinforcement.

Back to the future

Roman concrete

The Romans added volcanic ash and lime to their concrete which, as it then contained oxides of aluminium, silicon and iron, became extremely strong and waterproof. The result was virtually the same as modern concrete.

Any old iron

A London builder, Richard Walker, established a factory at Rotherhithe, UK, for making corrugated iron in 1828. Corrugating a sheet of iron gives it a strength beyond its thickness by making it rigid across its grooves.

'Portakabin'

In 1960, Donald Shepherd, a builder from York, UK, invented the first movable building: the 'Portakabin'. Since then, the multi-purpose modules have been used as offices, schoolrooms and even as accommodation.

HEALTH

FUTURESCOPE

• **In the developed world people are going to start to live for longer and longer.** A combination of better medical care, exercise and a healthy diet means that more and more people will live to a hundred. Anti-ageing pills and research into identifying the ageing gene will further increase the possibility of living longer.

• **New medicines will offer us endless possibilities to change the way we expect to live.** In 1998, the drug Viagra was introduced and immediately changed the lives of thousands of impotent men. Future breakthroughs could be a pill for stopping people getting fat, a male contraceptive pill and a vaccine for AIDS. However, the other side of the coin is an emergence of new, super-bugs, a result of the overuse of antibiotics.

• **Old diseases that were once thought to have been eradicated, such as TB, are re-emerging.** Added to this threat is the possibility of the spread of terrible new diseases, like Ebola and BSE, which up to now have remained on a small scale and in isolated outbreaks. As bacteria and viruses get stronger doctors will have to use stronger medicines to combat them.

• **In the operating theatre non-invasive surgery should replace the old-fashioned invasive surgery.** Techniques such as telesurgery and keyhole surgery will mean that patients will have to undergo far less physical trauma and will be left with much smaller scars. Even more extraordinary is the possibility of using artificial blood and animal organs in human surgery. With an increased demand for blood and organs, doctors will need to find suitable replacements. Scientists are even developing techniques to grow hearts and limbs in the laboratory.

• **Research into the brain and genetics will produce even more extraordinary results.** Although we are a long way from being able to understand how the brain functions, scientists are starting to identify certain basic areas – the parts associated with happiness, anger or ability at sport. The Human Genome Project, meanwhile, is slowly identifying all the genes in human DNA. Once the gene map is complete, doctors may be able to prevent diseases by the careful monitoring of people who have genes that make them most at risk.

NEW MEDICINES

EQUIPMENT

SURGERY

THE BRAIN

DISEASE

GENETICS

GENOME PROJECT

LONGEVITY

THIRD WORLD

TECHNO-BABBLE

ANDROPAUSE
The male menopause.

COSMECEUTICAL
A cosmetic pharmaceutical, a product marketed as a cosmetic, but with alleged pharmaceutical benefits.

SAD
Seasonal Affective Disorder, a depressive state brought on by dark, cold winter months.

GORK
From God Only Really Knows, a gork is a person with mystery ailments.

IRIDOLOGY
Diagnosing physical conditions by scrutinising the iris of the eye.

SURGIHOLIC
One who constantly undergoes cosmetic surgery in a vain attempt to beat old age and gravity.

COSMETIC UNDERCLASS
Those who can't afford plastic surgery.

TELWRIST
Repetitive stress injury caused by repeated computer game playing.

1937	US biochemist Max Tishler creates the first vitamin pill and in doing so launches what is to become a worldwide trend in dietary supplements
2010	A safe and acceptable male contraceptive pill is in common use

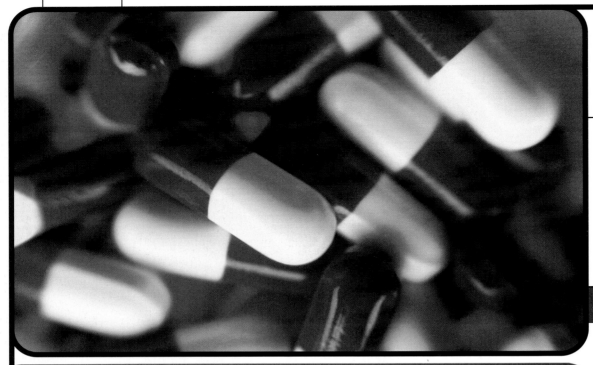

Left
As medical techniques become ever more refined, more complex tablets, combination drugs and gene therapies are fast replacing existing approaches.

NEW MEDICINES

DISCOVERIES

⏸ Pill that reduces stammers without the drowsiness

A new generation of milder tranquillizers could be close to bringing relief to the 5% of children and 1% of adults who are afflicted by stammers. Doctors believe that stammering results from an over-active brain producing too many signals for the sufferer to cope with. Trials using the anti-schizophrenia drug Olanzapine, have shown that it calms the flow of signals, thus reducing the stammer without causing the drowsiness of stronger tranquillizers.

▶ Male contraceptive pill will be a reality in the near future

Experts believe that an acceptable and safe male contraceptive pill is still 5–10 years away. The problem lies in the inadequacy and side effects of currently tested male hormone (testosterone) preparations. Dr Richard Anderson and Prof. David Baird from the Centre for Reproductive Biology, at the University of Edinburgh, UK, conducted surveys in Scotland, South Africa, Hong Kong and China, and found that, of the almost 2,000 men interviewed, between 48% and 68% said they would probably or definitely use a male contraceptive pill if such a thing existed.

▶ Anti-fat pill reduces appetites of mice and men

In most overweight people, genes account for an average of 50% of obesity. However, a research team at Rockefeller University, New York, USA, has reduced the weight of a strain of fat mice by 30% in two weeks using a course of leptin injections. Leptin is a hormone-like protein which tricks the mice's bodies into reducing appetite and increasing energy consumption. Another approach is to block the absorption of fat in the intestine. The first of these fat blockers, called Orlistata, was recently approved for prescription-only use.

▶▶ Too many white blood cells can cause asthma

Scientists believe that people who suffer from asthma produce too many white blood cells of a particular type in their immune systems which in turn cause the over-reactions to asthma triggers, such as house dust mites. At Edinburgh University, Edinburgh, UK, research is being conducted to develop a vaccine which would correct the imbalance of white blood cells.

⏸ Mice that produce unusual growth hormone drink

Scientists are already creating genetically modified animals and crops which can provide vaccinations or drug therapies. In the UK, a cow which produces milk beneficial to sufferers from cystic fibrosis has been created. Now a team headed by Dr Tung-Tien Sun and Dr Robert Wall at New York University School of Medicine, New York, USA, has designed a mouse that produces human growth hormones in its urine. Urine is, strangely enough, more convenient than milk because it is produced from birth by males as well as females, and does not contain the proteins and fats which make it difficult to separate drugs from milk. @ food p10

Left
An illustration of possible future medical applications. Here, nanorobots are destroying diseased tissue inside a human blood vessel. On the right, a robot with three rotating blades is destroying a tumour, while another, on the left, is attacking a blood clot.

▶ AIDS vaccine which works under laboratory conditions

According to 1997 figures from the World Health Organisation, up to 20 million people are HIV positive. HIV mutates as it is passed on and spreads within the body, which keeps it one step ahead of the scientists, and it may be that a 100% effective vaccine is an impossibility. A vaccine has been developed which produces antibodies in both humans and chimpanzees, but can only offer protection against laboratory strains of the virus. New research is focusing on the possibility that a number of vaccines and boosters could be used in conjunction to neutralize HIV.

❚❚ The unconventional cocktail that is dividing opinion

Luigi di Bella, an 85-year-old Italian professor, claimed to have discovered a cure for cancer. His cocktail of drugs includes small amounts of chemotherapy, but its main ingredient is the hormone somatostatin. Public belief in Prof. Di Bella's treatment is unshakeable, but doctors point to the lack of clinical evidence. Those patients who respond best to the treatment have often already undergone a course of orthodox treatment – their recovery could be a delayed reaction to these drugs, and a belief in the treatment may also play a part.

NATURAL SOURCES

❚❚ Bluebells lead the way in search for natural cures

Scientists are increasingly turning to nature in the search for new drugs. Researchers at the Institute of Grassland and Environmental Research in Aberystwyth, UK, believe that HIV and cancer treatments could be developed from the bluebell flower. The UK's Biotechnology and Biological Research Councils are teaming up with Xenova Discovery Limited to compile a library of plant compounds.

❚❚ Localized use of cannabinoids can relieve inflammation

Recent UK and US studies support new evidence demonstrating that cannabinoids – active chemical compounds in marijuana – provide safe and effective relief for a number of serious health conditions. Research in the USA has shown that the localized use of these compounds can greatly relieve the inflammation associated with arthritis and that certain cannabinoids can also block the onset of an extreme sensitivity to pain called hyperalgesia, a condition often associated with nerve disease and spinal-cord injuries.

▶ Dragon that can survive its own lethal saliva

The Komodo dragon, the world's largest living monitor lizard from the tiny Indonesian island of Komodo, produces a deadly saliva

which kills any animal it bites, including on occasion human beings. However, since the dragon frequently exposes itself to its own saliva through cut gums, it appears resistant to the poison. Biologists hope that, by isolating its natural vaccination, they will arrive at a 100% effective antibiotic.

NEW TESTING METHODS

▶ ECVAM wants to test human medicines on human cells

Based in Italy, The European Centre for Validation of Alternative Methods (ECVAM) was set up by the European Community in 1991 to develop alternatives to animal experiments. Besides the ethical concerns of using animals for medical and cosmetic research, the view that it is more scientifically productive to test medicines destined for human use on humans, is gaining currency. ECVAM researchers successfully use cultured human cells for phototoxicity tests which use light and laser for treatment, hoping to cut the number of animals used in experiments by up to 60%.

▶ Computers that estimate risk from existing knowledge

Computer programs are being developed which will screen new drugs for toxicity. Leeds University in Leeds, UK, already offers software called Derek (Deductive Estimation of Risk from Existing Knowledge) which assesses a product's potential toxicity before it undergoes testing. These computer programs will save valuable time and resources and, it is hoped, will ultimately prevent doctors from pursuing compounds that are too toxic.

Above
A Komodo dragon on Komodo Island, Indonesia, which biologists believe has evolved a natural resistance to its own venom. Increasingly, medicine is looking to imitate the simplicity of nature to develop preventative cures.

▶ Human corpses collected to conduct research on

Pharmagene, a UK based company founded in 1996, that pioneers research into drug discovery, rules out animal experimentation altogether. Instead, it prefers to take a higher ethical stance and conduct all its research into the discovery and development of drugs for the human body on human body tissues which are collected from mortuaries and hospitals.

♻ Back to the future

Riboflavin

In 1937, US biochemist Max Tishler developed the process which synthesizes riboflavin, Vitamin B2 – kicking off the mass production of vitamin tablets.

Tranquillizers

In 1952, Swiss pharmacologist Emil Schittler and British biochemist Robert Robinson created Reserpine, the first tranquillizer. In March 1955, *Time* magazine reported that Reserpine and new sedative Chlorpromazine had brought on a revolution in the treatment of mental illness, allowing patients to be treated faster and more effectively.

Watch injections

In 1991, Swiss watch-makers Swatch and UK company Elan brought out the Panoject, a wristwatch device which could be used to carry drugs such as insulin for diabetics. Underneath the watch case was a mini-syringe which could be electronically controlled by buttons on the watch face.

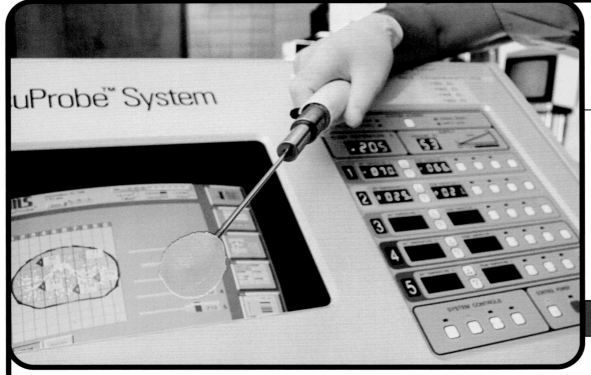

uProbe™ System

Left
A surgeon's hand holding a metal cryoprobe. The ice ball at its tip indicates its powers of cooling after being dipped in water. Guided by ultrasound, the probe is used in cryosurgery to freeze tissues – especially in prostate cancer where cancerous cells around the probe are frozen and then destroyed.

EQUIPMENT

DIAGNOSIS

Portable biocavity laser can identify cancer in minutes

Sandia National Laboratories in Albuquerque, USA, and the National Institute of Health, Bethesda, Maryland, USA, patented a portable laser device in 1997 which can identify blood disorders such as sickle-cell anaemia and cancerous cells within minutes. Called a biocavity laser, the device detects changes in cell size and shape after a blood sample is inserted into the laser itself. This data can be transmitted to an ordinary personal computer or laptop. The biocavity laser is far more efficient than a Pap smear, one of the most popular cancer tests, as it can survey millions of cells very quickly.

Portable X-ray machine is the size of a pizza box

In 1997, General Electric and EG&G, companies based in California, USA, created a portable, computerized X-ray the size of a pizza box. The US military, a founder of the project, plans to use the portable X-ray in mobile clinics. Not only will it serve remote and poorer communities but it can transmit images to hospital radiologists for specialist diagnosis.

Laser probes that detect 90% of pre-cancerous cells

A highly efficient laser probe capable of detecting stomach and intestinal cancers is set for commercialization. The optical detector is the work of a team of physicists at Oak Ridge National Laboratory in Tennessee, USA. It is over 98% accurate, and also registers 90% of pre-cancerous cells. Earlier diagnosis will enable doctors to commence treatment sooner, and so reduce deaths. @ surgery p106

Breast scans improve, thanks to tumour telescope

Telescope technology being developed by scientists at Louisiana State University, Louisiana, USA, is set to improve the quality of breast scans, and help doctors spot breast tumours. The CCD (charge-coupled device) is highly sensitive, and is more commonly used by astronomers.

Cholesterol tests: five minutes and a drop of blood

The Cholestech LDX System is new technology which allows pharmacists to check cholesterol levels. The machine requires just a single drop of blood to determine levels of cholesterol as accurately as hospital laboratories. Results are available within five minutes. Elsewhere, at Sandia National Laboratory in Albuquerque, New Mexico, US, scientists are developing a blood-analysing laser.

Mathematical theory helps to unravel lung disorders

Mathematical theory is helping scientists at Bristol University, UK, to design computer

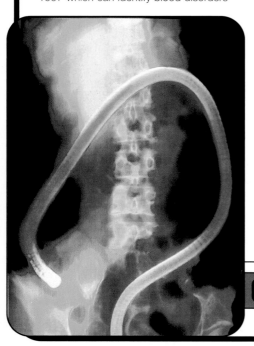

Left
A coloured X-ray of a fibre-optic (red) endoscope (colonoscope) passing through a colon. Having entered through the rectum, the colonoscope forms a loop allowing the surgeon to examine the intestine closely. The spine (green) and pelvis can also be seen.

software able to detect lung disease. Healthy lungs have a distinctive visual pattern, with branches like trees: when disease sets in, the branches look pruned. Computers can be programmed to recognise lung disease, and assess the severity. Additionally, the mathematical unpredictability of chaos theory is being applied to help understand what makes some people more susceptible than others.

AutoPap works alongside smear slide technicians

In the USA, a computer system called AutoPap is set to work alongside lab technicians, screening cervical smear slides. Marketed by NeoPath of Redmond, Washington, the computer acts like a spell checker, and can be used for the routine parts of the process, saving money and increasing reliability.

TREATMENT

▶▶ Intelligent bandages contain antibiotic molecules

Researchers at Kyoto University in Kyoto, and the Kuraray Company in Kurushiki, Japan, are to begin testing an 'intelligent' bandage on human beings. The bandage contains antibiotic molecules which are only activated if a wound becomes infected. Infected wounds release oxygen, which reacts with peptide in the dressing, and in turn releases the antibiotic.

▶ Holographic medical imaging for structural viewing

Representation of the body or parts of the body in 3-D is close to becoming a reality. Voxel, based in Laguna Hills, California, USA, has experimented successfully with new X-ray technologies to produce holograms while another firm, American Propylaea, has projected a hologram of a human liver. Holographic medical imaging will enable doctors to understand further the structure of tumours, and could provide medical students with invaluable experience.

❚❚ Carisolv is the instant gel that dissolves tissue

Swedish dentists have developed Carisolv, a painless alternative to the dentist's drill. Carisolv is a red gel which dissolves decayed tissue in less than 30 seconds, leaving the dentist to clean and fill the cavity. Although in some cases additional drilling is required, injections are not normally necessary. The gel, formulated by Swedish company Medi Team, will be particularly useful in developing countries where equipment and anaesthetics are scarce and costly. @ *third world p118*

❚❚ Painless laser is quicker than a drill and sterilizes, too

Premier Laser Systems, based in Irvine, California, USA, has designed a laser which removes tooth cavities painlessly. The Centauri is much quicker than a drill, and

sterilizes the cavity at the same time. Unfortunately, laser treatment is likely to be more expensive than drilling, and both patient and dentist will need to wear protective glasses.

▶ The incredible portable operating theatre

The Advanced Surgical Site for Trauma Casualties (ASSTC) measures 1.5 m by 1.5 m by 3 m (5ft x 5ft x 10ft), and weighs 2 tonnes; it is easily transportable by helicopter, and can be transformed into an operating theatre in just thirty minutes. The US Army hopes that it will save up to 25% of those soldiers who would usually die within an hour of having been wounded.

▶ Photodynamic Therapy is set to challenge lasers

Technology intended by NASA for growing plants in space has led to the development of Photodynamic Therapy. This therapy is similar to laser therapy, using tiny light-emitting diodes (LEDs) instead of lasers to activate the light-sensitive drugs. The LED system is the size of a suitcase, and is a much cheaper and more reliable light source than lasers. @ *space stations p146*

▶ Yag laser will zap tattoos and maybe gang allegiance

The breakthrough in tattoo removal came in the early 1990s in the USA with the arrival of the $80,000 (£45,000) laser. The Ytterbium Aluminium Garnet (YAG) laser removes tattoos simply and cheaply and, whereas early laser treatments relied on burning the tattoo, the YAG laser breaks up the ink colours into particles which the body can then dispose of via its own immune system. In the USA, it has inspired campaigns in some major cities offering the free removal of gang allegiance tattoos.

Above
Lasers are the scalpels of the future. Here, a young girl is receiving Argon laser treatment for a port-wine stain on her neck. The red pigment selectively absorbs the laser's blue-green light, and dilated vessels are burned and sealed off.

❚❚ Pan-European telemedicine points to global operating

A pan-European project is set to change surgical practice. The ground-breaking system allows a radiologist in one country to send ultrasound probes that are guided by a computer mouse, through the body of a patient in another country, and a co-ordinating robotic middleman will assess the situation and then inform the surgeon of the exact operation required.

♻ Back to the future

Ultrasound device

In 1976, US scientist Charles Kelman invented an instrument which fragments cataracts in the eye by ultrasound and then removes them while the patient is under local anaesthetic.

Novolet

In 1990, Danish medical group Novo Nordisk released Novolet, the smallest and lightest insulin syringe in the world. It holds enough insulin to meet a diabetic's needs for three to seven days, is disposable and is made of biodegradable plastic. A similiar British insulin syringe which gives a set dose and resembles a pen has won a design award.

Cyberspace Hospital

In May 1995, Cyberspace Hospital was launched by the National University of Singapore, with links to the best medical sites on the World Wide Web, providing specialist knowledge for doctors and medical researchers, as well as information about disease and the diagnosis and treatment of health problems for ordinary people.

1927	Prof. Philip Drinken designs the iron lung using two vacuum cleaners
2015	Human tissues and organs can be grown artificially at natural speed

Left
Human epidermis in a liquid culture flask being manipulated with forceps. Once treated with enzymes, the epidermis can be detached from the dermis on which it was cultured. Synthetic skin's uses include treatment of burns and testing cosmetics.

SURGERY

NON-INVASIVE SURGERY

⏸ Telesurgery and keyhole surgery

Telesurgery has already made it possible for surgeons in Italy, and Japan, to operate on a patient six miles away as detailed video footage of the patient's body is beamed back to the doctor who sees it on a screen. Keyhole surgery requires only a tiny incision through which an endoscope is inserted, which allows the surgeon to view the operation on a video monitor and helps to minimize the trauma of surgery.

⏩ Voice-operated robots that never get tired

The next step on from telesurgery is robosurgery. In the USA, one company is already applying to market a robosurgeon for use on humans. *Aesop*, engineered by Computer Motion, is a voice-operated robot capable of recognising 22 commands. Unlike a real-life surgeon, a robosurgeon does not get tired, its hands never shake and its delicate arms make it an ideal aid in keyhole heart surgery. The robot only responds to the normal speech patterns of one particular doctor, so there is no danger it would act on commands screamed by that doctor, or any other, in the heat of the moment. @ *robots p28*

⏩ Hermes automated theatres permit remote control

Computer Motion has also developed a voice-controlled operating theatre called *Hermes*, which allows the surgeon to control devices usually automated from outside the sterile theatre. In the far future, scientists such as K. Eric Drexler envision the advent of minute robots, tiny enough to be swallowed, and able to be programmed to perform internal operations such as repairing cells. @ *nanotechnology p154*

⏸ Laser surgery reduces post-operative trauma

One of the attractions of laser surgery is that it helps to minimize post-operative trauma and infection. A team at the National Medical Laser Centre at University College, London, UK, has developed a new treatment called photodynamic therapy which has already been tried on skin cancer and mouth tumours. Patients are given an injection of a light-sensitive drug, later activated by a laser which shrinks the tumour. Tests show that the treatment removes most of the cancer, and slows down the development of remaining cells.

▶ The advantages of blood substitutes are immense

A host of first generation blood substitutes are undergoing clinical trials. At present, real human blood has to be kept frozen at

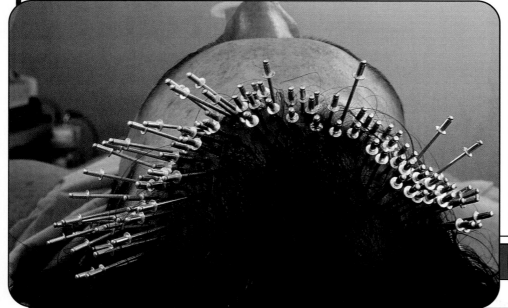

Left
A man's head during a hair transplant, using a cosmetic technique called 'punch grafting'. Metal 'pins' punch holes and remove areas of bald scalp which are then replaced with grafts of hairy scalp and left to heal.

-40°C and used within six weeks. The advantages of artificial blood are immense: it can be stored for longer, it minimizes the risk of disease being passed on through transfusions, and some substitutes can even be given to patients regardless of blood type. In the USA, Baxter Healthcare Corporation is developing Hemassist – a blood substitute that looks like the real thing and carries oxygen.

Open-heart surgery without a blood transfusion

At Cornell University Medical Center, New York, USA, doctors have successfully carried out open-heart surgery without blood transfusions. Patients receive a course of injections in the weeks leading up to surgery and this encourages the bone marrow to produce more blood. They are also given vitamin and iron supplements. During surgery, doctors administer a powerful clotting agent, and any spilt blood is mixed with an anti-clotting agent, purified, and pumped back into the body. Even blood which haemorrhages is not wasted – it is washed, filtered, spun down, and returned to surgeons for use again.

DESIGNER BODIES

Xenotransplantation gives humans animal organs

Scientists anticipate that animals such as pigs might be used to produce a number of human organs. Called xenotransplantation, this research is focusing on breeding pigs which can mimic human antigens, substances which aid the production of antibodies, because the main obstacle to transplanting organs is that the human body usually rejects them. Tissues such as heart valves have already been transplanted from pigs to humans, as well as liver and brain cell implants. However, some scientists still believe xenotransplantation carries too great a risk of animal infections.

Human skin that can be grown in two weeks

Scientists believe that, in the future, there is no reason why they should not be able to replicate any part of the human body. At Advanced Tissue Sciences, in San Diego, USA, human skin can be grown in just two weeks, bone in six weeks, and liver in eight weeks – the same speed of development as in the womb. Tissue is grown by injecting cells onto a 'scaffold' of biodegradable fabric, and feeding them a mix of vitamins, glucose, amino-acids, and serum proteins.

No danger of rejection for designer blood vessels

Using tiny amounts of a patient's own tissue, surgeons at the Laval University School of Medicine in Quebec, Canada, can create designer blood vessels for use in by-pass surgery. There is no danger of rejection, since the cultured vessels are grown from the patient's own cells, and are stronger than the body's own blood vessels.

Broken bones can be healed using titanium inserts

Researchers at Kyoto University, Kyoto, Japan, are pioneering a bone-healing technique by inserting small slivers of coated titanium into fractures, which act as anchors and promote synostosis – the process by which bones knit together after a break. Titanium is ideal, being durable, light and non-corrosive, but bone does not graft to it, so the researchers have found a way of coating small amounts of titanium – just 1 cm square and 1 mm thick – with a mixture of apatite, a complex mineral found in bone, and titanium oxide to which the bone grafts easily. @ equipment p104

Artificial bones are cut to order by computer

Researchers at the Argonne National Laboratory, Illinois, USA, are perfecting artificial bones which behave exactly like human bones once inside the body. The bones, made from thermoplastic mixed with ceramic powder, are porous, allowing human tissue to attach itself easily, and new computer software cuts the bones to order, using a 3-D X-ray. The result is a bone that fits exactly, unlike those carved from metal or from bone removed from a corpse, and they can also be made within an hour.

Headless organisms could be grown for spare parts

Scientists are one step closer to establishing organ factories following the creation of a headless frog embryo. Gene manipulation enabled Prof. Jonathan Slack from Bath University, Bath, UK, to suppress the growth of a tadpole's head. Added to the technology developed by the Roslin

Above
A neurosurgeon using a computer-assisted microscope with laser to find and operate on a cerebral tumour. The scene is relayed onto a video screen where a powerful MKM stereotaxic microscope plots the tumour's position.

Institute, UK, to clone Dolly the sheep, this advance could lead to headless human clones being created to grow organs for transplants. The organs would be grown from the patients' own cloned cells, making rejection a thing of the past, and easing the shortage of organs available for transplant. Without a central nervous system or brain, headless organisms would not qualify as being human, and so make the process legal. The ethics of such a procedure will, however, be extremely hotly debated.

Back to the future

Iron lung

In 1927, Prof. Philip Drinken from Harvard University, USA, designed the iron lung, made from two vacuum cleaners alternately producing positive and negative pressure on the human chest. It was tested on a young girl at Boston Hospital in Oct 1928 and, following this, used to treat polio victims.

Reattached arm

In 1962, Dr Donald A. Malt and Dr J. McKhann from the Massachusetts General Hospital, Boston, USA, reattached the right arm of a 12-year-old boy which had been completely severed from the shoulder.

Pig aortic valve

In 1965, French doctors J. P. Binet and A. Carpentier transplanted the first aortic valve from a pig into a human to replace a faulty valve in the aorta. The aorta is the main vessel which transports oxygen-rich blood from the heart to the rest of the body.

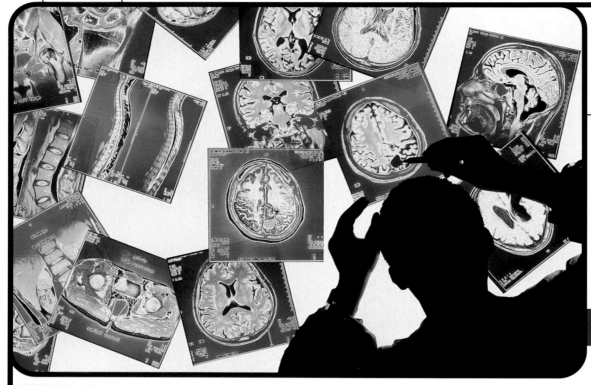

Left
A doctor examines a selection of magnetic resonance imaging (MRI) scans of the human body. On the right is the brain, and on the left, spinal and pelvic scans. MRI scanning, created from radio signals in a high-powered magnetic field, is excellent for studying soft body tissues.

THE BRAIN

PERCEPTION

▶▶ Synaesthesia is a baby's first way of seeing the world

Synaesthesia occurs when perceptions by one sense organ stimulate a reaction in another, in the same way that hearing a sound can immediately bring to mind a specific colour. US neurologist and author Richard Cytowic MD believes it has something to do with the limbic system, the oldest part of the brain, and is the way prehistoric man perceived the world. However, Daphne Maurer at McMaster University in Ontario, USA, believes that synaesthesia is the way babies perceive the world. Infants have many more neural connections than adults and slowly lose them as they begin to adapt to the world.

⏸ Interval clock that governs every movement

A team at Duke University, North Carolina, USA, has been researching the human interval clock, a part of the brain used to determine the amount of time between events. For instance, pedestrians use it to decide if they have enough time to cross the street before an oncoming car reaches them and musicians use it to synchronize with the drum beat. The research team used a functional magnetic resonance imaging machine (FMRI) to trace very fast flows of blood in the brain. They discovered that a very primitive part of the brain at the base of the skull, called the motor control centre, boosts the flow of blood to the desired region as and when it is required.

⏸ How and where the brain perceives language

Scientists at the Indiana School of Medicine in Indianapolis, USA, have discovered that different languages are perceived by different parts of the brain. Using Thai and English speakers, the research team ran a test in which the subjects' brains were monitored while hearing a series of Thai words. It was discovered that Thai speakers understand their language which, like Swedish and Mandarin, relies on intonation to convey meaning, with both the left and right parts of the brain. This contrasts with earlier tests which revealed that English speakers use intonation merely to convey emotion and use the right brain only to understand the mechanics of language.

⏸ Dyslexia and the puzzle of sound and vision

A research team at Yale University School of Medicine, New Haven, USA, announced in March 1998 that they had found the area in the brain which produces dyslexia. Using a magnetic resonance imaging (MRI) machine, they discovered that, in normal readers, there was activity in the forebrain, which is used to process the visual information in reading, and the back of the brain, which is the language centre and interprets information. However, in dyslexic readers, there was reduced activity in the language centre but increased activity in the part of the brain which processes sound. This means that teaching dyslexic children to read phonetically, focusing on words' sounds, is the best way to help them to overcome reading difficulties.

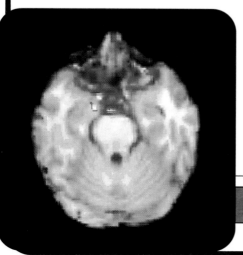

Left
A positron emission tomography (PET) scan of the human brain. The active area of the brain, colour-coded yellow/red, is the left amgdala, which tests suggest is the region which recognizes and responds to facial fear.

BRAIN POWER

▶ **Psychokinesis defies the laws of probability**

Scientists at Princeton University, Princeton, USA, believe they have evidence that man is capable of psychokinesis, the ability to control objects through thought. For 12 years, the team has been conducting tests using a special machine which generates a random sequence of ones and zeroes. Test subjects were asked to try to 'will' the numbers to be one or zero, and most were able to. And the odds on getting the same result? Less than one in 1,000 billion.

⏸ **The neural connection between epilepsy and religion**

Scientists at University of California, San Diego, USA, have a theory that religious feeling may be attributed to over-excited neurons in the inferior temporal lobe of the brain. In a test, three groups of people – sufferers from temporal lobe epilepsy, a religious group and an unreligious group – viewed a 40-word list of religious, violent and neutral words. Both the epileptic and religious groups responded to the religious words with activity in the inferior temporal lobe where epilepsy seizures occur, which may explain why many sufferers of epilepsy become obsessed with religion.

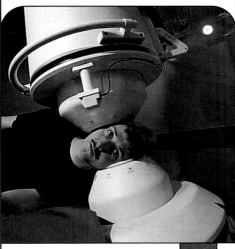

Above
Magnetoencephalography (MEG) uses a scanner that contains sensitive magnetic fields cooled in liquid helium. The neuromagnetometers are placed either side of the head and measure the magnetic fields generated from the brain's nerve cell activity.

▶ **The better the technique, the fewer cells required**

Brains are dynamic organisms which are able to produce and lose networks between neurons or brain cells. Children develop new networks in response to stimuli such as reading, playing and interacting with other humans. In 1997, researchers at the Wellcome Department of Cognitive Neurology at the Institute of Neurology, London, UK, discovered that people who are good at skilled movements such as playing musical instruments or sports, use fewer brain cells while performing their speciality than novices. @ *artificial life p152*

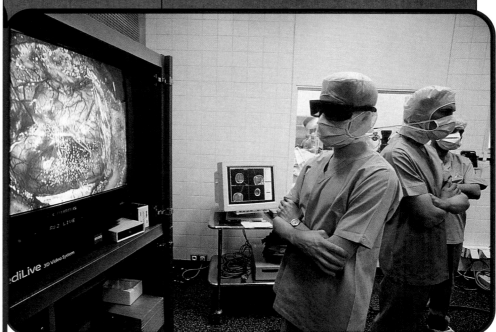

Above
Increasingly, surgery is becoming a remote activity. Here, neurosurgeons watch a computer-aided brain operation on a screen. An MRI scan helps create a 3-D virtual map which guides the surgeon's laser to the tumour with total precision.

DISCOVERIES

⏸ **The girl who was accidentally made to laugh**

An accidental discovery was made during a pre-surgery examination of an epileptic girl's brain by Dr Itzhak Fried and a team of Californian neurosurgeons. During their examination, they happened to stimulate a small region in the supplementary motor area of the frontal lobe with a weak electrical current – and the girl promptly laughed. Intrigued, the doctors gradually increased the current and found that the more they increased it, the more emphatically the girl laughed. It now appears that this accidental event may have found the hitherto unknown location for laughter in the brain.

▶ **Imprinted genes test helps to locate gender impulses**

Doctors at the University of Cambridge, UK, have discovered that children probably get their intelligence from their mothers and their basic instincts from their fathers. This finding comes from research into imprinted genes – genes that reveal from which parent they come. Experimenting with mice embryos, the researchers created two different types of mice, with tendencies to be either more 'male' or more 'female' – by switching off the male or female parts of the fifteen known imprinted genes. What resulted was that the more 'female' mice had larger executive brain parts, which are responsible for memory and conscious thought and are located in the cortex. However, the more 'male' embryos had larger emotional brain parts, such as the hypothalamus, which are responsible for survival instincts such as aggression, sex and eating. @ *genetics p112*

▶ **Pregnancy causes women's brains to shrink**

A study led by Dr Anita Holdcroft at the Royal Postgraduate Medical School in London, UK, revealed in 1997 that pregnant women often become emotional or have difficulty concentrating because their brains shrink during late pregnancy. Using an MRI machine, it was found that, after shrinking, the brain returns to its normal size within six months of giving birth.

♻ **Back to the future**

Time and temperature

In the 1930s, Dr Hudson Hoagland noticed that his wife, in bed with flu, complained that he had gone for a long time when he had left her for only a few minutes. He asked his wife to count to 60 several times while noting the time and her temperature. He discovered the hotter she was, the faster she counted and, therefore, the faster time appeared to pass.

MRI brain mapping

In 1977, Dr Raymond Damadian used a magnetic resonance imaging (MRI) machine to take the first pictures of the human body. The machine's field excites protons in the brain which, when they relax, leave a map of the degrees of brain activity.

Psychosurgery

During the 1930s, lobotomies were a common treatment for a variety of mental disorders from depression to schizophrenia. Psychosurgery was phased out in later years by the development of new drugs.

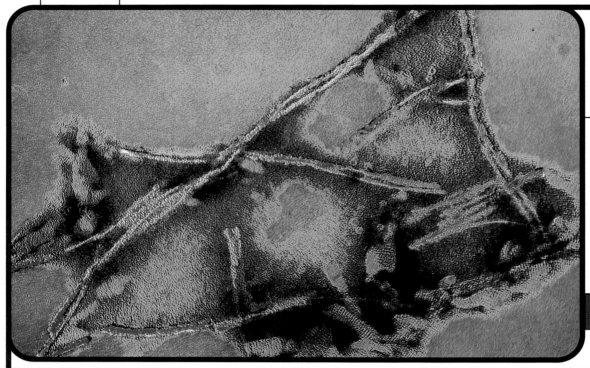

Left
Prions in the brain of a 'mad cow'. These elongated fibrils (pink) are thought to consist of the virus' proteins. The prions attack nerve cells causing neurodegenerative brain damage, the symptoms of which include glazed eyes and uncontrollable body tremors.

DISEASE

RESURGENCY

The Black Death that never really went away

Strains of the bubonic plague are still at large, and are as resistant to modern treatments as they were to leeches in medieval times. Researchers at the Pasteur Institute in Paris, France, have studied a strain contracted by a 16-year-old boy in Madagascar. Although the boy survived, it was no thanks to modern medicine: the virus resisted all the treatments which the scientists tried. Moreover, they found that the strain spread readily in controlled experiments, and fear that it could be just as easily transmitted in nature.

Most TB DNA components have been identified

Tuberculosis (TB) kills more people than any other infectious disease, claiming about three million lives worldwide each year. Its increasing resistance to antibiotics, allied with a growing pool of TB-prone HIV sufferers means that this figure is set to rise. However, a team of scientists at the Sanger Centre near Cambridge, UK, have identified most of the genes which make up TB DNA, and sequenced its four million components. @ genome project p114

Over-use of antibiotics has made superbugs resistant

An ever increasing number of microbes is developing resistance to antibiotics. One such 'superbug' is VRE (vancomycin-resistant enterococcus), which is even resistant to vancomycin, one of the strongest drugs available. VRE thrives on patients who are recovering from operations and causes infection after surgery. Microbiologists also fear that a common microbe, such as Staphylococcus aureus, which lives on human skin, may develop vancomycin resistance, causing post-surgery complications. In 1941, less than 1% of all Staphylococcus aureus strains were multi-drug resistant, and this figure has since leapt up to 38%. World Health Organization (WHO) officials cite over-use of antibiotics as a major cause of bacterial resistance.

OUTBREAKS

Chicken flu is virulent but also relatively weak

The first recorded case of H5N1, the virus known as chicken flu, was identified in Hong Kong in 1997, following the death of a young boy. Potentially lethal, chicken flu attacks the respiratory system and other organs, and is as yet incurable. Yet, despite its virulence, the virus has relatively weak powers of transmission, although human-to-human transmission has not been ruled out. Swift identification prevented the Hong Kong outbreak from claiming more lives, but a cure still remains elusive.

E-coli tests show antibodies can be produced in a week

Escherichia coli 0157, commonly known as E. coli, is potentially lethal especially for the

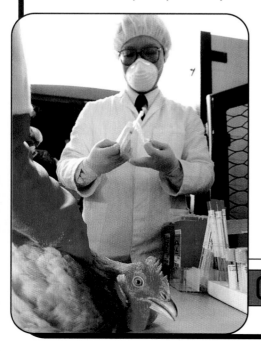

Left
A Hong Kong Agriculture and Fisheries Department official wearing protective sanitary clothes takes a blood sample from a live chicken batch arriving from China. The blood tests are part of health procedures to ensure that the chickens are free from H5N1 flu.

elderly and young children. In Scotland, it was responsible for an outbreak of food poisoning which killed twenty people in 1997. Scientists at the National Institute of Child Health and Human Development in Bethesda, Maryland, USA, are prototyping a genetically engineered vaccine, which encourages the immune system to produce antibodies that kill *E. coli* bacteria. Trials show that, in 80% of the healthy volunteers tested, it took a week for enough antibodies to be produced, and this response is fast enough to protect vulnerable people in case of another outbreak. The team hopes the vaccine can be adapted to protect cattle, in which case the vaccine need only be used on humans during an outbreak.

▶ Australia prepares for the arrival of a deadly disease

Australia is preparing for the arrival of one of the world's most deadly diseases. Japanese encephalitis is spread by mosquitoes, infecting about 15,000 people each year and leaving many permanently brain-damaged or paralyzed. Since it was identified in Japan in the 1930s, the disease has spread through southeast Asia, as far as Bali. From Bali, it spread to Papua New Guinea, probably carried by a water bird, and it is predicted to hit Australia by the millennium. The disease is rife among herds of feral pigs, which act as 'amplifiers'. However, a human vaccine is now available.

▶ The search continues for a BSE and nvCJD cure

Bovine Spongiform Encephalopathy (BSE) was first recorded in 1986 in the UK. It is one of several forms of transmissible brain disease found in animals. Scientists believe that BSE is caused by an infectious agent called a slow virus, or a prion, which affects the brain and spine, causing sponge-like changes that are visible under a microscope. It is believed that BSE may have been caused by feeding cattle with protein from infected sheep. Independent studies show that the same prion strain in BSE causes new variant Creutzfeldt-Jakob disease in humans (nvCJD), suggesting that nvCJD is the human form of BSE. The disease was most likely transmitted through exposure to infected bovine offal. Although the number of reported cases of nvCJD in the UK is decreasing, the average incubation time remains unknown, so the figure could rise yet.

▶ Ebola guinea pigs could help to immunize Africa

Ebola is one of the most feared viruses in the world, causing massive bleeding and throwing the body into shock. Easily transmitted through blood and body fluids, the virus was first recorded in the Democratic Republic of Congo (then Zaire) and has since spread to Sudan, Gabon, and the Ivory Coast. Four cases were reported in Johannesburg, South Africa, in 1996. An effective vaccine is urgently needed, and researchers at the University of Michigan, Ann Arbor, USA, have found one which protects laboratory guinea pigs from the virus. @ *third world p118*

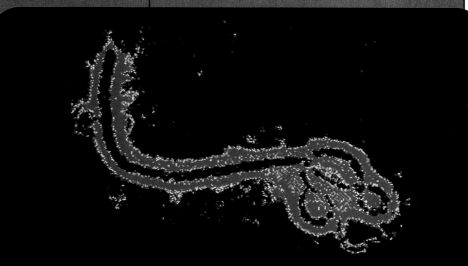

DISCOVERIES

⏸ Malaria is public health enemy number one

The World Health Organization has recently labelled malaria, 'Public Health Enemy Number One'. Each year, it infects between 300 and 500 million people and kills up to 2.7 million of them. What is more, it is becoming resistant to most of the drugs currently depended upon to treat it. So great is the need for new anti-malarial medicines, that researchers from around the world have now begun to map the genome of the causative organism, *Plasmodium falciparum*. Efforts to build a co-ordinated global strategy for malaria control, spearheaded by The National Institutes of Health and France's Institut Pasteur, now involve several major international bodies, including, WHO, USAID and the European Union (EU), as well as private charities such as Britain's Wellcome Trust.
@ *new medicines p102*

▶ Enzyme marker that can turn immune cells on and off

Researchers at the Toronto Hospital, Toronto, Canada, and the Canadian Red Cross have discovered a new marker for the HIV virus. The marker is an enzyme which turns immune cells on and off. The enzyme responds very quickly to HIV, becoming chronically turned on within 30 minutes of infection. Their findings point towards a new way of testing, which would allow for swifter diagnosis, and so reduce the opportunity for the virus to be spread.

▶ Cancer cells are the ones that don't self-destruct

Rapid advances in the understanding of cancer are pointing scientists towards new treatments and faster detection.

Above
Coloured Transmission Electron Micrograph (TEM) of the Ebola virus. It is similar to, yet distinct from the Marburg virus, the cause of green monkey disease. Outbreaks of Ebola have occurred in equatorial Africa since 1976.

Scientists at Johns Hopkins University in Baltimore, Maryland, USA, have discovered that cells are dependent on sugar and self-destruct if their glucose supply is interrupted. It is known that cancer occurs when the suicide mechanism, by which malfunctioning and diseased cells kill themselves, fails. Scientists had thought that this abort mechanism was located inside the cell, but research carried out by Anne-Odile Hueber and Gerard Evans proves that it operates from the surface of the cell. This discovery paves the way for the development of other repair drugs that could trigger the reverse response.

♺ Back to the future

The last smallpox case

In 1966, WHO launched a worldwide vaccination campaign against smallpox. The last recorded case of a death from it was in 1978 when the victim, who was a medical photographer, was infected by a laboratory sample at Birmingham University, UK.

Leishmaniasis

In 1989, a research team from the University of Minas Gerais in Brazil developed the first vaccine against leishmaniasis, a tropical disease which causes swelling of the liver and spleen. Along with other lethal diseases, it has been prioritized by WHO for eradication.

Coronary culture-contrasts

Coronary heart disease is the biggest killer in developed nations. In Bulgaria, in 1997, eight people in 100 suffered fatal strokes, the highest in the world. By contrast, these diseases are practically unknown in the Inuit peoples of Canada, Russia and Greenland.

1865	The science of genetics is discovered by an Augustinian abbot
2002	Geneticists in Cambridge, UK, will be able to choose the sex of calves

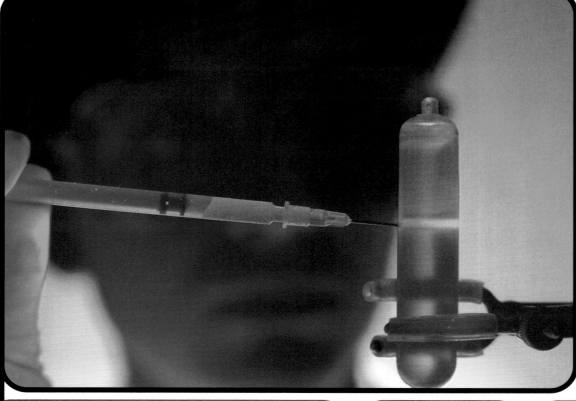

Left
With the help of ultra violet light, it is now possible for scientists to separate samples of DNA. A sample of DNA is put into a container, and clamped in place under ultra violet light. The scientist can then remove a small sample using a hypodermic syringe.

GENETICS

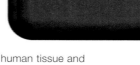

GENETIC EXPERIMENTS

 Parents can choose their child's gender

Since the beginning of time, parents have tried to influence the sex of their babies. Geneticists working with cattle in Cambridge, UK, think they may be able to offer a reliable method of sex selection by 2002. Using a method called flow cytometry, they can enrich sperm samples with either male- or female-bearing sperm. A fluorescent dye is placed on the X or Y chromosome and then the sperm is sorted in a laser beam.

▶ Cloned animals have medical uses

A major advance in the field of cloning occurred in 1997, when the Roslin Institute near Edinburgh, Scotland, announced the birth of a sheep named Dolly – the world's first cloned animal. She was created by transferring the nucleus from an adult animal to an enucleated egg. The 'pharming' of cloned animals could assist in the search for cures for diseases, and provide useful products for the pharmaceutical industry. Most people object to the idea of producing 'carbon copies' of genetically identical

people, but cloning human tissue and organs could revolutionize medical science.
@ agriculture p128

▶ Scientist develops cloning tank

A Japanese scientist has developed an artificial womb which he claims will be able to grow human foetuses within the next decade. Professor Yoshinori Kuwabara's invention is a plastic tank filled with amniotic fluid which is kept at body temperature and constantly replenished with oxygen. Feeding and blood cleaning is done by a dialysis machine attached to the umbilical cord. So far he has successfully managed to support goat foetuses for periods of three weeks until they are ready for birth.

⏸ Geneticists produce fatherless cow

Geneticists at Yamaguchi University, Japan, have successfully impregnated cows without male sperm. The technique is called parthenogenesis and means that men could be eliminated from the reproduction process

altogether. Under the guidance of Professor Tatsuyuki, an unfertilized egg was removed from a cow's womb and bathed in a series of chemicals which stimulated the growth of the egg into an embryo which was then put back into the womb. The team used only X chromosomes from the mother and only female offspring were produced.

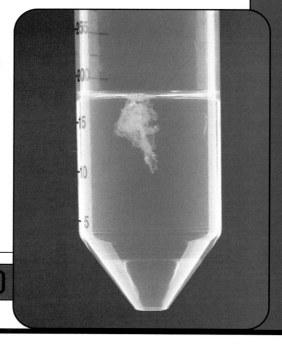

Right
Contained within this test tube is a sample of human DNA, which contains between 50,000 and 100,000 genes. The sample has precipitated in the phenol to form a white cloud. It was obtained from a patient's white blood cells, called lymphocytes.

Scientists discover the 'sober' gene

A fast metabolism may not be the sole reason why some drinkers get tipsier than others. Animal tests conducted at the RIKEN Brain Science Institute in Wako City, Japan, have indicated that alcohol sensitivity could be influenced by genes expressed in the brain. Mice lacking a brain enzyme called Fyn kinase took twice as long as others to stand up after being injected with alcohol and placed on their backs. Scientists believe the enzyme may counteract the depressive effect which alcohol has on neurons by adding phosphates to a receptor called NMDA.

GENE THERAPY

Method for localized gene therapy developed

Researchers at the University of Chicago, USA, have developed a technique which will allow doctors to target genes at specific parts of the body. Previously, injected therapeutic genes could not be directed to specific cells and would circulate though the whole body, possibly leading to dangerous side-effects. The new gene therapy attaches a weakened virus to a

Above
Scientists can cut out specific genes for cloning by staining DNA fragments and putting them in an agarose gel. They show up as fluorescent violet bands under ultra violet light, and can be separated by size using an electric current.

newly identified control element found in smooth muscle cells which allows it to be guided to a target. The therapy could soon be used as a common treatment for ailments such as asthma, heart disease and irritable bowel syndrome.

Disabled cured through genetic manipulation

Humans may be able to grow new limbs in the way that lizards and starfish re-grow lost tails and arms. Scientists at Allegheny University in Philadelphia, USA, have cured mice of osteoporosis, the brittle bone disease, by injecting their bone marrow with genetically manipulated young cells. The scientists also hope to treat paralysis by regenerating cells in the central nervous system which have been damaged by spinal cord injuries.

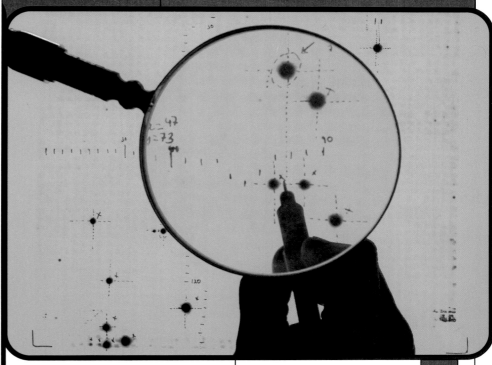

Trials to test treatment for AIDS

In the USA, a number of clinical trials have been approved to test gene therapy for treatments of genetic disorders such as cystic fibrosis, brain tumours and even AIDS. Results from tests into ADA deficiency, a genetic disease that affects the immune system, suggest that gene therapy could be used to help patients to destroy HIV-infected cells. Genetically altered T-lymphocytes or stem cells might prevent the failure of the immune system in AIDS patients.

Discovery could lead to cancer prevention pill

Scottish scientists have identified a single gene that protects against the cancerous chemicals common in tobacco smoke. Polycyclic hydrocarbons, the chemical agents found in cigarette smoke, were tested on the skin of laboratory mice and it was discovered that those animals lacking the gene developed three times as many precancerous tumours as those with the gene. Because it is easier to manipulate one particular gene than many, this breakthrough means scientists could use genetic engineering to prevent certain cancers, and a cancer prevention pill could potentially be undergoing clinical trials within a decade.

Pocket device that gives a genetic profile

We may soon be able to analyse our genetic profiles and assess our susceptibility to disease, with an easy to use, pocket-sized instrument, thanks to

Above
This grid of DNA fragments represents human chromosome 17, the site of a defective gene linked to many cases of inherited breast cancer. An X-ray plate is superimposed onto the grid, which allows scientists to map genes on a chromosome.

advances made in the US by Affymetrix, a company based in Santa Clara, California. Copies of all 6,200 genes found in baker's yeast have successfully been grafted onto a chip about the size of a thumb nail. By applying fluorescently tagged RNA extracted from yeast, researchers are able to identify the active genes simply by checking the glowing spots. It is believed that eventually a chip could be produced for any organism whose entire gene sequence has been mapped – including humans. @ *genome project p114*

Back to the future

Genetics

Genetics was first discovered as a science by Gregor Johann Mendel, an Austrian biologist and Augustinian Abbot of Brun. He combined his knowledge of plants with his love of mathematics.

Gene theory

In 1910, Thomas Hunt Morgan, Professor of Experimental Zoology at Columbia University, New York, USA, announced the idea of gene theory after he had studied thousands of generations of the fruit-fly *Drosophila*.

Abnormal genes

In 1982, Dr Robert Wienberg of MIT and Dr Mariano Barbacid in the National Cancer Institute, Maryland, USA, identified abnormal genes for the first time.

Left
The Human Genome Project aims to build a complete genetic map. This means conducting detailed biochemical surveys of each gene on all 23 pairs of human chromosomes.

GENOME PROJECT

BEGINNINGS

What is the Human Genome Project?

The Human Genome Project is one of the most exciting endeavours ever undertaken, comparable in size and importance with the programmes which put man on the Moon. It is a 15-year effort to identify all the genes in human DNA (the human genome), and to determine the sequences of the 3 billion chemical 'bases' that make up human DNA. DNA (deoxyribonucleic acid) is a biological code found in all living things. It is made up of four similar chemicals called 'bases' or 'nucleotides': A,T,C and G. Organisms use this DNA code to produce proteins and build all their component parts. A gene is a sequence of these bases that codes for one particular protein. The human genome contains an estimated 60,000 to 150,000 genes. Locating and understanding these genes will hopefully lead to revolutionary new ways to diagnose, treat and prevent all forms of human disease, and insights into other important areas from agriculture to pest control. Parallel studies are also being carried out on selected model organisms such as the bacterium *E.coli*, the fruit fly *Drosophila* and the laboratory mouse.

Birth of the Human Genome Project

The Human Genome Project arose from government research in the USA into the effects of atomic bomb radiation. It had become clear that atomic radiation could have severe repercussions, not only on those initially exposed to it, but also in their offspring – through effects on their genes. It was decided that only by creating a reference 'library' of the entire genome could these effects be totally understood. Planning began in 1986 and in 1990 the US Congress approved funding for a five-then 15-year programme. Now, at least 18 countries have human genome research programmes, including Australia, China, France, Germany, Israel, Russia, Sweden, and the UK. The Human Genome Organisation (HUGO), which helps to coordinate international collaboration, has about 1,000 members from 50 countries.

Mapping the human genome

According to the Genome Database (GDB), the public repository for human genome mapping statistics, by March 1998, 6,147 genes had been mapped to chromosomal locations. In addition, a further 39,000 genes have been identified but their locations have yet to be assigned. (To find a constantly updated gene count, visit the GDB web site at http://gdbwww.gdb.org). The first low resolution genetic map of the entire human genome was published in 1992. In 1995, high resolution maps of chromosome 16

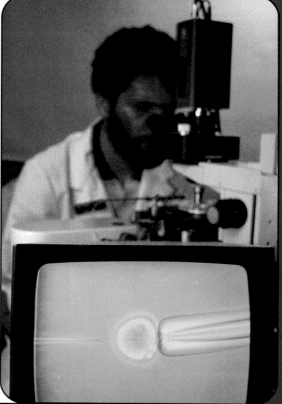

Right
Microinjection allows scientists to introduce DNA directly into the genetic make-up of a cell. It has to be done with a microscope, and displayed on a VDU screen. A suction tube stabilizes the cell while the DNA is introduced on a probe.

and 19 were produced, plus moderate resolution maps of chromosomes 3, 11, 12 and 22. The first non-human whole genome was sequenced from the bacterium *Haemophilus influenzae* and later that year sequencing from the smallest bacterium, *Mycoplasma genitalium*, showed scientists the minimum number of genes needed for independent existence was 0.58 million bases. In 1996, the genome sequencing of an organism called *Methanococcus jannashcii* confirmed the existence of a completely new, third branch of life (animals and plants being the other two). In 1997, high resolution maps of chromosome 7 and the 'female' chromosome X were completed, together with the *E.coli* genome sequence.

Legislation to protect the codes to life

In 1994, the first piece of legislation, the US Genetic Privacy Act, was proposed to regulate the collection, analysis, storage and use of DNA samples and the genetic information obtained from them. This was followed in 1996 by the Healthcare Portability and Accountability Act which prohibits the use of genetic information by health insurance companies in the US.

How closely related are different organisms?

Humans are not genetically very different from many of the animals that surround us. It appears that all mammals contain more or less the same number of genes, and most of these look very similar. The genomes of man and mouse, for example, have roughly the same number of nucleotides, there is a correspondence between most of the genes in the two species, and we share virtually all of our genes with apes. The differences occur in only a small number of areas, maybe between 20 to 30% in mice and as little as 10% in apes – perhaps as few as 100,000 very subtle changes in base sequencing. However, this is enough to generate the enormous physical differences we see between the species.

APPLICATIONS

Research reveals clues to why people get diseases

Changes in a single base sequence within a gene can produce an inappropriate protein and prompt the development of a disease. Researchers are looking at diseases including cancer, heart disease and AIDS to find which genes are altered. Illnesses such as sickle cell anaemia and cystic fibrosis are caused by alleles (different versions of the same gene) that produce proteins so unlike the original that they do not work. Other alleles create a predisposition that will lead to an illness only if other factors are present. For example, a form of mental disorder called phenylketonuria, is caused by the combination of a faulty gene and a chemical found in foods called phenylalanine. It seems that most diseases are caused by a combination of faulty genes and environmental factors. It will

eventually be possible to predict precisely what diseases a person will be liable to develop. However, this information can present a dilemma: a woman knowing she has a BRCA-1 gene, which increases the risk of breast cancer, will have to decide whether to have a preventive mastectomy at an early age or remain vigilant for signs. Worse, a person with a gene for an incurable condition can do nothing but wait for the disease to appear. And should such information be given to employers or insurance companies?

New drugs promise personalized gene therapy

Two US companies, Incyte Pharmaceuticals and Human Genome Sciences have set up their own private genome projects and are using short cuts to sequence thousands of genes. Genes themselves make up only about 2% of the total DNA – the role of the rest is imperfectly understood, but is often referred to as 'junk'. These companies are working to discover and sequence only the active genes and are collaborating with big pharmaceutical companies to allow them to develop new drugs. They have found that a gene known as apoE is at the heart of Alzheimer's disease. It exists as three alleles: apoE2, 3 and 4, and people with apoE4 are at greatest risk. Drugs are being developed that target specific alleles, allowing for tailor-made therapy.

DNA chips allow rapid laser screening

In order to reap the rewards of the Human Genome Project, rapid screening techniques will need to be developed. Most

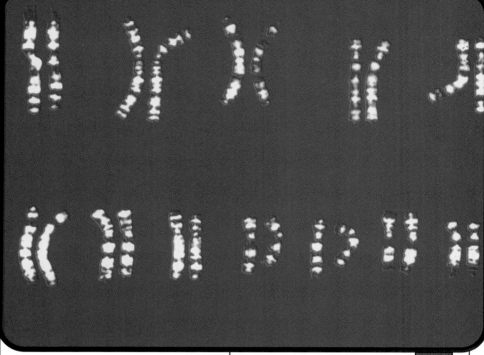

Above
This coloured karyotype shows the chromosomes in a male with Down's Syndrome, the most common diagnosable cause of mental handicap. It is hoped that the information gathered by the Genome Project will enable greater diagnosis.

current methods are messy, lengthy and expensive. Now something better is in sight – a 'chip' that will identify a piece of DNA from among a small number of known variants. The idea of DNA chips, which will be made of glass, not silicon, was dreamed up by Steve Fodor. The DNA to be screened is first labelled with a chemical that fluoresces and then applied to the chip. The chip is then scanned by a laser and the sequence of the sample read off.

Back to the future

Atomic bombs

It was through studying the effects of atomic radiation on survivors of the atom bombs in Hiroshima and Nagasaki, together with those affected by the extensive use of atomic energy as a power source during the 1960s, 70s, and 80s, that the idea for a gene library – the Human Genome Project – was born.

Frederick Sanger

In 1975, English chemist Frederick Sanger became the first person to perform gene sequencing experiments. Together with his co-workers, he worked out the entire sequence of DNA molecules for a virus containing 5,375 nucleotide pairs. His work on DNA won him the joint Nobel Prize for chemistry in 1980, making him one of only four people to have won two Nobel Prizes (he won his first in 1958).

1948	William Ivy Baldwin, aged 82, walks on a 38.1-m tightrope
2025	Regeneration of human tissue becomes possible

Left
A still taken from a commercial for the insurance company Equitable Life showing hundreds of old people sunbathing. As the possibilities of extending life spans increase so companies are quick to realize the financial implications of more people living for longer and longer.

LONGEVITY

LIFESTYLE

The continuing role of grandmothers

A study by a team from Utah University, USA, has revealed a new clue to longevity which lies in the family structure of people still living in rural tribes. Even when they are too old to bear more children of their own, tribal women continue to gather food to feed their grandchildren. By doing this, these grandmothers increase their grandchildren's long-term chances of survival, and thus secure their own genes' transmission and promote longer life spans in the human species.

Restricted lifestyle could extend life span by 20 years

Research shows that fruit flies and rats whose calorie intake is reduced by 30% lead a 30% longer life, as well as being healthier. A study from the National Institute on Ageing in the USA reveals that monkeys respond in the same way, so that a cut in calorie intake slows their metabolism. As the body metabolizes glucose it uses up oxygen, which in turn releases free radicals, a major factor in ageing. @ *animals p134*

People in their nineties can develop beneficial muscles

Although some surgeons are now warning that jogging can hasten the ageing process by encouraging the body to sag, the anti-ageing benefits of regular exercise remain undisputed. Researchers are discovering that even people in their nineties can develop beneficial muscle mass, while the Chinese martial art t'ai chi is proven to reduce the risk of falls and broken bones in the elderly.

Two glasses of wine a day fights heart disease

In a recent study conducted in Nancy, France, drinking habits emerged as one of the most significant factors of increased longevity. The lowest rate of mortality was found among men who drank between two and three glasses of wine a day. The research, led by Dr Serge Renaud from the University of Bordeaux, France, shows that

Left
An elderly man defies his age by water-skiing. Ageing – and definitions of age – are changing as medical advances and technology combine to alter perceptions and possibilities. Soon, elderly people will outnumber younger people for the first time.

moderate drinking reduces the mortality rate from cardiovascular disease by 35% and from cancer by 20%. Drinking three glasses of wine a day reduces the risk of death from all causes by up to 30%.

MEDICINE

▶ When the nematode worm starves it lives longer

By examining worms, Gary Ruvkin of Massachusetts General Hospital, USA, has identified a gene which could well be central to the ageing process. DAF-2 regulates glucose in the nematode worm and seems to be the equivalent of the human insulin receptor gene. When the worm goes short of food it lapses into a state of suspended animation and extends its 14-day life span to two months. If scientists can discover how the DAF-2 gene makes cells burn glucose more efficiently, an anti-ageing drug could be manufactured.

⏸ Drugs developed to stop the ageing process

The human growth hormone (HGH) is one of the most expensive anti-ageing hormones available. Until recently, it had to be extracted from human corpses. Advocates of HGH claim it increases bone density, promotes mental alertness, and helps the development of youthful tissue.

⏩ Limbs and organs grow back after being removed

Newts, lizards and starfish are some of the many creatures capable of growing new limbs and scientists see no reason why tissue regeneration of human body parts, such as livers, should not be possible. Scientists at Allegheny University in Philadelphia, USA, are working with 'stem' cells found in the bone marrow. These cells function like plant stems, growing other cells like leaves. The team hopes that extracting and manipulating stem cells will pave the way for human regeneration.

▶ Biomarkers: the new way of telling someone's age

In the US-based clinics of Dr Vincent Giampapa's Longevity Institute International, staff determine the 'biological age' of patients. Rather than counting the years, they test 'biomarkers' which include the cardiovascular system, bone density, skin elasticity, reaction times and lung capacity. Therefore, a 70-year-old may come out of the tests healthier and 'younger' than someone of 35.

▶ Scientists try to identify the ageing gene

Research into the rare condition of Werner's Syndrome may help scientists unravel the ageing puzzle. Victims of Werner's Syndrome age prematurely, turning grey at 20, and rarely live beyond 50. It is caused by faults in a gene called WRN. A team of scientists led by Leonard Guarente of the

Massachusetts Institute of Technology, USA, have identified faults in the yeast version of this gene, called SGS-1, which causes yeast cells to grow old quickly, indicating that this gene may be a longevity factor for many other species too.
@ genetics p112

▶ Humans and birds don't age in the same way

Most mammals die after 1 billion heart beats. If the same thing applied to humans, we would die at 20. Steve Austad, Professor of Zoology at the University of Idaho, USA, is using evolutionary theory to understand why species age at different rates. His work so far suggests that ageing is the result of evolutionary adaptation in different species.

AFTERLIFE

▶ Space funerals may let you live on forever

Thanks to the Celestis Earthview Commemorative Spaceflight Service Inc. it is now possible to have some of your ashes sent into space. A fee of $5,000 (£3,000) buys one a place on board a satellite launcher, plus a mini-obituary on the Celestis web site. Other Internet services include Perpetual Memorials, which promises a full-length on-line obituary, complete with photographs, video clips and taped eulogies from loved ones. @ cryogenics p156

⏸ Astronomer to be given special Moon burial

NASA plans to send the ashes of astronomer Eugene Shoemaker, discoverer of the Shoemaker-Levy comet, to the moon

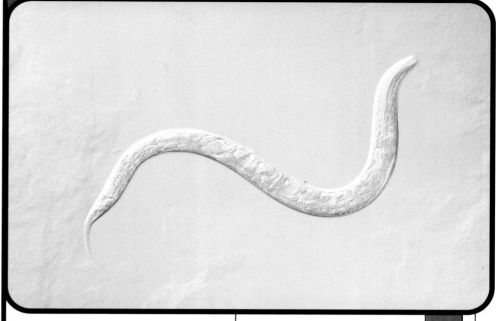

Above
A light micrograph of a soil-dwelling bisexual worm, *Caenorhabditis elegans*. Because it matures quickly and reproduces itself identically through self-fertilization, it is a model for genetic research. Scientists already have a map of its nervous system.

in 1998. Shoemaker died in a car accident in July 1997. However, the American Navajo Nation organization, which represents native American Navajos, has raised an objection to the plan because the moon is still a sacred object in Navajo culture.

▶ In Japan, bar-coded burials cut down on costs

In Japan, where land prices are high, a traditional grave can cost more than ¥1.5 million (£7,500). Now, a Japanese company called Sanryoku Infomedia is offering burial space for half that price in warehouses in Tokyo and Osaka. Families of the deceased are issued cards and visit temples attached to the warehouses. The card is slotted into a special altar which then calls up the urn. The warehouses are only two storeys high and six coffins wide, but can accommodate 1,500 small tombs.

♻ Back to the future

W. B. Yeats's creative juices flow

In 1934, the 69-year-old Nobel Prize-winning Irish poet W. B. Yeats (1865-1939) had the controversial Steinach operation to increase his sexual drive. While it certainly caused his literary output to perk up during his final years, its sexual effect awaits further investigation.

William Ivy Baldwin

In 1948, geriatric gymnast William Ivy Baldwin successfully crossed a 97.5-m (320-ft) tightrope 38.1 m (125 ft) above the South Boulder Canyon in Colorado, USA, on his 82nd birthday.

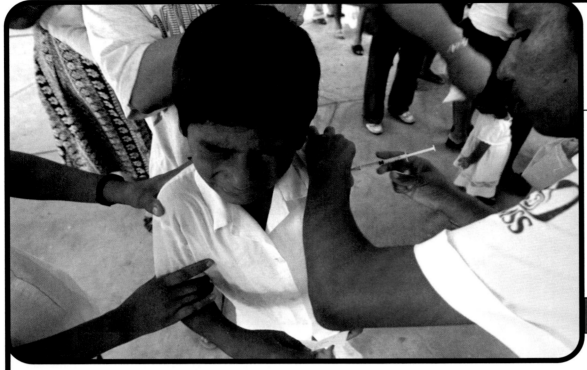

Left
A young boy receives a tetanus injection in Acapulco, Mexico. Without the resources to provide routine vaccination against diseases such as cholera and tetanus, many under-developed countries are caught unprepared when natural disaster strikes. Vaccines still need to become cheaper and easier to transport.

THIRD WORLD

THE FUTURE

▶ Predictions for a future – growing world

By 2000, there could be 22 cities in the world whose populations exceed 10 million, 18 of which will probably be in the Third World. It has been predicted that water consumption from rivers could be so high that five of the world's biggest rivers (the Nile, the Ganges, the Amudar'ya, the Yellow River, the Colorado River) may no longer empty into the sea for months at a time.

⏸ Global population continues to swell, despite hunger

With the world's population fast approaching 6 billion, sustenance is a crucial problem. Half of the people on Earth already do not have enough food, and as the global population increases at a rate of 90 million a year – three times the population of Canada – food producers are being put under mounting pressure. In 1990, Britain managed to reach its target of producing more food than it consumes.

▶▶ An increasing population demands more energy

The difference between the world's rich and poor is growing: the US is increasing its energy consumption at six times the rate of Bangladesh, which has a faster-growing

population; Bangladeshis each consume three barrels of oil annually, whilst Americans each consume 55 barrels. The projected global population of 11.2 billion by 2100 would require new food technologies, 20 million km^2 (7.7 million m^2) of land, and 80% of all forest and woodland in developing countries in order to survive. @ *food p10*

▶▶ WHO issues warning on global TB crisis

The World Health Organisation (WHO) has warned that the number of tuberculosis cases will be rising by between 7 and 10 million each year by 2015. Countries which are most affected include South Africa, Nigeria, Ethiopia and Mexico. Many richer countries have been criticized for failing to invest enough money in combating the disease. Other countries such as Peru have had success with the directly observed therapy, short course (DOTS), which involves supervising patients throughout a six-month combination drug course. However, this costly option remains out of reach for many countries, and it is hoped that by 2010 drugs companies involved in TB research will have developed cheaper, more effective methods of treatment. @ *disease p110*

DRUG AID

▶ Sugar-glass beads aid drug transportation

Minute beads of sugar are set to smooth the journey for much-needed medical supplies across the developing

Right
The WHO estimates that up to 80% of Africans receive some or all of their medical care from traditional healers. In the search to find new cures and vaccines, scientists are looking increasingly to herbal remedies to provide the answers.

world. In the past, medication has reached remote areas of Africa, Asia, and South America along complex cold chains of refrigerators, to ensure that the molecules in drugs do not lose their structure or degrade through dehydration and over-heating. Biochemists and pharmacologists are perfecting ways of keeping medicines in suspended animation with glass-like beads of sugar. This method could also be used with insulin, so making painful injections a thing of the past for millions of diabetics.

▶ UN HIV/AIDS programme to open the doors to drugs

The Joint UN programme on HIV/AIDS will make HIV/AIDS drugs more accessible in developing countries, where over 20 million people live with the virus and resources are limited. Four countries – Chile, the Ivory Coast, Uganda and Vietnam – have been chosen to participate in the pilot phase of the project, which involves adapting local health infrastructures to ensure an adequate distribution of the latest tested drugs. Diagnostic companies will provide virological services and tests for patient monitoring, and the drugs, which will be subsidized by a number of pharmaceutical companies, will be selected according to the needs of each country.

▶ Dehydrated plasma aids doctors in disaster zones

Dehydration technology developed by a research team at Pafra in Cambridge, UK, could allow doctors to store plasma at room temperature for years at a time. By removing nearly all the moisture, scientists are left with a glass-like mass which can be re-hydrated at any time. Hampshire Advisory Technical Services have developed a thin membrane, punctured with microscopic holes, which filters ordinary water and eliminates any alien particles. This technology will be especially useful on battle fields and in disaster zones, and also makes it possible for people to store their own plasma stocks.

▶ Vaccines could save a million infants each year

Rotaviruses were not discovered to be a cause of infant diarrhoea until 1973. Every year five million infants die from diarrhoea, and 20% of all those deaths are caused by rotaviruses – this represents a million deaths each year caused by a germ which we have only been able to recognize for a generation. Several research teams are currently striving to produce an efficient vaccine against rotaviruses. A vaccine need not necessarily be 100% effective in order to work efficiently, and latest trials show 70% effectiveness.

PREVENTION

⏸ South Africa focuses on primary health care

In an effort to reduce the pressure on hospitals and improve access to health care in South Africa, the government has shifted the focus towards primary health care and increased the number of clinics around the country. Pregnant women and children under the age of six are given free medical attention at these clinics and people living in informal settlements and rural areas are being given better access to health care for the first time. Studies conducted since the project was launched by President Nelson Mandela in 1994 show that it is helping to promote the principle of preventive health care as well as greater equality within the health sector.

▶▶ Dumped pesticides could wreak havoc

Much of the Third World is sitting on a toxic timebomb in the form of 100,000 tonnes of obsolete pesticide stored in inadequate and leaking dumps. The statistics emerged from a report by the UN Food and Agriculture Organisation, which claims that the chemicals in Africa alone will cost an estimated $80 million (£48 million) to clean up. Most of the pesticides were donated by Western countries before being banned.

▶ Waterless toilet set to cut outbreaks of disease

A new-style toilet has been developed for shanty towns and refugee camps which could help reduce incidences of waterborne diseases such as cholera and typhoid. The toilet, designed by Australian parasitologist Paul Turner from the James Cook University, Townsville, operates like a sewage treatment plant but requires no water. Waste enters two sealed tanks where it is anaerobically digested by bacteria before being pumped into a gravel pit. The bacteria count is about 10,000 times lower than in a septic tank.

▶ Simple arsenic filter could save lives and health

Soil contaminated with arsenic is one of the most serious health problems in the Third World, especially in countries such as Bangladesh and Bengal where groundwater can contain up to 400 times the WHO's drinking water safety limit for the chemical. Nikolaos Nikolaidis, environmental engineering professor of the University of Connecticut, USA, has developed a basic filter made of sand and iron filings which converts the arsenic through oxidization into an insoluble compound, trapping it in the filter. Nikolaidis is still working on a prototype which could filter 5,500 litres a day.

▶▶ 'Fast food' mycoprotein offers nourishment

Protein derived from the cultivation of microbes is already popular among

Above
Some fear that the planet's natural resources will not be able to sustain ever-expanding global population. This is particularly true of the developing world, as demonstrated by these two women carrying supplies from an oasis.

vegetarians. It is marketed as 'mycoprotein' or 'textured vegetable protein (TVP)'. Food produced in fermentation vats could be used to provide under-nourished people in poorer parts of the world with large amounts of protein. A beef animal doubles in weight in 3 months and a pig in 1 month, but British biologist Brian Ford has shown that 1 kg (2 lb 3 oz) of microbe protein could require as little as an hour to become 8 kg (17 lb 10 oz), making it a much more efficient source of protein than meat.

♻ Back to the future

Third world

In 1952, Alfred Sauvy came up with the term 'Third World' to describe countries that do not have sophisticated industrialized economies. The term comes from the French Revolution where there were three estates – the clergy, the aristocrarcy and the people – 'Like the third estate, the third world is nothing and wants to be something'. The term was first used at a conference in Indonesia.

Water disinfection

Scientists have known since the early 1900s that ultraviolet light can disinfect drinking water, but UV technology has only recently become affordable for disinfection on a large scale. A device developed in the US passes water through a chamber, where it is bathed in UV light, which kills viruses, moulds and other pathogens by deactivating their DNA.

It is estimated that 2.47 acres of forest are cut down every second

ENVIRONMENT

- **Dramatic and potentially catastrophic changes in the world's climate** will affect us all in the next hundred years. With global warming and unusual weather patterns caused by El Niño millions of people will be killed or made homeless by droughts, floods, hurricanes and tornadoes. Weather prediction systems that can correctly warn of natural disasters will be vital for our planet's continued existence.

- **Recycling waste will become a boom industry**. Plants and flowers will be used to mop up waste products; waste will be recycled to make secondary products, such as glue; new recreational areas, such as ski slopes, will be created out of old slag heaps and waste dumps; old tyres could be used as building materials.

- **Solar and wind power will be used increasingly** to generate electricity. Fungi and bacteria are known to generate enough energy to be used as alternative forms of fuel. Other solutions to the planet's fuel crisis could be underwater 'wind'mills and methane mining in the sea.

- **New farming methods should help to meet increasing demands for food**. Aquaculture, hydroponics and organic farms are three examples. Greater farming efficiency will be achieved via the use of automatic farms where everything can be controlled and carried out from a farm office. Machines will do the picking, sensors will detect unhealthy plants and satellites will be used to aid farming.

- **Much of the planet's surface and sea has still to be properly explored**. The next hundred years will see new animal discoveries, both on land and in the sea. In South Africa, the extinct Quagga is being reintroduced through breeding programmes and in Vietnam recently a new type of goat was discovered. The next breakthrough will come when it is possible to reproduce an extinct animal using its DNA. Before long, we might be able to visit a real 'Jurassic Park'.

CLIMATE

RESOURCES

WASTE

AGRICULTURE

THE EARTH

THE SEA

ANIMALS

TECHNO-BABBLE

AQUACULTURE
Fish farming as a source of mass-produced food.

BIONOMICS
Blending biological and economic thought.

BIOSPHERE
A self-contained environment capable of supporting life. The most familiar biosphere to most of us is Earth.

DOUGHNUT PATTERN
The process whereby richer urban residents move towards the edges of cities, leaving poorer areas at the centre.

ENDOCHRINE DISRUPTER
Mainly industrial chemicals which disrupt the usual actions of endocrines in the human body, causing widespread physiological problems.

HYDROPONICS
The science of growing plants in nutrient solution.

PHARMING
Pharmaceutical farming, the art and science of creating transgenic plants and animals which have genes that can help produce pharmaceutical drugs.

1967	Scientists claim for the first time that global temperatures are rising because of the levels of carbon dioxide in the atmosphere
2002	Japan's Virtual Earth computer program is completed, allowing scientists to propose solutions to avoid natural disasters

Left
Part of the CHEOPS-3 (Chemistry of Ozone in Polar Stratosphere) project at Kiruna, Sweden, in Feb 1990. A scientist wears a radiation protection suit after inspecting the radar dome used to track balloon-borne experiments that measure and sample the amount of pollutants in the atmosphere.

CLIMATE

GLOBAL WARMING

 Man-made climate is set to get hotter and hotter

Although the greenhouse effect is a naturally-occurring phenomenon, greenhouse gas levels have increased by 25% in the last century, largely due to industrial activity and deforestation. Infrared radiation emitted from Earth into space is trapped by these greenhouse gases and reflected back to Earth. The Earth is getting hotter, with an average temperature rise of 0.5°C (0.9°F) over the last century. Some sophisticated computer climate models suggest that by 2100 the Earth's average temperature will have increased by 2°C (3.6°F), with sea levels rising by 50 cm (20 in) due to water expansion and the melting of land-based ice.

 New ice age to balance out global warming

Swiss researchers at the University of Bern predict that the greenhouse effect will make Great Britain colder by turning off the warm Gulf Stream. This north-flowing, warm and salty current will be diluted by fresh water running off the North American continent and out of the Arctic due to global warming.

Solar cycles are responsible for climate changes

While global warming is widely attributed to increasing levels of carbon dioxide in the atmosphere, scientists from the Naval Research Laboratory, Washington, USA, estimate that at least half the climate change of the last 150 years can be attributed to the Sun's 11-year cycle as it waxes and wanes, giving rise to solar flares or sunspots. Investigations have found that 71% of the earth's temperature shifts are a direct result of the Sun's cycle.

El Niño brings heavy rainfall and drought

The El Niño weather system disrupts oceanic and atmospheric conditions

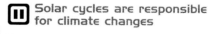

 Left
The effects of the weather phenomenon El Niño at Piura, northwest of Lima, being surveyed from a helicopter by the Peruvian president, Alberto Fujimori, in Jan 1998. Heavy rains caused serious flood damage in areas of north and central Peru.

through a mixture of the waning of Pacific trade winds, causing equatorial waters to heat up, and the reversal of surface oceanic currents. This can lead to heavy rainfall in South America and severe droughts in southern Africa and eastern Australia.

⏸ La Niña also brings heavy rainfall and drought

The El Niño cycle is balanced by a La Niña, or Anti-El Niño, phenomenon which occurs when waters off Peru receive an injection of cool water, causing the surface of the eastern Pacific to cool and leading to floods in Australia and drought in South America.

FORECASTS

⏩ Earth Simulator Program hopes to help solve it all

NEC in Japan is developing the world's fastest parallel processing computer to run a Virtual Earth program intended to help resolve environmental problems. The Earth Simulator Program, promoted by the Science and Technology Agency in Tokyo, Japan, and to be completed by 2002, will investigate environmental problems and propose solutions to avoid natural disasters.

▶ Drilling into Antarctica for a climate prediction

Teams from the US, Europe, Japan and Australia are drilling at depths of up to 3 km (1 ³/₄ miles) below the surface of the ice caps of Antarctica and Greenland to obtain ancient ice containing information about how the climate operated more than 110,000 years ago. Initial results from this research indicate that climate changes in the past may often have been rapid and dramatic: temperatures around the North Atlantic fluctuated by 14°C (25.2°F) during the millennia that preceded the last Ice Age, which began about 130,000 years ago.

⏩ Spectrometers that link the weather to magnetic fields

Weather forecasting and electrical storm prediction could be improved following the development of two wide-angle, neutral-atom spectrometers that should help meteorologists study the link between weather and the Earth's magnetic field. The $18-million (£10.7-million) spectrometers, to be completed by 2004, will be mounted on satellites and will film magnetic particles as they enter the magnetosphere.

⏸ Sensing for earthquakes by reading the rocks

Panayiotis Varotsos of the University of Athens, Greece, claims it is possible to predict earthquakes, sometimes weeks in advance, by detecting electrical currents in the Earth's crust. Most seismologists are sceptical about this, even thought Varotsos successfully predicted three earthquakes in 1995 along once-dormant faults by using electrodes buried in the earth that were able to read the stress in the rocks.

Above
Jim Scoggins with his invention, the 'Jimsphere', a weather balloon, at the European Space Agency's Ariane launch site in French Guiana. Its stability is enhanced by 400 conical surface projections, and it is used to measure temperature and humidity.

▶ Storm detection technique is eighty per cent accurate

The Center for the Analysis and Prediction of Storms (CAPS) at the University of Oklahoma, Oklahoma, USA, has enjoyed an 80% accuracy rate in forecasting local mammoth thunderstorms, known as supercells, using the Advanced Regional Prediction System (ARPS). This computer system uses Doppler radar to indicate convection patterns in the upper atmosphere, and reads temperature, wind and humidity reports from ground stations.

MYSTERIES

⏸ Ball lightning somehow captured in flight

For centuries, meteorologists have been disputing whether ball lightning exists, and, if so, what it could be. On 21 Aug 1996, researchers were monitoring the top of a thunderstorm in Sarpy County, Nebraska, USA, and captured a ball of light in six video frames, whose velocity was timed at 4,660 km/s (2,900 miles per second).

⏸ Sprites flash from the tops of storm clouds

Captured on video by John R. Winckler, at the University of Minnesota, Minnesota,

USA, sprites, a species of lightning, are caused when the upper part of a thundercloud, usually positively charged, disperses itself in a large electrical field created between the top of the cloud and the ionosphere. This creates intense flashes at altitudes up to 50–90 km (31–56 miles).

♻ Back to the future

Friedrich Humboldt

In the early 19th century, Friedrich Humboldt persuaded Nicholas I of Russia to set up a chain of weather stations across the country. These stations provided the main source of weather information right up until the second half of the 20th century.

Netherlands flooding

In Feb 1953, strong winds and high spring tides drove the North Sea over the Dutch dykes, flooding Zeeland in the southern Netherlands. 1,855 people were drowned and 47,000 homes were lost.

Greenhouse effect

In 1967, scientists claimed for the first time that global temperatures were rising because of the increasingly high concentration of carbon dioxide in the atmosphere.

1978	Idea to use pedestrians to generate power for street lighting
2010	Norway opens its first underwater 'wind'mills that use tidal power to generate electricity

RESOURCES

NEW INDUSTRIES

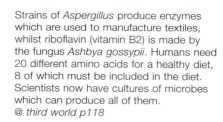 **Desalting the sea could solve the water shortage**

It has been estimated that by the year 2000 3.6 billion people will lack adequate drinking water, and governments have responded by looking into the desalination process which creates fresh water from sea water. Britain has built its first desalination plant on its east coast, and is able to produce one in every thousand parts of drinking water by desalination. Most such plants are found on the coasts of oil-rich nations, with 60% located on the shores of the Persian Gulf.

 **Fungus factories manufacture future products**

Biologists have realized that fungi can be useful. The mould *Rhizopus* transforms unusable maltose into valuable glucose.

Strains of *Aspergillus* produce enzymes which are used to manufacture textiles, whilst riboflavin (vitamin B2) is made by the fungus *Ashbya gossypii*. Humans need 20 different amino acids for a healthy diet, 8 of which must be included in the diet. Scientists now have cultures of microbes which can produce all of them.
@ third world p118

Bacteria prove useful in the mining industry

Bacteria can be used to recover minerals including gold and silver, and can even help extract heavy metals such as cadmium, lead and uranium from low-grade ores. *Thiobacillus* bacteria can utilize copper, iron and sulphur, and are able to metabolize metal wastes to release energy. A solution of metal sulphate leaches out, from which it is easy to extract the pure metal. Unlike conventional industrial processes, these microbes require no external fuel supply.

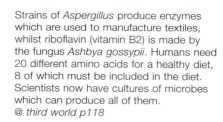 **Waste management fuels the eco-industrial park**

An eco-industrial park is where waste products from one organization are used as a resource in another. The best example is

the Kalundborg eco-industrial park in Denmark, which houses a power station, oil refinery, concrete producer, pharmaceutical company, fertiliser producer, fish farm, household heating authorities and other enterprises. Through their cooperation they benefit from cheaper materials and energy, minimize disposal costs and reduce the environmental impact of their activities.

FUEL

▶▶ Methane hydrate as a new source of energy

The latest energy source to be discovered is deep-sea methane hydrate, a strange substance made of a waxy solid which is formed by methane molecules trapped in water. Investigations of mining methods are progressing rapidly, and include plans to release methane by warming the hydrate. The deposits around Japan, if successfully mined, could match current consumption rates of natural gas for at least 100 years.

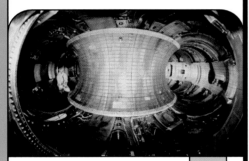

Above
The Tokamak Fusion Tes Reactor in New Jersey, USA, was the world's most powerful solar reactor. It set a record for fusion power, generating 10.7 million watts for about one second – enough to power 10,000 homes.

⏸ Capturing solar energy through plants

Plants use photosynthesis to convert solar energy effectively. The process splits the molecules of water, generating high energy electrons and releasing oxygen. In plants, these electrons are required to reduce carbon dioxide and produce carbohydrates. Scientists are looking into ways of converting the electrons generated by photosynthesis directly into electricity. The electricity would be created by living plant cells, ruling out the potential for energy to be lost in interim stages.

⏸ Giant windmills generate cleaner electricity

Believing that people will pay more for cleaner electricity, a small, city-owned utility in Traverse City, Michigan, USA, has used subsidies from the US Department of Energy to erect a giant wind turbine as a pilot alternative to fossil and nuclear-fuelled power. Some 145 residents have opted for the greener stream of energy generated by the 600-kilowatt windmill with blades 44 m (144 ft) in diameter. The company has promised that rates will not increase, since the fuel is free.

▶ Tidal mills harness the ocean's power

Norway is planning to build the first 'tidal mill' power station. While most proposals for tidal power necessitate the building of dams across estuaries, Thorkild Carstens of the University of Trondheim, Norway, plans to submerge turbines in the strong tidal currents of the Kvall Sound where they will spin like windmills.

⏸ Researchers improving rechargeable batteries

Researchers at the University of Texas, USA, have synthesized a new type of cathode in the quest for lighter, longer-lasting rechargeable batteries for future generations of laptops and mobile phones. Lithium ion batteries, the most promising candidates so far, usually contain cobalt, which is costly and toxic. Manganese oxide cathodes are more environmentally friendly, but they cannot be recharged often enough. The structure of the synthesized manganese oxyiodide cathode promises to overcome such problems.

▶ Council waste can be processed into fuel

Municipalities can recover valuable new products from the garbage they collect. Since 1979, East Sussex County Council has been processing the town's rubbish into dried pellets. Each year 20,000 tonnes of refuse is processed to produce 5,000 tonnes of pellets. Some are used as fuel to heat council offices, some are sold to local companies. Other councils in the south of England are planning to introduce similar schemes. @ waste p126

▶▶ Slime could become the fuel of the future

Algae, the green slime found on ponds and waterways, could be an important fuel source in the next millennium. Researchers at the University of the West of England, UK, are about to launch a revolutionary biotechnology project that will harness the energy released from burning algae to use as a substitute fuel for diesel.

▶▶ Household refuse as a clean fuel source

Pyrolysis is a new technique for recycling domestic waste. Refuse is heated to 800°C (1,472°F) in closed chambers. No oxygen is admitted so the refuse does not burn, and instead forms a friable material similar to coke. It is easily transported, and makes a clean-burning fuel. A pyrolysis plant works at a lower temperature than an incinerator, and costs only half as much money to build.

Above
The amount of solar energy reaching the Earth each day is equivalent to 180 million power stations each operating at 1,000 megawatts. We only use 0.01% of this energy, but research is underway to improve our methods of harnessing it.

⏸ Cow pats fuel power station to create 'biogas'

The first UK power station fuelled by cow dung went into operation in 1998. The 'biogas' plant cost £1 million to build, and is located in Holsworthy, Devon. It is intended that the plant will produce enough biogas to meet all the electrical demands of the local residents.

♻ Back to the future

Power from people

If an idea patented in 1978 comes to fruition, pedestrians and motorists could be providing power for lights and other urban services. Van Allyn Inc. of New York envisages roads and pavements inlaid with strips which depress under the weight of a passing wheel or foot, serving as a piston connected to a flywheel and an electric generator. The power output could be fed either directly into local street lighting or used to charge batteries.

Nature causes chaos in a biosphere

The Biosphere 2 project in Arizona, USA, attempted to create a self-sustaining microcosm of Earth. Eight scientists were sealed into a 3-acre greenhouse-like structure in 1991 to provide human interaction with over 3,000 species of insects and plants. The experiment was humbled by nature in 1996, however, when the biosphere was overrun by crazy ants and morning glory plants.

1919	National Scrap Federation used workers with hammers, chisels and hacksaws to reclaim scrap metal
2020	New compounds Calixarenes are used to clean up water supplies

Left
A use for old disused tyres has been developed by Günter Menning and Hannes Michael of the University of Chemnitz, Germany. They suggest heating pulverised tyres and adding a polymeriser to the mixture. This rubber can be repeatedly melted and reused and stretches to double its original size.

WASTE

TOXIC WASTE

Smart plants could help rejuvenate contaminated sites

New York sculptor Mel Chin and Rufus Chaney, a botanist from Maryland, USA, discovered that alpine pennycress, a member of the mustard family, is highly effective in removing zinc and cadmium from the soil of former industrial sites. They made the discovery whilst conducting experiments on the process by which plants absorb pollutants from the earth. In another project, hybrid poplar trees are being used in Oregon, USA, to help break down toxic organic compounds in the soil following an accidental spillage of hundreds of gallons of trichloroethane. The trees will probably be harvested and burnt to destroy the chemical once the soil is clean.

Flowers soak up chemicals in radioactive water

Proving to be more than just pretty faces, sunflowers are fulfiling a very important purpose – decontaminating radioactive water. Scientists working independently at a research company called Phytotech in New Jersey, USA, and at Kiev's Institute for Cell Biology and Genetic Engineering, Ukraine, have shown that, if sunflowers are placed in floats of growth medium on contaminated water, their roots will grow down into the water and absorb more than 90% of the radioactive uranium, caesium and strontium contained within it.

Ridding the world of waste using microorganisms

Chemically purifying the world's poisonous waste dumps would take 50 years and cost $100 billion (£60 billion). Using microorganisms to degrade waste costs less than one-third as much, and takes half the time. A company named Resource Engineering at Houston, USA, showed that, using traditional methods, a polluted site could be reclaimed in eight years at a cost of $135 million (£81 million). Bacteria could cleanse the same site in three years and

Left
As it meets cool air, the water vapour in hot exhaust gases condenses, making these plumes white, but the harmful chemicals within are invisible. The production of industrial waste is still at dangerous levels, despite increased monitoring.

cost $50 million (£30 million). Some of the most toxic land in the UK is being made fit for construction using fungi which eat their way through soil contaminated by industrial, cancer-causing poisons, and convert them into harmless compounds. The project is being pioneered by Colin Grant of Bio-Logic Remediation in Glasgow.

▶ Injecting industrial waste into the bowels of the Earth

If you cannot dispose of industrial waste, bury it. This philosophy has spawned waste disposal by deep injection in the US. Currently, 60% of industrial waste is disposed of by being squirted into rocky strata more than 1 km (1,056 yd) below the surface. However, at Kern County, California, plans to dispose of 750 million gallons annually have been challenged because the site is in an earthquake zone.

⏸ Poisonous waste product finds a use in India

Lignite, or brown coal, is mined across India. Each month, the Neyveli Lignite Corporation was left with five tonnes of waste phenol from this process. Since it could not be disposed of, it accumulated in large tanks. Fortunately, research by the Indian Plastic and Chemical Company showed how it could be used to make glue, timber preservative and an antioxidant for the plastics industry. The 450 tonnes of stored phenol has now all been reprocessed.

Above
Scientists hope to develop a cheap method of sunflower-powered decontamination for treating the vast quantities of radioactive water existing near derelict nuclear reactors worldwide.

INDUSTRIAL WASTE

▶ Cosmetic industry to use old tyres for lemon fragrance

Researchers in the US have discovered that when cooked, used tyres can produce the same oil found in lemons. The oil – limonene – is extracted by heating the tyres to a temperature of 725°C (1,337°F). The resulting black substance is then vapourized, forming individual isoprene molecules which later reform as limonene. Scientists are working on methods of

Above
Technology shows no signs of slackening, and each new development leaves a heap of out-dated hardware in its wake. It is hoped that in the future, we will find ways to recycle used electronic devices.

creating an uncontaminated, better-smelling oil which could eventually be used in the cosmetics industry as lemon scent.

⏸ Japanese create cement from sewage sludge mixture

In Japan, the Kansai Electric Company attains a massive waste recycling rate of 92%. Gypsum plaster is generated by some of their thermal power plants and all 83,000 tonnes of the waste plaster is recycled for use in cement and the manufacture of plasterboard. Kansai has also found ways of recycling other waste materials, including old concrete poles which are used in road foundations and the sludge created from wastewater treatment in cement making.

▶▶ Power station waste used to beautify the environment

What can be done with power station by-products? Broken pieces of heat insulation and gypsum scraps removed from inside power station gas cleaners were formerly disposed of in landfills. Now, they are playing a crucial role in an initiative to preserve the environment. In Japan, for example, materials recovered from flue-cleaning plants are made into building blocks and plant containers.

⏸ Turning deserted coal mines into ski resorts

China clay waste in Cornwall, UK, is being used locally to construct domestic dwellings in the Cornish Unit House. Mounds of waste dumped from coal-mines have also been given a new lease of life and are being

used for recreational purposes. In the US, for example, ski slopes have been built on former mine spoil heaps at Mount Transmore. Meanwhile, in the north of England, heaps of waste left over from abandoned coal-mines have been planted with grass and humourously renamed the Wigan Alps by locals.

♻ Back to the future

Love Canal

The Love Canal in the US was used for over 20 years as a dump for toxic chemicals. In 1953, homes and schools were built at the canal, but in 1976 the dangers of toxic waste were exposed when a flood caused chemicals to leak and the entire area had to be evacuated as the site became flooded with toxic chemicals.

National Scrap Federation

In 1919, when the National Scrap Federation was established, man power was used to reclaim the metal. Workers used hacksaws, hammers and chisels to break up the metal. Today, hydraulic shears are used.

Karin B

In 1985, an Italian company illegally dumped toxic waste in Nigeria. They were forced to remove the waste on a ship, the *Karin B*, which sailed round Europe for months before it was eventually taken back to Italy.

Left
Sweet sorghum is the world's most extensively cultivated crop, and is very efficient at photosynthesis. Scientists hope to create more resistant varieties and farm them to generate environmentally-friendly bioenergy. Methods might include making ethanol from plant sugars, or producing gas and oil from dry plant pulp.

AGRICULTURE

NEW FARMING METHODS

⏸ Organic food promises healthier lifestyle

Organic farms are smaller and more labour-intensive, producing nutritious food by maximizing the health of the soil, crops and animals. Traditional methods such as crop rotation, composting and natural pest control minimize pollution, and synthetic pesticides and animal antibiotics are forbidden. Organic farming is governed by strict regulations enforced by European law, and every farm is inspected annually.

⏸ Growing plants without the soil

Hydroponics is the science of growing plants in a nutrient solution which supports the roots in a medium other than soil. It originated with the Aztecs, but is used increasingly in dry climates where water is scarce. In Hawaii, USA, the Aloha 'Aina Hydro Farms grow tomatoes hydroponically on a large scale in enormous greenhouses.

A soilless environment eliminates 95% of earth-borne diseases, requiring very few pesticides and chemicals, and the water is recycled.

⏸ Plants that are better than nature intended

Biotechnology allows genes to be moved from one plant to another to create new varieties of crops which are more nourishing and resistant to insects and disease. Cheaper plant varieties with a longer shelf life have been produced, which increase farmers' crop yields by between 10 and 15%. A new generation of vaccines can also be grown in plants such as maize and bananas. However, genetic engineering has highlighted ethical and health concerns, as well as a large degree of consumer

Right
Ostriches are the world's largest living bird. Their meat is high in protein and low in calories and cholesterol, and although ostriches have been bred commercially for over one and a half centuries, it is poised to become a rapidly expanding global market.

mistrust. It is dominated by US company, Monsanto, which sells its modified seed on condition that the crops are treated with Roundup, its own brand of herbicide which the biotech seed is engineered to resist.

Aquaculture solves fish shortage

With the ocean's wild fish stocks seriously depleted from over-harvesting, fish farming, or aquaculture, is becoming a viable source of mass-produced food. Shellfish, salmon, trout and catfish are some of the fish currently being farmed. Aquastar, near Songkhla on the south-east coast of Thailand, is one of the world's largest black tiger prawn farms. Begun in 1987, it is a collective operation which trains local people to run their own seawater farms. The project's 360 farms produce 4,000 tonnes of prawns a year, which are sold in Japan, the US and Singapore.

Livestock pharming could save lives

'Pharming' involves using farm animals to produce pharmaceutically useful products. Due to advances in genetic engineering and cloning, it could soon be a huge industry. UK company PPL Therapeutics has announced that if clinical trials succeed, 50 cloned

Above
Workers at one of Thailand's fish farms situated near Bangkok. Black tiger prawns provide a substantial share of the profits for Thailand's fishing industry. There are 360 farms producing 4,000 tonnes of prawns every year.

sheep could satisfy the £100 million world market for the Factor IX blood clotting protein. Four US companies are developing pigs whose organs are coated with human proteins so that their kidneys, lungs and hearts can be transplanted into humans.

SMART FARMS

Satellites used as aid for farming

The Silsoe Research Institute in Bedfordshire, UK, and agricultural machinery manufacturer Massey Ferguson have developed precision farming systems using satellite technology. Global Positioning System satellites are used to draw detailed

maps of each field, complete with information about persistent weeds, soil chemistry and yields. The data allow pesticides and fertilisers to be applied in precisely the right places and quantities, ensuring greater profits and reduced use of chemicals. Unfortunately, the technology is still too expensive for most farmers.

Machines replace harvesting by hand

Orange growers in Florida, USA, are testing a mechanical harvester which they hope will help them to compete with produce from Brazil where labour costs are lower. The harvester was designed by a US Department of Agriculture engineer and consists of giant arms with 2-m (6-ft 6-in) long nylon spikes that slowly rotate, shaking the fruit onto a conveyor belt below. The machine harvests fruit at a rate of between seven and nine trees a minute, making it 15 times more efficient than hand picking.

Slug-fuelled robots patrol the fields

The Intelligent Autonomous Systems Engineering Laboratory at Bristol University, UK, has received government funding to build robots to patrol fields in search of slugs. Slug pellets cost British farmers £10 million a year; the slug-killing robots will be a cheap, autonomous system. A colony of four or more robots will move about fields collecting slugs, then return to a base and deposit them in a fermenter. The corpses will produce biogas which will power a generator to recharge the robots' batteries.

Sensor developed to detect unhealthy plants

Plants can be given instant health-checks with a sensor called a spectrophotometer.

Above
There are many potential applications for genetic engineering in agriculture. These two calves, George and Charlie, were bred in the US using a combination of newly developed cloning techniques with genetic engineering.

Developed by scientists at Oregon State University in the USA, the sensor detects disease by monitoring the fluorescent light which plants give off. Problem leaves are known to exhibit patches of leaked fluorescent light, and the sensors can pick up on this and alert the farmer. Early detection means that spraying can be targeted at specific, smaller areas, alleviating pressure on both the environment and the farm's budget. Scientists are currently investigating the possibility of developing a satellite-mounted variation which would be able to monitor whole regions, together with a hand-held version designed for the individual gardener.

Back to the future

Music for plants

In the early 1960s, a scientist working in Madras, India, noticed that if he played violin or Indian music to plants they would grow taller and stronger. When he took his music to paddy fields, the harvests increased by 60%.

DDT

In 1972, the insecticide DDT was banned by the US Environmental Protection Agency. The insecticide was used for years by farmers despite growing evidence that it damaged wildlife and people.

The tractor

The first tractor which could be produced in large numbers was invented in 1902 by D. Albone of the UK. The tractor was petrol driven and had wheels of steel.

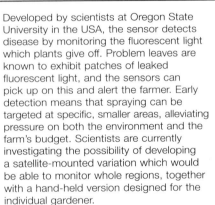

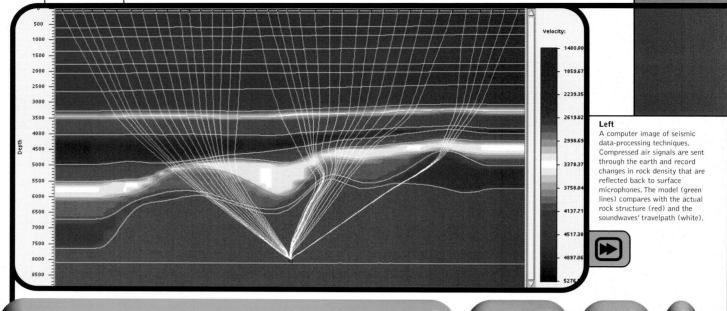

THE EARTH

PLANTS

The community that turned out to be a single plant

It was first discovered in 1969, but it was another 27 years before the unique biological importance of a mile-long expanse of king's holly shrub, *Lomatia tasmanica,* was realised. Scientists originally assumed that it comprised an entire community of separate plants, which occupy two river gullies in southwestern Tasmania and stand up to 8 m (26 ft) high. In Oct 1996, however, Australian botanist Dr Stephen Harris and colleagues revealed that this 'community' was actually a single plant, composed of numerous genetically-identical clones. Moreover, its leaves are identical to those of nearby fossils dating back 43,000 years, thus making it the world's oldest living plant.

Lost palm of the Pharaohs is alive and doing well

In ancient Egyptian times, a species of palm tree called *Medemia argun* was traditionally placed in tombs, but that was several thousand years ago, and this species was thought to be extinct. In March 1996, however, palm tree experts Martin Gibbons and Tobias Spanner revealed that, after driving across the Sudanese desert from Khartoum, they had met an old camel herder who led them to a single living specimen, standing outside a remote abandoned town called Murrat Wells. Seeds were taken from this remarkable tree, and have been donated to Kew Gardens and other botanical centres around the world.

Unsolved: the carnivorous trees of Madagascar

Since time immemorial, the island of Madagascar has been associated with fanciful tales of huge man-eating trees. These are undoubtedly imaginary, but there may be a less dramatic real-life mystery tree here. Czech researcher Ivan Mackerle recently discovered that, in 1935, a former British army officer called L. Hearst spent four months in Madagascar, and took photos of a strange tree known locally as the tepe, under which lay skeletons of various sizeable animals. The photos were later published, but no one today seems sure where, and Hearst is dead. Mackerle, however, planned an expedition to Madagascar in 1998 to seek the mysterious tepe, in case it really is an unknown species of large carnivorous plant.

Nature's chance to get its own back on herbicides

Dioxin is a highly-toxic contaminant of certain man-made herbicides, and can cause skin cancer. In 1997, scientists at Ehime University, Matsuyama, Japan, revealed that they had discovered a species of wood-rotting fungus that consumes this deadly chemical. They now hope to culture a more efficient strain. @ *disease p110*

Left
A piece of blue aerinite rock which lay forgotten for fifteen years in a geologist's home and which the Natural History Museum, London, UK, was later unable to identify. It was finally identified by the Moroccan Ministry of Mines.

Unknown conifer turns out to be a living fossil

In 1994, a group of peculiar trees was encountered by a National Parks officer in an inaccessible gorge within Wollemi National Park, New South Wales, Australia. When examined, they were found to be an unknown species of ancient conifer, dating back 150 million years, and were christened *Wollemia nobilis*. Only 39 were discovered in the wild, and botanists feared that this 'living fossil' might soon die out. However, since 1996, attempts to cultivate the Wollemi pine from seed have been very successful, thus guaranteeing its survival.

Four-leaved clovers that can be grown to order

Since the early 1990s, plant researcher Terry Michaelson-Yeates from the Government Plant Breeding Station at Aberystwyth, Wales, has been developing a true-breeding strain of four-leaved clover. Normally, this traditionally lucky plant only arises once in every 10,000 normal three-leaved clovers, but Michaelson-Yeates now believes that he has uncovered the genetic basis for its occurrence, and hopes to grow four-leaved clovers to order in the future.

Wise plants know when the storm is coming

Botanist Dr Andrew Goldsworthy from London's Imperial College is researching the remarkable possibility that plants can actually predict the onset of thunderstorms and thus increase their metabolism in readiness for an accelerated period of growth, harnessing the impending downpour of rain. Goldsworthy believes that their powers of prediction involve detecting the atmospheric electricity accompanying a storm and this is their cue for growing.

Ultrasonic plants mould themselves for bats

Bats navigate in the dark by emitting ultrasonic squeaks and listening to the echoes bouncing back from nearby objects. A Costa Rican vine-like pea, *Macuna holtoni*, is pollinated by bats, and scientists have now learnt that each blossom has specialized concave petals which reflect echoes from bats flying close by, thus alerting them to the pea's existence and increasing its chances of being pollinated.

EARTH MYSTERIES

Forgotten aerinite blue rock that exists after all

While visiting Morocco in 1981, geologist Anna Grayson purchased a beautiful piece of intensely blue rock, but was unable to identify it. For the next 15 years, it remained forgotten at her home near Watford, UK, until she decided to show it to experts at the Natural History Museum, London, UK. In March 1996, they announced that this

mineral might be new to science, but Dr Mohammed Bensaid, of the Moroccan Ministry of Mines, revealed that it was actually a little-known type called aerinite.

Beaches and the sound of singing sand

Many stretches of beach or sand around the world are famous for the mysterious musical sounds they emit. Now, doctors from Laurentian University, Ontario, Canada, believe that they have found out how. They took some normal sand and converted it into the singing variety by repeatedly grinding, separating and polishing. In addition, they discovered that the presence of silica gel coating the sand particles is required if the sand is to sing – they even found that a bottle of commercial silica gel will sing if shaken.

Rocks that can predict earthquakes

Experiments performed on site in Greece during 1995, and later replicated in the laboratory at Athens University, suggest that several days, possibly even weeks, before the onset of an earthquake, subterranean rocks that are being gradually pressured release small electrical currents detectable at the earth's surface. Using buried electrodes, scientists have successfully predicted three earthquakes along hitherto dormant faults. @ *climate p122*

Could there be subterranean life on Mars?

Swedish scientists have discovered life, in the form of fossil microbes, inside a

Above
Researchers monitoring movement of the San Andreas fault at Parkfield, California, USA. A laser bounces light off 18 reflectors situated 18 km away and can detect movements of less than 1 mm over a distance of 6 km.

1.8 million-year-old layer of granite 182 m (600 ft) beneath Sweden's Baltic coast. Clay, also obtained from the same site, was covered with a layer of calcite, which was shown under an electron microscope to contain bacteria-like microfossils. These findings led scientists to speculate that microscopic life could also exist deep underground on Mars. @ *exploration p142*

Back to the future

Toxic lake

In Eastern Russia in 1973, scientists explored the most hazardous lake on the volcanic Kamchatka peninsula. The waterless lake is a mixture of hydrofluoric, hydrochloric and sulphuric acids, so they wore gas masks and sailed in rubber dinghies that soon dissolved.

Art museum closes

In Lascaux, France, in 1940, four boys stumbled across caves that contained some of the most impressive prehistoric art ever found. When the caves were opened to the public the paintings began to fade so, in 1963, the caves were closed up again.

Balloon blizzard blunder

Salomon Andrée, Swedish engineer, was the first person ever to reach the North Pole by balloon. Despite his ballooning prowess, he and his team were unable to survive the arctic conditions and, 33 years later, the windswept remains of their base camp were found.

| 1938 | In South Africa, Marjorie Latimer buys an unusual fish thought to have been extinct for 75 million years from a local fisherman |
| 1997 | Scientists claim to find evidence on the seabed of the remains of the asteroid that killed off the dinosaurs |

Left
Deep Star 4000, a manned research submersible, seen here off the coast of Cozumel, Mexico, is capable of reaching depths of 1,200 m (4,000 ft). Diving technology now enables detailed studies of the ocean floor and the identification of new species from the depths.

THE SEA

NEW SPECIES

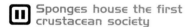

Sponges house the first crustacean society

Insects are well known for living in colonies whose members have different functions. In June 1996, however, marine biologists revealed the existence of the first-known social crustacean, a shrimp called *Synalpheus regalis*, whose colonies each contain non-breeding workers and a fertile queen. They occur inside living sponges on the coral reef off Belize in Central America.

Washed-ashore skull could belong to rhinoceros dolphin

As recently as 1996, a totally new species of beaked whale, *Mesoplodon bahamondi*, was scientifically documented for the first time, based upon a skull washed ashore on Chile's Robinson Crusoe Island. Judging from the skull's dimensions, the complete animal might be as large as an elephant. Some excellent sightings have been reported of a bizarre type of spotted Pacific dolphin with a fin on top of its head, but no specimen of this 'rhinoceros dolphin' has so far been obtained.

Giant squid could be shy or simply non-existent

Although it is one of the world's biggest animals, the southern giant squid, *Architeuthis longimanus,* is known only from dead specimens, including several found around New Zealand. In Feb 1996, marine biologist Dr Clyde Roper from the US National Museum in Washington led the first expedition seeking to film a living giant squid. They spent over two months searching the seas around South Island, which include such likely squid haunts as the 6,000-m (19,500-ft) deep Kaikoura Canyon. Sadly, they failed to spy one, but there are plans to continue the search in the hope of one day observing this mighty monster from the depths.

Left
The beak of a giant squid. The giant squid is the largest and most complex of invertebrate animals, often reaching a length of 18 m (59 ft) and weighing up to 3 tonnes. They live at depths of around 300–600 m (1,000–2,000 ft) in oceans across the world.

Oarfish aren't sea serpents – they just swim vertically

The oarfish *Regalecus glesne* is a 9-m (30-ft) long elongated marine fish that is reminiscent of a laterally flattened snake with a vivid red crest. Until recently, it was known only from beached specimens, and was assumed to swim horizontally, undulating its body from side to side. Consequently, some zoologists believed that oarfishes were responsible for reports of giant 'sea serpents'. However, while swimming off the Bahamas recently, diver Brian Skerry spied a living oarfish and, to his great surprise, he saw that this mysterious animal did not swim horizontally at all, but held its body totally upright instead, like a vertical pole.

Cadborosaurus receives a name in case it is found

A long-standing mystery animal that seems likely to be discovered in the near future is *Cadborosaurus*, frequently reported off the coast of British Columbia, Canada, particularly near Vancouver Island and Cadboro Bay. Said to measure 9–18 m (30–60 ft) long, it has a large camel-like head, lengthy neck, forked tail and a very long silver-grey body that arches when swimming. British Columbia University biologist Dr Ed Bousfield and retired oceanographer Prof. Paul LeBlond have been researching *Cadborosaurus* for many years, and are so sure of this beast's reality that in 1995 they published a formal zoological description of it in the scientific journal *Amphipacifica*, christening the still-uncaptured species *Cadborosaurus willsi*.

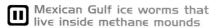

Mexican Gulf ice worms that live inside methane mounds

The Mexican Gulf's sea floor, about 240 km (150 miles) south of Louisiana, USA, bears some sizeable mushroom-shaped mounds of yellow and white methane ice, which have always been thought to be too poisonous to sustain any form of animal life. In July 1997, however, a team of scientists from Pennsylvania State University, USA, journeyed to the Gulf's sea bottom in a mini-submarine, and found considerable numbers of a previously unknown species of flattened pink polychaete worm thriving on, and burrowing inside, the methane mounds. @ seacraft p84

Archaeans that are no longer bacteria, they're different

Archaeobacteria have long been known to science, and inhabit such inhospitable regions as areas near rift vents on the oceanic bed where the water temperature can exceed 100°C (212°F). Following a detailed genetic study of these primitive organisms during the early 1990s by Dr Carl R. Woese and his team at Illinois University, USA, however, it has now been revealed that they are not bacteria at all. Renamed archaeans, they comprise a wholly separate group of organisms, totally unrelated to all other life forms on our planet.

Hypothetical creatures that hang around seabed vents

According to biologist Dr David Jones, there might be some still undiscovered organisms that live around deepwater hydrothermal vents on the seabed and he refers to these hypothetical species as Carnot creatures. He envisages one such Carnot creature as a 0.9 m (3 ft) long tube-dwelling worm that could plant one end of its body on a hot rock surface and dangle the other end in cold seawater to reject heat waste.

New species of spectacular giant jellyfish found

A new species of huge jellyfish has just been formally described and named by Dr Joel Martin from the Natural History Museum of Los Angeles County in the USA. Christened *Chysaora achlyos*, this mysterious and spectacular jellyfish has a smooth purple-black bell spanning 0.9 m (3 ft) in diameter, and light pink tentacles measuring up to 2.7 m (9 ft) long. It is now known to occur in large numbers off southern California, USA, and Mexico's Baja California peninsula.

Antarctic cold produces enormous marine animals

In Sept 1997, Dr Lloyd Peck from the British Antarctic Survey revealed that a host of giant marine animals had been discovered in the frozen seas around Antarctica, whose icy temperatures had promoted their remarkable growth. Among the newly-revealed giants were marine relatives of woodlice measuring 18 cm (7 in) long, a 3 m (10 ft) tall sponge big enough for human divers to clamber inside, enormous pycnogonids (sea spiders) spanning more than 33 cm (1 ft) from leg tip to leg tip, and 2.7 m (9 ft) long ribbon worms armed with protruding mouths that can snatch fish and swallow them whole.

Tasmanian globster was thought to be octopus

In Jan 1998, a 4-ton, 6-tentacled, 6-m (20-ft) long, and exceedingly decomposed, fibrous carcass was washed ashore on Tasmania's Four Mile Beach. Similar carcasses, nicknamed globsters, have been washed ashore here and elsewhere around the world, but have never been satisfactorily identified. The most popular conservative identity is that they are simply decayed masses of whale blubber. However, analysis of tissue samples taken from a globster washed up on a Florida beach in 1896 suggests that this one may have been a huge octopus, far bigger than any species currently known to science.

OCEAN FINDS

Seabed mining for precious metals in the Bismarck Sea

Vast quantities of precious metals have recently been discovered in shallow water in the Bismarck Sea just north of New Guinea, opening up the novel prospect of seafloor mining operations in the future. Gold, silver, copper, and zinc were found in samples taken by an international team of geologists investigating how metal ores are formed on the seafloor in the Manus Basin.

A natural explanation for the Bermuda Triangle

A natural explanation for the Bermuda Triangle mystery has been proposed by oceanographers from the international Ocean Drilling Programme. They believe that, if ships are indeed disappearing mysteriously in this stretch of water, it might be due to sudden, massive releases of giant methane gas bubbles, which are normally maintained in a frozen state on the seafloor and which could overwhelm a vessel on the surface, causing it to sink.

Dinosaur asteroid remains found on ocean floor

Some scientists believe that the dinosaurs were killed off 65 million years ago by the impact of a colossal asteroid from space and now evidence for this theory has been unearthed on the Atlantic Ocean's floor. Researchers from Virginia's National Science Foundation in the USA revealed in

Above
A giant waterspout in the warm waters of the Bermuda Triangle region. It occurs when an inverted cone-shaped cloud descends until it connects with rising sea spray. The spout can be several hundred feet high and last for half an hour.

Feb 1997 that core samples taken from 91 m (300 ft) beneath the sea floor of Florida's eastern coast contain a layer of glass-like green pebbles that may have been formed by a massive explosion accompanying the impact of an asteroid. Just above this layer was a rusty brown layer containing iridium, the most corrosion-resistant metal known, which is believed to have been the asteroid's vaporized remains. @ astronomy p138

Back to the future

Coelacanth

In 1938, Marjorie Latimer, the curator of a museum in East London, South Africa, bought an unusual looking fish from a local fisherman for the museum. It turned out to be a coelacanth thought to have been extinct for 75 million years and was given the Latin name *Latimeria chalumnae* after Ms Latimer and the River Chalumna where the fish was netted.

Titanic

In 1985, French and American scientists used an unmanned submersible to locate the wreck of the *Titanic*. The luxury liner was found on the ocean floor in two pieces at a depth of 4,000 m (13,100 ft).

Deepest Life

In 1950, a Danish deep sea exploration team found signs of life deep under the ocean. The Galanthea team found living organisms in the Pacific Ocean 10,370 m (34,000 ft) down.

Left
So far, the albino axolotl, *Ambystoma mexicanum*, has never been found in adult form. This kind of salamander is specific only to Lake Xochimilco, Mexico, and, though able to breed, remains a larva all its life.

ANIMALS

NEW SPECIES

Vu Quang ox is finally found to be alive

Discovered in 1992 in Vu Quang, northern Vietnam, the Vu Quang ox, *Pseudoryx nghetinhensis*, is one of the most important new mammals to have been discovered for over 50 years. The size of a buffalo, it has long, slender legs and horns, and was previously only known from skins and skulls.

The mysterious holy goat of Vietnam

Even more recently-discovered and more mysterious than the Vu Quang ox is the holy goat, *Pseudonovibos spiralis*. It was first made known to science in 1994, when some strange spiralled horns were spotted in a market at Ho Chi Minh City, southern Vietnam. Identical horns have since been obtained in Cambodia. Local people claim the holy goat resembles a cow, but no scientist has ever seen a specimen.

Skulls are the only clue in the Peruvian big cat hunt

For several years, zoologist Dr Peter Hocking has been investigating native Indian reports concerning two unidentified types of big cat allegedly inhabiting the cloud forests of Peru. Both types are said to be as large as a jaguar, but one is striped like a tiger, and the other has tiny speckles instead of the jaguar's normal rosettes. In 1994, Hocking obtained a female skull of each of these mysterious cats, and has shown them to several scientists. Opinion is currently mixed but he now hopes to obtain a complete specimen of each for conclusive identification.

New species of Brazilian monkey and porcupine

During a year spent in Brazil in 1996/97, Dutch zoologist Dr Marc van Roosmalen discovered four completely new species of monkey. One of these was a new species of marmoset with a pink face, orange legs, and black tail. Another was a new titi monkey, distinguished by its reddish-orange beard, and known to the local Indians as the zog-zog, after its characteristic call. Roosmalen also discovered an unknown species of tree porcupine, armed with an array of sharp yellow spines.

Left
A sample of tissue from the woolly mammoth, *Mammuthus primigenius*. Their ancient remains are often extremely well-preserved due to having been deep-frozen in permafrost, and this can allow analysis of internal organs, heart and brain.

Forest spotted owlets and warty pigs

In Nov 1997, after trekking for 12 days through wooded country northeast of Bombay, India, a scientific team led by Dr Pamela C. Rasmussen from Washington DC's National Museum of Natural History filmed two forest spotted owlets, *Athene blewitti*, a species believed extinct since 1884. In March 1997, Australian mammalogists documented the recent finding in Vietnam of a skull belonging to the Vietnamese warty pig, *Sus bucculentis*, thus confirming the existence of a species last reported over a century ago.

British pipistrelles are a unique strain

In May 1997, mammalogist Dr Gareth Jones of Bristol University, UK, announced that the pipistrelles in England did not all belong to the same species, as traditionally thought. Some belonged to a previously undetected, totally new species – identical in outward appearance, but with readily distinguishable DNA, and emitting ultrasonic squeaks at a different frequency.

Symbion pandora almost defies categorization

Danish zoologist Prof. Reinhardt Kristensen discovered a small but new animal species which, in Dec 1995, he named *Symbion pandora*. Living parasitically on a diet of lobster mouthparts, this bizarre creature exists in several different forms during its complex life cycle, and is so different from all other known animals that it has been classified as the only member of a new phylum – the highest category in the classification of organisms into groups.
@ the sea p132

Snapping turtle should have been already extinct

In May 1997, Australian zoologists found an unusual snapping turtle in Lawn Hill National Park, Queensland, Australia, belonging to the *Elseya lavarackorum* species, which have been 'officially' extinct for between 20,000 and 50,000 years.

'Giant ants' put to work in Persian goldrush

Greek scholar Herodotus claimed that Himalayan ants the size of small dogs were used by the Persian Empire to unearth gold, and in 1996 these 'giant ants' were finally identified. French anthropologist Michel Peissel returned from the Himalayas with reports of a large species of marmot as big as a very small dog, with a Persian name translating as 'mountain ant'. The soil it disturbs when burrowing is collected by locals who sieve it for gold deposits.

Suede lizard immortalizes corduroy rock musician

In 1997, on an expedition to the Kalahari Desert, Botswana, Prof. Charlemagne Nkoba from the University of Durban, Durban, South Africa, discovered a new species of gecko, which is a kind of lizard. Prof. Nkoba has named the animal, which has blue eyes and corduroy-like brown skin, Codling's gecko, after Neil Codling, the keyboardist in British rock band Suede.

Mexican axolotl shows the difference a gene makes

Randal Voss and Bradley Shaffer from the University of California, USA, discovered in Dec 1997 that, incredibly, genetic changes can occur after just a single mutation. Voss and Shaffer have been studying a species of salamander called the Mexican axolotl. Usually, salamanders are land animals that go into the water to breed. But, among the axolotls that behave in the conventional manner, are others which have become fully aquatic, and the indications are that it is a single gene that makes the difference.

EXTINCT SPECIES

Dinosaur colours stored in chromatophore fossils

In Aug 1997, Australian biophysicist Dr Andrew Parker revealed that he had identified chromatophores (pigment-producing cells) preserved in several different fossil animals, including prehistoric crustaceans, worms, and fishes. It now seems likely that chromatophores will be located in dinosaur fossils too, finally revealing what colours these animals were.

Gargantuavis was the original non-flying bird

Until recently, no species of flightless bird larger than a turkey was known to have existed alongside the dinosaurs but, in Jan 1998, Paris University palaeontologist Prof. Eric Buffetaut documented a newly-unearthed fossil bird dating back 72 million years, which he aptly named *Gargantuavis* ('gargantuan bird'). This is because it is estimated to have weighed about 141 kg (310 lb) and was therefore too heavy to fly.

Plans to replicate the original world's tallest bird

Up to 3 m (10 ft) tall, New Zealand's flightless, ostrich-like giant moa, *Dinornis giganteus,* was the world's tallest bird before its extinction. Now, biologists at Hirosaki University, Aomori, Japan, are seeking to resurrect this huge bird, by extracting DNA from bones, replicating it, and then injecting it into chicken embryos.
@ genetics p112

Quagga is slowly being bred again following extinction

The quagga, a yellowish-brown zebra-horse

Above
The Quagga breeding programme in Cape Town, South Africa. This sub-species of zebra has a slow reproductive pattern: it takes two to three years for zebra mares to reach maturity and four to five years for stallions.

with stripes only on its head and neck, was hunted to extinction in southern Africa by the 1870s but, since 1987, a team of scientists in Cape Town, South Africa, have been re-breeding the extinct animal over successive generations of zebra. The scientists have managed to breed nine zebra with quagga characteristics, but it will take many more generations before a true quagga is produced.

Back to the future

Elephant chit–chat

In 1985, US scientists in Oregon discovered that elephants emit sub-sonic sounds to communicate. The sounds, below the threshold of human hearing, last for 10–15 seconds and convey a variety of meanings.

Coal toad

In May 1919, in Netherseal Colliery, UK, a miner found a small toad in a seam formed 200 million years ago. The toad was probably buried alive when the seam was formed.

SPACE

- **Living in space may soon become a practical reality**. The Americans and the Russians are laying the foundations for life in space with their space station research. Besides studying the chemical properties of galaxies the Russian space station MIR has been carrying out experiments in plant growth to discover if it is possible to grow plants at the same rate as on Earth. So far, they have successfully managed to grow a type of cabbage. The ISS (International Space Station), with a joint Russian and American crew, will look into how weightlessness affects the human body. They also hope to be able to develop bioregenerative, or self-supporting, systems. It is hoped that one day this accumulated knowledge will allow entire communities to survive in space without support from Earth.

- **New, faster spacecraft are being developed to replace the Space Shuttle**. Named X-33, X-34, X-36, X-38 and X-40, these unmanned craft should take away the need and risk of using astronauts. The successful voyage to Mars of the Pathfinder mission showed the effectiveness of using robots controlled from Earth instead of sending humans.

- **Space probes will bring back new information about the planets**. By 2001, the Mars Surveyor will have started to undertake experiments on the soil of Mars, while the Deep Space II probes will bring back rock samples to Earth. Other probes are being sent to investigate the Moon's water source, the atmosphere of one of Saturn's moons and sounds in the Sun.

- **We will have made contact with extraterrestrial life by 2025** according to some scientists. The search for extraterrestrial life, or SETI, and the subsequent Project Phoenix have been searching the skies for artificially produced signals for years. Sooner or later, they will pick up a signal. But until then we will have to make do with the *X-Files*.

FUTURESCOPE

ASTRONOMY

HUBBLE

EXPLORATION

SPACECRAFT

SPACE STATIONS

ALIEN LIFE

TECHNO-BABBLE

AAAA
Alternative Association of Astronauts aims at providing space travel outside of NASA and ESA. They hold conferences to discuss ways of building low-cost spaceships.

HST
The Hubble Space Telescope.

OORT CLOUD
A vast cloud thought to surround our solar system.

QUANTUM SHIMMER
Anti-gravity which stops the universe from collapsing in on itself.

EXOPLANET
Any planet discovered orbiting around a star other than our Sun.

WORMHOLE
A black hole in one universe connected to a black hole in another universe. It can be considered a type of black hole time machine.

AREOLOGIST
A geologist, but one whose primary study material is rocks from the planet Mars.

Left
The Hale-Bopp comet briefly rivalled Halley's comet in the public consciousness as our best known celestial visitor when it passed close to Earth, as this image of it over an abandoned building in Cape Breton Island, Nova Scotia, Canada, on 26 March 1997, vividly illustrates.

ASTRONOMY

NEW INSTRUMENTS

Internet telescopes give kids a chance to see the stars

Plans are afoot to create a £10-million network of more than a dozen robotic telescopes across the world which could be accessed via the Internet, enabling millions of schoolchildren all over the world to gain access to astronomy. The first telescope in the project (which is also the world's first fully robotic telescope), built by Dr John Baruch of Bradford University, UK, and sited in Yorkshire, is currently linked to the Internet and receives about 40,000 visits a week. It is controlled via computer from Bradford University and has a focal length of 2 m (6 ft). The scheme is also democratic, in that the telescope points to whichever portion of the sky is most requested by users logging on to the system.

▶ Exploding a star with lasers in a laboratory

Physicists at the Lawrence Livermore National Laboratory in California, USA, are using a three-storey-high laser, one of the most powerful in the world, to simulate an exploding star. Ten large laser beams are set up to collide on a 3-mm long concave target of plastic and copper, focusing 30 trillion watts on a target 40 trillion times smaller than a chunk of supernova. The experiment is vital to help explain the explosion of Supernova 1987A, which exploded 160,000 years ago but which has only been visible for 11 years. When 1987A exploded it released as much energy in the first few seconds of its blast as all the other visible stars and galaxies in the universe combined.

▶▶ Space camera could show us evidence of other worlds

Dust clouds surrounding four of the nearest stars to earth, Beta Pictoris, Fomalhaut, Epsilon Eridani and Vega, are providing the most convincing possibility that there may be other worlds beyond our solar system. Scientists at the Royal Observatory in Edinburgh, UK, using the pioneering £1 million Scuba camera attached to a

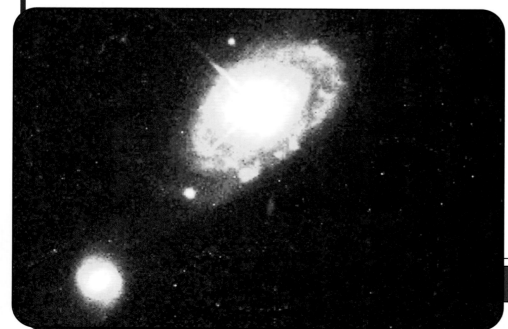

Left
The bright object is Quasar 0052+251, otherwise known as a Black Hole. Several billion times brighter than a normal star, it swallows all the matter in its surrounding galaxy. Luckily for us, it is about 1.4 billion light years from Earth.

microscope, can photograph objects from the microwaves they give off. The dust clouds are thought to contain a system of planets similar to our own, which could offer the possibility of intelligent life on other worlds. @ *alien life p148*

ⅠⅠ Virtual Universe program points to our void existence

An international team of researchers have developed a computer simulation of the Universe which indicates that we may live in a void. The program, which runs from 300,000 years after the so-called Big Bang to the present, predicts that space may consist of a number of giant voids and superclusters of galaxies. These galaxies could be about the same size as the area of the Universe that astronomers have investigated so far.

ⅠⅠ Cheaper telescope with the world's largest mirror

A giant telescope, with a mirror 11 m (36 ft) across, has been built at the McDonald Observatory in Texas, US, at 15% of the cost of similar instruments. The Hobby-Eberly Telescope (HET), costing less than $13.5 million (£8.4 million), is simpler than other telescopes in that it cannot be raised or lowered and is permanently angled at 35°. It can rotate on its base, however, to view more than two-thirds of the sky.

▶ Composite mirror technique to provide first space maps

Astronomers will be able to produce maps of space following NASA's development of a mirror that can focus high-energy X-rays, instead of allowing them to pass through. The mirror, made by coating metal foil with numerous micro-thin and alternating layers of platinum and carbon, can reflect X-rays of up to 40,000 electronvolts.

FINDINGS

▶ Ultra-high-speed cosmic rays could be neutrinos

Scientists think that the rare cosmic rays jetting through the Universe at close to the speed of light could in fact be neutrinos. They were initially thought to be protons, but as protons can only travel about 150 million light years (and the origins of these puzzling particles are probably active galaxies, such as quasars, which are further away than this) they are more likely to be neutrinos – particles which become strongly interacting at high energies. So far, only eight rays have been recorded, travelling in the upper atmosphere at energies of up to 10^{20} electronvolts. A team of physicists from the Rutherford Appleton Laboratory, near Oxford, UK, will test the hypothesis during the observation of a cosmic ray shower.

▶▶ Distant supernova gives clues to Universe's future

Results from supernovae investigations point to the possibility that there is too little

mass in the Universe to stop it expanding in future – and it will probably continue to grow forever. Astronomers at the Lawrence Livermore National Laboratory in California, USA, have been studying a supernova about 7 billion light years away, and by comparing statistics from this and other supernovae, have been able to estimate the amount of matter in the Universe and how quickly its expansion is slowing down.

▶ Black hole research gives clue to fate of matter

Scientists at the California Institute of Technology, USA, are closer to finding out how the jets of matter emitted by black holes form after watching a black hole swallow matter from a nearby star and then emit it at close to the speed of light. Black holes are the tiny areas of space that form around the collapse of a star. They are extremely dense and have an intense gravitational field which can often suck in matter from another star before releasing it as X-rays. Jets of matter or infrared flares appear each time the X-rays fade.

▶▶ Sun's brightness set to increase into 21st century

Satellite research has shown that the Sun is getting brighter and could make the Earth warmer by about 0.4°C (0.72°F) in the 21st century. The amount of solar energy absorbed by the earth increased by 0.036% between 1986 and 1996. Scientists are still unsure whether current greenhouse warming effects are due to industrial emissions from Earth or sun spot activity – or both. Whatever the answer, it's going to get hotter. @ *climate p122*

Above
The attractively-named Asteroid 253 Mathilde as photographed by the NEAR Near Earth Asteroid Rendezvous spacecraft. Mathilde forms part of the asteroid belt, orbiting the Sun at a distance of 290–500 km (180–311 miles) every 4.3 years.

ⅠⅠ Ground-based astronomers discover new moons

Astronomers in Canada and the US have discovered two new moons orbiting Uranus. These moons, the faintest around Uranus to have been spotted from Earth, bring the total number of the planet's moons to 17. As Earth- and space-based telescopes develop, many more discoveries are likely.

♻ Back to the future

Halley's Comet

Halley's Comet reappears every 76 years and is the most famous of all comets. It was examined for the first time in 1986, the last time it visited Earth, by the *Giotto* Spacecraft and was found to be 15 km (9 miles) long and 8.3 km (5 miles) across.

Radio telescope

In 1931, Karl Jansky, a radio engineer with Bell Telephone Laboratories, USA, became the first person to pick up radio emissions – as opposed to more traditional and common light waves – from the Milky Way using an improvised aerial.

Airborne observatory

In 1982, NASA launched the first airborne astronomical observatory. The observatory was set up inside a modified C-141 jet airplane which was capable of flying at heights up to 12,424 m (41,000 ft).

1990	Space shuttle Discovery deploys Hubble 600 km above the Earth
2002	COS is installed to gather clues about the birth of the universe

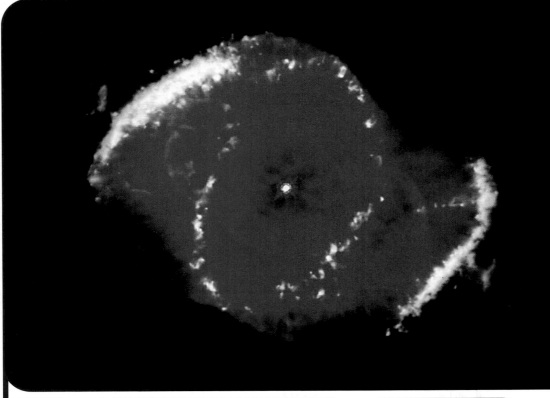

Left
This is the Cat's Eye Nebula as photographed by the HST. The red and green gas has been expelled by a dying star, seen here in the centre in blue.

HUBBLE

TECHNICAL MATTERS

▶ Hubble gets servicing in space

The Hubble Space Telescope (HST) was initially scheduled to return to Earth for refurbishment and be relaunched every five years, but concerns about contamination led to a change of plan. NASA decided that on-orbit servicing would be adequate to maintain the 15-year design life of HST and a three-year cycle of servicing was adopted, with successful missions completed in Dec 1993 and Feb 1997. In Dec 1999, the 1970s-era Faint Object Telescope will be replaced by the Advanced Camera for Surveys which can offer twice as much detail and a larger view of the sky. A fourth servicing mission is planned for mid-2002.

▶ COS lets astronomers look back billions of years

When Hubble is next serviced, in 2002, scientists will install the Cosmic Origins Spectrograph (COS). The instrument will gather light from distant stars, galaxies and quasars, allowing astronomers to study the very early Universe. About the size of a telephone box, the COS is 20 times more sensitive than anything currently in operation,

and will offer a glimpse of how galaxies and chemical elements were formed 10 billion years ago. It will be constructed at the University of Colorado, USA, and is expected to cost around $25 million (£15 million).

❚❚ Natural phenomena hamper Hubble's work

It takes the HST 96 minutes to orbit the Earth, but observation is interrupted for up to 45 minutes when the Earth blocks the target. In practice, the time lost is even greater, because the sensitive instruments cannot observe objects within 15.5 degrees of the bright Earth. Fortunately there are Continuous Viewing Zones (CVZs) and astronomers are encouraged to choose targets within these zones as more data can be obtained. The observing efficiency of HST has improved from 20% in 1990 to 46% in 1995.

❚❚ Thermos required for new infrared instrument

The Near Infrared Camera and Multi-Object Spectrometer (NICMOS) was installed during the $350 million servicing mission in

1997. The instrument extended the telescope's capability into the infrared light wavelengths, longer than the red light humans can see in the electromagnetic spectrum. The infrared detectors in NICMOS must operate at very cold temperatures, so scientists fitted it with a thermally insulating container, called a cryogenic dewar, which operates much like a thermos bottle. The dewar contains frozen nitrogen ice which can cool the detector for years, much longer than any previous space experiment.

Right
These gas pillars are made up of dense molecular hydrogen and dust in the Eagle Nebula, which is about 7,000 light years from Earth. The halo is created by light from young stars, and the small bumps in the pillars are embryonic stars.

Hubble can look in many directions at once

Space Telescope Imaging Spectrograph (STIS) has been called Hubble's "colour vision" and it replaced earlier versions in 1997. A spectrograph spreads out the light gathered by the telescope so that it can be analysed to determine the chemical composition, temperature, magnetic fields and rotational velocity of celestial objects. The STIS has the capability for two-dimensional spectroscopy, which means it can look at as many as 512 locations or objects in space at the same time.

Preparation for the next space telescope

Plans are already under way for Hubble's successor, the Next Generation Space Telescope (NGST). The NGST will be larger than the HST and its primary goal is to study the very early Universe. The NGST will be up to 1,000 times more sensitive, partly because it will orbit the Sun rather than the Earth. It will cost $500 million (£300 million), and it is likely that a further $400 million (£240 million) will be spent over its planned 10-year lifetime. Four designs are being considered, and a decision is expected in 2002, with construction beginning the year after. The Space Telescope Science Institute in Baltimore, Maryland, USA, will manage the NGST science programme.

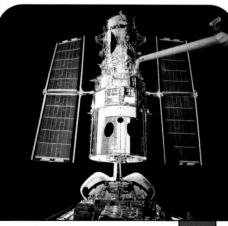

Above
The HST must be serviced every few years, with the next one due in 2002. The servicing is an opportunity to install new equipment and replace existing components, and generally requires astronauts to perform spacewalks.

OBSERVATIONS

Hubble photographs aurorae on Saturn

The HST has beamed back UV images of Saturn's aurorae from the Space Telescope Imaging Spectrograph. They are ten times sharper than earlier pictures, and show charged particles streaming from the Sun and striking the planet's atmosphere, where they excite molecules and make them glow. They will help to work out the composition of Saturn's atmosphere. Astronomers still cannot explain two bright streaks between the atmosphere and Saturn's moon.

New camera studies planets' weather

The HST's NICMOS has been used to study the atmosphere of planets Saturn and Uranus. Astronomers can compile a clearer picture of the weather on Saturn because NICMOS takes advantage of the infrared absorption properties of methane. The *Voyager* missions gave poor visuals of the bland, blue atmosphere of Uranus, while the NICMOS's first images detected six distinct cloud features and the dark rings were easily seen. Because of the camera's narrow field of vision, each image it produces is a mosaic constructed from three individual images.

Hubble captures the biggest star

In Oct 1997, Hubble's NICMOS captured an image of what might be the brightest star in the Milky Way. It has been named the Pistol Star because of the shape of its nebula, and it appears to be 100 times larger, and 10 million times brighter, than the Sun .The giant star, which is hidden away deep amid dust clouds near the centre of the galaxy, is exhausting fuel at a dramatic rate, which means that it is likely to die in a spectacular explosion within three million years.

Observing the fireworks of dying stars

The HST has produced breathtaking new images of dying stars, showing bubbles of super-hot gas which glow brightly as the stars erupt with such violence that they can evaporate planets. The dying stars form remarkable shapes like pinwheels, goblets and jet sprays as they spin into space. Astronomers believe the patterns may be caused by interaction with unseen companions – planets, brown dwarfs or smaller stars – which draw off gas and dust and set themselves in a swirling motion. The pictures also provide a preview of how our own Sun will swell by 200 times as it approaches its death in about six billion years time.

Hubble observes distant galaxies

The Hubble Deep Field optical survey, launched in 1996, turned up 3,000 faint galaxies, some believed to be the most distant objects observed to date. Unlike ground-based observatories, Hubble is able to image details of the shapes and configurations of galaxies. Elliptical galaxies

Above
This coloured, ultra violet image taken from Hubble's Space Telescope Imaging Spectrograph shows the atmospheric aurorae in Saturn's polar regions. The aurorae extend approximately 2,000 km (1,243 miles) above the clouds.

contain some of the oldest stars in the Universe. Researchers also now believe that large galaxies are not always born huge, but instead tear star clusters away from smaller neighbours.

Archives provide clues to the future

Astronomers at NASA's Jet Propulsion Laboratory in Pasadena, California, US, are searching the archives of Hubble images in search of asteroids. They have scanned 28,000 images over a three-year period, and hope that their findings will help them estimate possible risks of asteriods hitting the Earth with greater precision.

Back to the future

Hubble's discovery

The $3 billion (£1.8 billion) telescope was named after Edwin Hubble, who discovered the expansion of the Universe in 1929, since it is helping astronomers understand the Universe from its vantage point in orbit above the earth.

Take-off for the HST

The 2.4 m (8 ft) telescope weighs 12 tonnes and travels at 8 km/sec (5 miles/sec). It was deployed in low-Earth orbit – about 600 km (373 miles) – by the crew of the space shuttle *Discovery* on 25 April 1990. Hundreds of scientists based at the Goddard Space Flight Center in Greenbelt, Maryland, and the Space Telescope Science Institute in Baltimore, USA, analyse the 20,000 exposures and coordinate the 200 observing programmes per year. The planned 15-year mission has been extended by at least five years, to 2010.

Left
Part of a 360° panoramic mosaic image taken by the Imager for Mars Pathfinder (IMP) in July 1997. The sojourner rover vehicle can be seen sampling the rock known as 'Yogi' with its Alpha–Proton X–Ray Spectrometer. *Pathfinder*'s ramp is on the left.

EXPLORATION

THE PLANETS

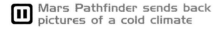

Mars Pathfinder sends back pictures of a cold climate

In July 1997, the Mars *Pathfinder* probe sent back panoramic images of Mars at 2,250 bits per second across 100 million miles of space to Earth. *Pathfinder*'s findings showed that temperatures can change drastically, dropping up to 22°C (40°F) in minutes. Ever since the 1970s scientists have suspected that Mars, which has an average temperature of 220 Kelvins, 53 Kelvins below water's freezing point, was once warm and had running water.

Mars Surveyor and the 10-year sampling programme

The Mars Surveyor mission is NASA's 10-year, multi-spacecraft programme to explore Mars. The programme includes the *Mars Surveyor 2001 Lander*, which is due to arrive on Mars in Dec 2001, and will undertake experiments with soil to test its

acidity and toxic properties. In 1999, NASA will be launching the *Deep Space II* probe to analyse soil beneath Mars' surface, and after 2005 it is planning to launch a mission to bring back rock and soil samples to Earth. Two further probes will make the voyage in 2003 and 2005.

The physical dangers of putting man on Mars

Though robotic probes are cheaper to send to Mars than manned missions, and are seen by some as the future of space exploration, NASA is still considering manned missions for the future. The chief

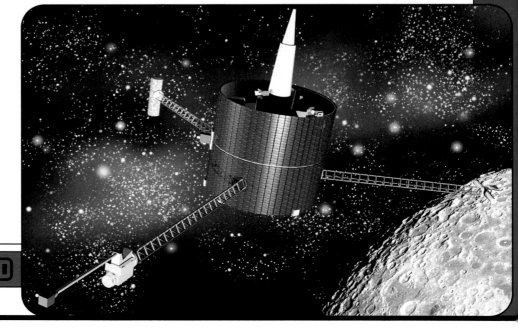

Right
A computer image of the *Lunar Prospector* (LP) orbiting the moon at a distance of 99 km (61 miles). Its instruments will analyse the composition of rocks, water and minerals, volcanic and tectonic activity, as well as attempting to extract data about the lunar core.

obstacle to manned travel is the health risk. Besides the drastic weakening of the bones and muscles in microgravity, there is the risk of cancer from the Sun's radiation, which on Earth is mostly absorbed by the atmosphere. @ space stations p147

Galileo probe sends Jupiter's slush back to earth

Launched by NASA in 1989, the *Galileo* probe arrived in 1995 to investigate Jupiter, which is larger than all the planets and moons in the Solar System combined. In March 1998, pictures arrived on Earth of what appears to be slush that had risen through cracks in the ice and had frozen at the surface temperature of -120°C (-248°F).

Cassini mission is expected on Saturn in 2004

The *Cassini* probe was launched by NASA in Oct 1997 and is expected to arrive at Saturn in 2004. It will orbit the ringed planet and drop the *Huygens* probe built by the European Space Agency (ESA) onto Titan, one of Saturn's 19 known moons. *Huygens* will sample the moon's thick atmosphere, which scientists believe resembles that of Earth earlier in its history.

Pluto Express launch is a remote possibility

Smaller than the Moon, Pluto, the ninth planet from the Sun, is the one we know least about. There is even argument over whether or not it is a planet. In the early 1990s, a region of mysterious orbiting bodies too small to be planets were discovered between Neptune and Pluto. This has been named the Kuiper belt and some astronomers believe that Pluto is merely the biggest of these bodies. In 2002, NASA will launch the *Pluto Express* probe to investigate Pluto and the Kuiper belt.

The missing planet in the solar system

Dr D. Christodoulou from Louisiana State University, Louisiana, USA, discovered that the Solar System may have 'lost' one of its planets long ago. He had been studying how the Sun and the planets may have condensed from a cloud of primordial dust and gas. After taking into account the effects of gravity, rotation and magnetic fields, he discovered that the asteroid belt and the planets were situated in the localities predicted by his calculations, except for Mars. A gap existed between Earth and Mars where his calculations predicted another planet should be.

OTHER BODIES

Lunar Prospector finds millions of tonnes of water

In March 1998, NASA's *Lunar Prospector* detected what appeared to be ice in vast craters at the Moon's north and south poles. Some scientists believe that sub-surface water might have been driven to the surface to form ice during the Moon's formation, while others believe it comes from comets and asteroids that have pounded the Moon over millions of years. NASA has estimated that there is between 10 and 300 million tonnes of water on the Moon, which has raised hopes that human colonies will soon be populating its surface.

The Near Earth Asteroid Rendezvous mission

In 1999, a probe will orbit one of the asteroids in the belt between Mars and Jupiter. Launched by NASA in 1996, the *Near-Earth Asteroid Rendezvous* (Near) mission will fly within 48 km (30 miles) of the asteroid Eros and measure its magnetic field, composition and mass distribution.

Private US citizen hopes to sample asteroids

In the USA, computer software businessman James Benson has established the Space Development Corporation, through which he is raising $50 million (£31 million) to send a privately-owned probe to the asteroid belt. The University of Texas at Austin, USA, is contracted to build the probe called the *Near-Earth Asteroid Prospector*. Benson aims to launch it before 2000 and wants to take mineral and ice samples from an asteroid, with a view to mining or using asteroid water in future inter-planetary exploration. @ space stations p146

SOHO manages to detect sounds in the Sun

The Solar and Heliospheric Observatory (SOHO) was launched jointly by NASA and ESA on 2 Dec 1995. The two-tonne craft uses 12 instruments to monitor the Sun's activity constantly in unprecedented detail.

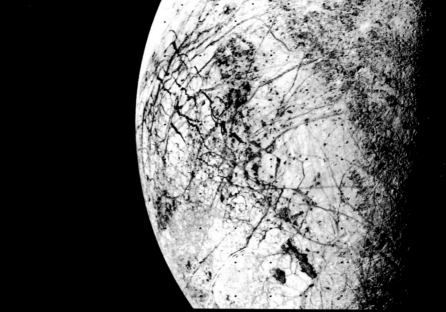

Above
Europa, the smallest and brightest of Jupiter's four satellites, photographed from 241,000 km (150,000 miles) by *Voyager 2*. It is thought to be covered by a crust of fractured ice 75-100 km (47-62 miles) thick.

It is positioned at a point known to astronomers as the inner Lagrangian point, where the pull between the Earth and the Sun's gravity is balanced. In this way, *SOHO* orbits the Sun together with the Earth. Among the findings the probe has made is that the Sun produces sound: *SOHO* has picked up a throbbing motion on the surface of the Sun which rises and falls over a period of about five minutes. These movements are caused by sounds that bounce around the interior of the Sun.

Back to the future

Pluto

In 1930, astronomer Clyde Tombaugh at Lowell Observatory in Flagstaff, Arizona, USA, spotted a new planet in our Solar System, soon to be named Pluto. The planet was found in the part of the sky where the founder of the observatory, Percival Lowell, who died in 1916, had predicted.

Moon landing

In 1948, the *Science Digest* magazine argued that a manned landing on the Moon posed so many problems that it would not happen for another 200 years. Only 21 years later Neil Armstrong proved it could be done.

Mars

In 1972, photographs sent back from the *Mariner 9* satellite revealed that, far from being a barren wasteland, Mars was a world of volcanoes, dust storms and gully-like terrain that seemed to have been modelled by running water at some stage.

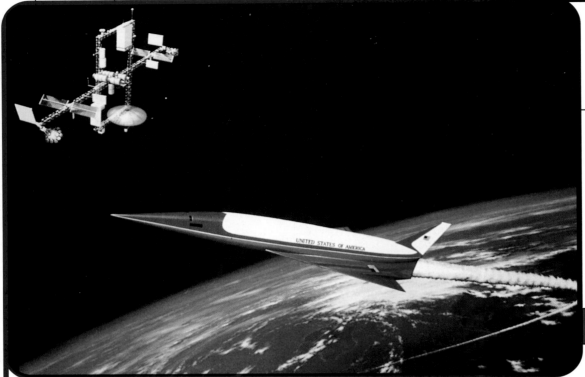

Left
The experimental X-30 is an aeroplane which will be capable of taking off from a runway and travelling at hypersonic speed to go directly into orbit. The craft will also be able to land like a conventional airplane creating many possibilities for commercial space flight.

SPACECRAFT

SPACECRAFT

Four space shuttles set to become more fuel-efficient

Following radical cuts to the US space budget, it is important that NASA creates a fleet of more fuel-efficient, re-usable manned spacecraft. In 1998, four existing shuttles, *Atlantis*, *Endeavor*, *Discovery* and *Columbia*, were upgraded to include new propellant tanks weighing 3 tonnes less than the conventional 30-tonne tank, enabling a greater payload consisting of equipment and goods. These shuttles could be in commission until 2010 and will cost an estimated $1 billion (£600 million) to build, with each mission costing an additional $500,000 (£298,000).

Tests to start soon on X-33 and X-34 unmanned craft

NASA has developed the X-33 and X-34 unmanned wingless craft and aims to begin test flights in 1998 and 1999. The X-33, which could one day be the shuttle's successor, is designed, like the shuttle, to be launched vertically with rockets and land

horizontally like an aeroplane. The chief difference between the X-33 and the shuttle is a V-shaped 'aerospike' engine which maximises lift by igniting gases on its outside surface rather than the conventional bell chambers which are currently in use. The X-34 is smaller than the X-33 and the unmanned test flights are designed as a trial for new heat resistant materials and navigation systems.

Wingless lifeboat aircraft relies on its shape to fly

A prototype of the X-38 (the 'X' stands for 'experimental'), intended as an emergency escape lifeboat for crews of the *International Space Station* (*ISS*), made its first successful atmospheric test flight in March 1998. The wingless aircraft was airlifted under the wing of a B-52 and dropped at an altitude of

Right
During the 1970s many believed that shuttles would be launched on a weekly basis in the future, but it soon became clear that the high costs involved would prevent this. More fuel-efficient, re-usable alternatives are in development.

6,977 m (23,000 ft) to make its flight before landing using a huge parachute. Everything on the spacecraft is controlled by mission controllers on Earth. The X-38 is scheduled to begin operations on the *ISS* in 2003. @ *space stations p146*

The X-36 flies without a tail which boosts its stealthiness

McDonnell Douglas, the US aeronautical corporation, built X-36 to test remote piloting techniques and provide data on the performance characteristics of aircraft without tails. The craft's 6-m (18-ft) long jets are remotely controlled by a pilot in a ground station cockpit (a technology called fly-by-wire), complete with a head-up display. Test results should enable the development of agile, tailless fighter-type craft with reduced weight and drag and enhanced stealth. @ *aircraft p82*

Hyper-X's engine breathes oxygen instead of carrying it

NASA, with the help of a team of Russian aeronautical engineers, is in the process of developing the Hyper-X, a unique craft which will use an 'air-breathing' engine. The Hyper-X's engines will suck in the oxygen from the atmosphere for use in combustion instead of carrying oxygen on board. Conventional shuttles have to carry approximately 542,000 litres of liquid oxygen, leaving only 2% of their total weight for payload. Although the Hyper-X will have to carry some oxygen on board for use when it reaches the upper atmosphere, where oxygen is thin, NASA calculates that the craft's payload will account for around 25% of its total weight.

ROCKETS AND ROBOTICS

Laser technology may be used to propel aircraft

Funded jointly by the US Air Force and NASA and developed by Prof. Leik Myrabo, lightcraft are propelled into the air using laser beams. These hollow, 30-cm (1-ft) high aircraft are made out of aluminium and have already been successfully tested using the US's most powerful laser at the White Sands Missile Range in the New Mexico desert. Each craft is fitted with a mirror at the bottom which focuses the light on a ring-shaped combustion chamber; the concentration of light energy there is strong enough to rip electrons from molecules, forming plasma and creating an explosive force which lifts the lightcraft.

Amateur rocket enthusiasts prepare for launch

British DIY rocket enthusiast Frank Sharman is preparing to launch his latest construction – a 6-m (20-ft) rocket powered by a new type of solid fuel. The unmanned rocket, which will be a world first for independent space launching, will be flown into the upper atmosphere on a balloon from where

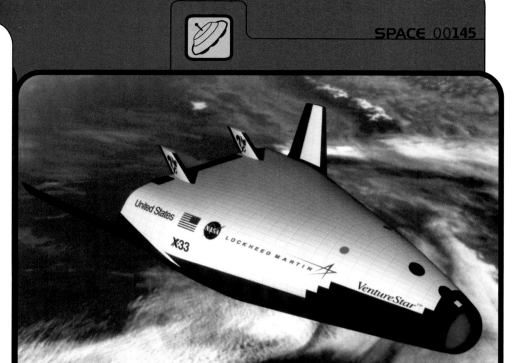

it will launch into space accelerating to a speed of 112 km/h (70 mph). Another amateur rocket scientist, Derek Willis, founder of the Space Quest Foundation, UK, plans to launch *Space Quest II*, a 3.3-m (11-ft) projectile, to an altitude of 2 km (1¼ miles). The rocket motors, inspired by the Aero chocolate bar, contain solid propellant comprising billions of resin-hardened air bubbles.

SPACE TRAVEL

Incentive offered to design low-cost space travel

The X-Prize is a privately funded competition open to all aerospace companies. Designed to kick-start a low-cost space travel industry, the X-Prize Foundation is offering $10 million (£6 million) to the first design team able to fly three people 101 km (63 miles) above the Earth – the official astronaut level – and return them after a suborbital 'up-and-down' flight, twice within a two-week period. One contender for the prize is *Cosmos Mariner*, developed by Dynamicar Research, Houston, USA, which is hoped will reach the required altitude, flying at eight times the speed of sound with the help of two Russian-built rocket motors and a titanium alloy heat-resistant covering.

Roton helicopter could launch space tourism

Two DIY rocket enthusiasts in the US, Bevin McKinney and Gary Hudson, have teamed up to form their own company, HMX Inc.,

Above
The test flight of the X-33 is planned by NASA to take place in 1999. Details of the craft's revolutionary wingless design have emerged from a cloak of security in place during the Cold War.

through which they hope to raise funds to test and build the world's first space helicopter. Their design, which they have named the Roton, uses rocket engines fitted to the tip of each of the four rotor blades. McKinney and Hudson believe that the Roton will play a central part in space tourism, offering fun rides into space as well as ferrying guests to orbiting hotels. @ *holidays p18*

Back to the future

Meteorite crash in Siberia

An enormous meteorite crashed into Tunguska, Siberia, and devastated miles of forest in 1908. The landscape was left desolate and ruined, but the remoteness of the area meant that nobody was hurt.

The first beings in space

In 1959, two monkeys from the US became the first living creatures to return to earth unharmed after a journey into outer space. Their spacecraft crashed into the Atlantic ocean after a 580-km (360-mile) high flight above the earth.

A real disaster in a simulated orbit

Three astronauts were killed during a flight simulation in Cape Canaveral, USA, on 27 Jan 1967. The astronauts were practising for a 14-day orbit when an electrical fault caused a fire to break out.

Left
Assembly of the *International Space Station* began in 1998 and will require 44 flights to complete it by 2003. The largest space project ever undertaken, it involves unprecedented international co-operation.

SPACE STATIONS

MIR

Cosmonauts have been living and working on the 120 tonne Russian Mir space station since it was first manned in March 1986, although the final module was launched in 1997. Travelling 483 km (300 miles) a second and orbiting Earth every 92 minutes, Mir is to be deorbited in 1999 and most of it will burn up while re-entering the atmosphere. Any surviving fragments will fall into the Pacific.

Progress brings food and takes waste to burn

Mir is made up of five main modules and is fitted with solar panels which permanently point towards the sun in order to provide electricity for the station. At *Mir*'s height – between 299 and 386 km (186–240 miles) above the planet – the outside temperature is 400°C (752°F) in sunlight and -100°C (-212°F) in the Earth's shadow. Liquid waste is recycled with the help of an electrolysis unit which provides the station's oxygen. Originally, solid waste was ejected from *Mir* into space but this was stopped after world-wide concern over the growth of space debris. Now the *Progress* supply ships which bring water, fuel and supplies to *Mir* from Earth, are used to carry away rubbish and waste. The supply ships, along with their cargo, burn up on re-entry into the Earth's atmosphere.

▶ Kvant research, quasars and active galaxies

Many cosmonauts are trained scientists (others are pilots) and conduct experiments in laboratories while they are in space. The *Kvant-1* module is also the astrophysics laboratory in which cosmonauts study the physical and chemical properties of space bodies such as quasars and active galaxies. *Kvant-2* examines electronics and building materials in micro-gravity. In addition, the two *Priroda* and *Spektre* modules investigate our planet's atmosphere and climate, and the *Kristall* craft studies material processing.

Right
An image of the *ISS* orbiting over Europe and preparing to dock with the European *Automated Transfer Vehicle* (*ATV*) in the background, left. The *ATV* is planned to be a supply vehicle to the *ISS*. Centre bottom is the conical European crew transfer vehicle.

'Bee-sticks' plant experiment takes root in space

Many manned and unmanned spacecraft have conducted experiments in plant growth. British-born Michael Foale planted a dwarf variety of seed, *Brassica rapa*, on *Mir* in 1997 and they became the first to germinate in space. Close relatives of *Brassica rapa* include turnips and Chinese cabbage. Foale had to hand-pollinate the plants with 'bee-sticks', toothpicks with the

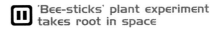

pollen-collecting organs of bees glued to them. He also had to maintain airflow around the plants and deliver water to the roots in microgravity. His plants grew nearly as fast as if they had been on Earth.

▶ Health hazards, exercise and mould in space and time

The Russian Space Agency and NASA have learned much from living on *Mir* about how the human body responds to zero-gravity. Exercise is important – the lack of friction on the body causes bones to weaken through the loss of calcium – and on *Mir* cosmonauts have to exercise three to four hours a day. It was also discovered that the body's immune system is suppressed in space. Mould that had grown in *Mir* during its 11 years in space was found to cause hay fever, and common colds become difficult to cope with in space because zero-gravity stops mucous draining down the back of the throat and nose.

ISS

In 1984, US President Ronald Reagan directed NASA to build a space station for launch in 1992. Launch dates have been postponed many times and the station has metamorphosed into one of the biggest co-operative technological projects ever undertaken. The first module, the Russian-built Functional Cargo Block, *which will serve as the station's nerve centre, was planned to blast off from Baikonur, Kazakhstan, in 1998. The second component to be launched will be the USA-made* Node 1, *which will serve as an attachment segment for more modules. It will take 44 flights to assemble the 410-tonne station and it is scheduled for completion at the end of 2003. The* International Space Station (ISS) *will be 108 m (354 ft) long and 40 m (131 ft) wide – about the size of a football pitch.*

⏸ International co-operation on space station designs

In Feb 1995, Russians and Americans started sharing Shuttle missions and living on *Mir*, kicking off the first phase of the *ISS* project. The second phase, which covers the building and assembly of the station, has already begun. Russia has been contracted by NASA to build three of the first four modules. There are 16 countries involved in the design and assembly. The major partners are: the USA; Russia, which is providing research and service modules with their own life and habitation systems, a Science Power Platform that supplies electrical power, and a *Soyuz* spacecraft; the European Space Agency, which is contributing a pressurized laboratory; Japan, which is building a laboratory with an area exposed in space; and Canada, which is building a 17-m (55-foot) long robotic arm for assembly and maintenance tasks. NASA expects the total cost for the station to be $20.6 billion (£13 billion) but the *Wall Street Journal* newspaper predicted in March 1998 that it would amount to $24 billion (£15 billion).

▶ Five three-person crews to man ISS

In mid-1999, a Russian *Soyuz* spacecraft will ferry the first crew, consisting of Bill Shepherd from the USA and Sergei Krikalev and Yuri Gidzenko from Russia, to the *ISS*. NASA and Star City in Moscow have agreed on the first five three-person crews – seven Americans and eight Russians – which will man the station up to the end of 2000. There are already 22 spacewalks scheduled for crew members and 30 for visiting cosmonauts, which will be a vital part of the building and maintenance of the station. When complete in 2004, a crew of six will live in what will be the pressurized volume equivalent to the passenger areas of two jumbo jets. The Dexterous Robotics Laboratory at NASA's Johnson Space Centre, Houston, USA, is studying designs of different robots which will eventually service the *ISS*.

▶ Research into burning and growing in space

Research on the *ISS* will focus on the effects of weightlessness on the human body, experimenting with new and biological materials, and studying combustion – or how things burn in space. Experiments on *Mir* demonstrated that protein crystals grow more slowly in microgravity and, therefore, proteins form more perfectly in space than they do on Earth, making space protein suitable for the design and testing of new medicines. Although the new station will be used for Earth observation, it will not be used for microgravity experiments because movements from the six-strong crew will make it too jittery for precise measurements to be taken. @ *materials science p160*

▶▶ Bioregenerative chambers to expand their role

NASA is developing bioregenerative chambers: self-supporting eco-systems that will eventually be used on the *ISS* and lunar bases. These chambers, which run on solar power, supply food to the cosmonauts and have systems that can recycle human waste materials back into the food chain. NASA scientists are also experimenting with growing potatoes, rice, soya beans, carrots, lettuce and tomatoes in space, and they believe that cosmonauts will one day be able to choose from as many as 15 to 30 different kinds of crops, supplemented by 'luxury' foods – meat, dairy products and flavour concentrates – brought from Earth. They hope that, besides acting as an orbiting space laboratory, the *ISS* will provide a refreshment station and base camp for the manned mission to Mars. @ *exploration p142*

Above
A test subject rinsing her hair inside the space station *Freedom*'s Whole Body Shower. Designed for zero-gravity use, a vacuum hose removes excess water. There is a foothold and overhead handhold, too.

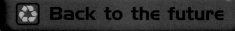

♻ Back to the future

Salyut
The first orbiting space station was *Salyut*, launched by the USSR in 1971. Between 1971 and 1982 seven *Salyuts* were launched, each carrying up to four crew members into space for up to several months at a time.

Skylab
In 1979, an attempt to bring back to Earth the US space station *Skylab* failed. It burned up on re-entry and surviving pieces crashed into a remote area of Australia. In 1993, sheep farmer Mark Grewar found *Skylab*'s 2-m (6-ft) long titanium oxygen tank on his land on the Nullarbor Plain. Grewar telephoned the *New York Times* newspaper in order to place an advertisement to sell the tank but they hung up, apparently convinced it was a hoax. NASA was not interested in retrieving it either.

Garlic nightmare
In Jan 1987, *The Times* reported how a French astronaut took some garlic-laden delicacies with him on a Soviet space flight. He was clearly unaware of garlic's flatus-producing effect, and the air conditioning was said to have been unable to cope.

1973	British Rail patents the idea of a 'nuclear-powered' flying saucer
2020	The spacecraft Voyager 1 reaches a point 20 billion km from Earth

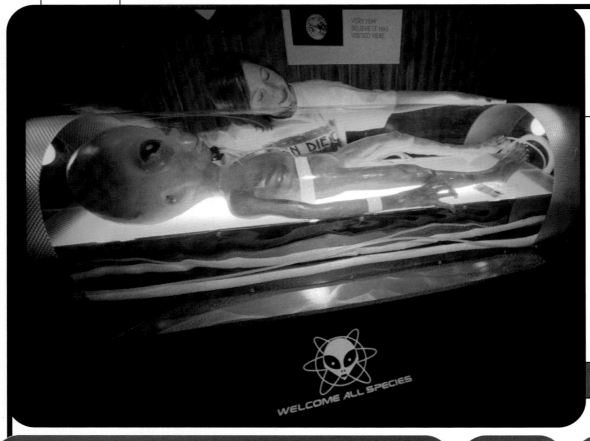

WELCOME ALL SPECIES

Left
The possibility of alien life continues to capture our imagination, and rather than waiting for them to come to us, scientists are launching probes equipped with ever more sophisticated technology, able to relay their findings directly to Earth, and even broadcast pictures on the Web.

ALIEN LIFE

ET EVIDENCE

Panel of experts to study evidence of UFOs

The Society for Scientific Exploration seems to think there may be more to UFO evidence than verbal reports. In Oct 1997, a panel of nine scientists from France, Germany and the US was convened to review evidence including, spectroscopic data, video records, photographs, material specimens, radar records, and radiation-type injuries sustained by witnesses, in an effort to scientifically unravel this 50-year-old mystery.

Alien embryo pronounced a hoax after extensive tests

In Sept 1997, a vial-like jar containing a strange embryo was found in the car of a murdered man in Puerto Rico. Police officers at the crime scene described the find as a "fetus of non-human appearance", resembling the fabled Chupacabras, a Puerto Rican creature with large almond eyes that purportedly attacks animals and people. Despite high-security forensic testing, the local television station later claimed the embryo was only a souvenir key-chain with a plastic alien figurine inside a crystalline jar.

Fossilized Martian life found in meteorite

In Aug 1996, researchers announced that a meteorite known to have come from Mars displayed characteristics indicative of ancient Martian bacterial life. The meteorite, designated ALH84001, is about the size of a potato, and was found in Antarctica in 1984. Although sceptics have dismissed the claims, arguing that the fossils would have had to have been formed at temperatures too high for life to survive, these findings potentially confirm that there could have been life on Mars.

Communication on a canvas of crops

Crop circles have mysteriously appeared in fields all around the world. Crop circles are areas of flattened crop, usually circular in shape and often forming very elaborate patterns. Researchers investigating the phenomenon admit that many crop circles are man-made, created in order to lend support to the hoax idea, but still more

have genuinely unknown origins. Careful study has revealed themes in the formations, such as the proliferation of insectograms, and more recently solar system patterns. More curious still is the fact that as yet there is no adequate explanation to account for the mechanical and electrical failures experienced within certain crop circle formations.

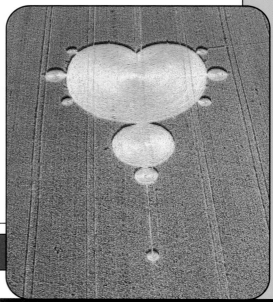

Right
This crop circle at Ickleton, near Cambridge, UK, is in the form of the Mandelbrot Set, a mathematical method. Some believe crop circles to be the work of extraterrestrial beings, but science-based theories, such as 'plasma-vortex', have also been advanced.

⏸ Allegations of astronauts, close encounter in space

According to a 1997 Internet posting, the Space Shuttle *Endeavor* narrowly avoided a collision with a gigantic UFO during its 12-day mission in Sept 1995. American author William Kliner is reportedly in possession of a copy of the top-secret NASA audio tape which proves it. Kliner believes the STS-69 incident is "dazzling proof that UFOs not only exist, they are piloted by extraterrestrials who are interested in our technology".

⏩ Drilling for evidence of aliens under ice

Xenobiologists looking for evidence of alien life are hoping for a breakthrough here on Earth. If they succeed in finding evidence of life in Lake Vostok, buried 3.7 km (2½ miles) below the Antarctic ice sheet, it implies that life could exist under the ice in similar lakes on Europa, a moon of Jupiter. Ice cores retrieved from a depth of 100 m (328 ft) of the lake revealed 200,000 year old frozen algae which was brought back to life in a laboratory.

SPACE

⏸ Searching for extraterrestrial intelligence

SETI (Search for Extraterrestrial Intelligence) is an effort to detect evidence of the existence of technological civilizations elsewhere in the universe. NASA's SETI Program, known as the High Resolution Microwave Survey, ended in 1993 after congressional funding was cut. The SETI Institute is a non-profit organization which acts as the institutional home for research relating to the study of life in the universe.

▶ NASA searches for other earth-like planets

Scheduled to set out on its mission in the first decade of the next century, the Terrestrial Planet Finder (TPF) will search for other Earth-like planets and characterize their atmospheres as part of NASA's Origins Program. The TPF contains an interferometer, which is a type of observatory consisting of several telescopes which function as one to produce an extremely sharp image. To ensure maximum sensitivity the TPF will be sent into deep space, perhaps even as far as the orbit of Jupiter.

⏸ Project Phoenix has radio astronomers listening in

Successor to NASA's SETI Program, the privately funded Project Phoenix is the world's most comprehensive search for extraterrestrial intelligence. Radio telescopes of up to 300 m (984 ft) in diameter are used to scrutinize the vicinities of nearby, Sun-like stars to detect artificially produced signals. About 1,000 stars have been targeted for observation. So far no clearly extraterrestrial transmissions have been found, but the observation phase is scheduled to run until the year 2001.

⏸ Earthlings send greetings to Saturn, just in case

Titan, one of Saturn's moons, has a thick atmosphere composed mostly of nitrogen, much like the Earth's, although with a surface temperature of -178°C (-288°F) it is unlikely that life could exist there. Just in case, the European Space Agency's *Huygens* space probe, launched in Oct 1997, will be carrying one million messages from Earthlings to Titan's inhabitants, collected on the ESA Web site.

⏸ Flying saucers really do exist

The LTAS Corporation in Nevada is testing several flying saucers which are almost silent and propelled by huge tilting solar-powered electric fans. The saucer shape provides the volume for the helium lifting gas. The Hyper, a 212-m (696-ft) diameter hypersonic flying saucer, could be launching satellites into low-Earth orbit in the near future.

⏸ Voyager takes travel brochure into space

Since their launch in 1977, *Voyagers 1* and *2* have revealed many mysteries of our solar system. They have enough radioactive plutonium to operate the measuring and navigation equipment until about 2020, when *Voyager 1* will be 20 billion km (12.4 billion miles) from Earth. In case aliens should encounter either *Voyager*, NASA has included an audio-visual travel brochure.

⏩ Shoppers soon to be motoring on the moon

Armchair astronauts may soon be able to navigate the craters on the surface of

Above
This flying-saucer-like object is in fact the platform above a 305-m (1,000-ft) radio telescope dish, illuminated by lights. The US-based Project Phoenix is using radio telescopes to try and detect life around 1,000 sun-like stars.

the Moon. US-based company LunaCorp is preparing to land two lunar roving robots on the Moon by the year 2000. Interactive simulators installed in shopping malls and theme parks would allow shoppers and games enthusiasts to drive the buggies around the lunar landscape by remote control. During their 1,000 km treck the robots will allow scientists to explore the moon's surface at the bargain price of $7,000 (£4,200) per hour. @ *shopping p12*

♻ Back to the future

Flying Saucers

In 1973, the UK state-controlled company British Rail patented the idea of a nuclear-powered flying saucer hoping that it would one day become the public transport of the future. However, the flying saucer was never built.

First crop circles

A pamphlet of 1678 shows an illustration of a crop circle, caused by a 'mowing devil', in a field in Hertfordshire, UK. Explanations for their appearance range from animals, over-fertilization and landing marks left by UFOs.

First reported flying saucer

In 1947, Idaho businessman Kenneth Arnold claimed to have seen nine flying disc-shaped objects near Mt Rainer, Washington, USA, while piloting a Callair aeroplane. The term 'flying saucer' was later coined by a journalist covering the story.

Proposed nanocomputers can store one million trillion bytes of memory in one cubic millimetre

NEW SCIENCES

FUTURESCOPE

• **In the future, computers will be able to think for themselves,** we will share our homes with robotic cats and dogs and our everyday domestic appliances will use fuzzy logic and learn from the problems they encounter. 'Biomorphic' robots will emulate evolution based on animal behaviour and smart systems will allow us to become characters in a virtual world. Artificial life is not far off.

• **Virtual reality will have enormous benefits for business, health and defence.** VR has the potential to be used in therapy – to allow sufferers to confront their fears – in nuclear weapons simulation and in place of the operating theatre for trainee surgeons. In the next century, business conferences will be carried out on the Internet in a virtual environment.

• **Manufacturing technology could be replaced by nanotechnology,** the science of building objects on a molecular level. Tools thousands of times smaller than human cells and the smallest microchip could revolutionize industry. In medicine, nanorobots could go inside the body to look for viruses and bacteria and then destroy them, or blast through blood clots. Nanocomputers might run in the region of a billion cycles per second. And all of this will be done with low production costs and raw materials that last a long time.

• **Reviving the dead may become a reality** if cryogenics works. Alcor Foundation, a company that freezes patients in liquid nitrogen, hopes to be able to revive its clients once they have perfected a system that won't damage the body's cells. However, at a cost of up to $120,000 per person, cryonic suspension will be something reserved for the rich.

• **Amazing new materials are being developed in the manufacturing industry.** We will be able to have glasses that remember their own shape when we accidentally sit on them, smart clothes that change temperature according to the weather and plastics that stop fizzy drinks going flat. In sport, titanium tennis rackets and carbon-fibre composite cricket bats will allow every amateur to hit aces and sixes at will.

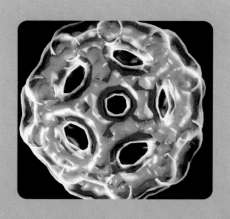

ARTIFICIAL LIFE

NANOTECHNOLOGY

CRYOGENICS

VIRTUAL REALITY

MATERIALS SCIENCE

SPORTS SCIENCE

NEW THEORIES

TECHNO-BABBLE

AUXETIC
Materials that get thicker when they are stretched.

BOTS
A new form of computer life, an intelligent agent that can be programmed to carry out tedious and repetitive tasks.

YESTERTECH
The technology of the past, often used in nostalgic tones.

COLD FUSION
The holy grail of energy science. Cold fusion is the fusing of hydrogen atoms to make helium and energy, but at temperatures that are manageable.

INTELLIGENT AGENT
A bot or other software agent that travels the Internet or corporate databases searching for particular information.

MECHATRONICS
A cross between mechanics and electronics, mechatronics is the use of microelectronics in the control of mechanical systems.

BETA
Anything new and hence still in the embryonic stage.

BARFOGENESIS
Nausea caused through wearing virtual reality headsets.

Left
Marvin Minsky is one of the pioneers of artificial intelligence, having designed and built, in 1951, the first neural network-based learning machine based on the human brain. In 1985 he co-founded MIT's Media Lab, which is at the forefront of current research into the creation of thinking machines.

ARTIFICIAL LIFE

DEVELOPMENTS

Computers are beginning to get aLife

The study of artificial life, or 'aLife' to its devotees, may eventually develop machines that can 'think' for themselves. A common type of aLife computer program is one such as Polyworld, a virtual environment where computerized bugs exist – some say evolve – within a 3-D plane. The bugs are programmed to carry out certain tasks – to find food or a mate – and within those parameters are left free to develop their own survival methods. While this sort of program may seem little more than a game, it has significant applications for more advanced technologies, perhaps leading towards machines that can fully reproduce human thought processes.

De Garis's 'artilect' vision of the 21st century

Hugo de Garis, a senior research affiliate at the Centre for Artificial Intelligence Evolutionary Systems Department, Kyoto, Japan, sees the goal of evolutionary engineering as the creation of artificial intellects, or 'artilects', more complex than human intelligence – and far superior to it. By the late 21st century, the computing capacity of such systems could have more than 10^{30} components, compared to the human brain's 10^{10} neurons (tens of billions), each no more than the size of a molecule. @ nanotechnology p154

The world's first truly intelligent robotic kitten

The first artificial brain is being built by Advanced Telecommunications Research (ATR) in Kyoto, Japan, in collaboration with former electrical engineer Mikhail Korjin of Colorado, USA, and Hugo de Garis. The CAM-Brain Machine will be used to create an intelligent robotic kitten by 2000. It is believed that if this project is completed successfully it will open the way for the process of evolving a million neural net modules to create artificial brains. The kitten brain will feature a 10,000-module brain with a million neurons, compared to the human brain's tens of billions.

The role of fuzzy logic in tomorrow's systems

Many artificial intelligence networks make use of fuzzy logic systems, which enable computers to analyse imprecise situations where things are not simply black or white, on or off, but somewhere in between. Fuzzy logic has already been incorporated into domestic electrical devices, such as washing machines, where the machine can sense how much soap to use depending on how dirty the dishes are. It is also being used in more complex situations, such as

stock markets, and Japanese scientists are even working on systems that will one day be able to write novels. @ money p30

The first conscious machine begins to explore

Following six years of research, a computer has been designed that its creators at Imperial College, London, UK, claim is 'environment aware'. The lap top, called Magnus, has been designed with neural networks, simulating a basic collection of brain cells, which enables it to learn from the problems it encounters. The program explores virtual 'worlds', learning the names

Right
The Cybernetics Department at Reading University, UK, has created a series of so-called dwarf robots that it uses to demonstrate robot technology to schoolchildren. The dwarfs can 'think' simple thoughts, such as when to avoid objects in their way, through infra-red signals sent out by their antennae.

and meanings of objects it comes across. Magnus has shown that it comprehends its actions, which makes scientists think it is becoming aware of its own existence and could one day begin to exert 'free will' by choosing between many possible actions.

⏸ Test shows computers are still not intelligent enough

In March 1998, the Electronic Telegraph and the BBC's *Tomorrow's World* programme ran the world's largest artificial intelligence test. Internet users were invited to carry out the classic test devised by the British mathematician, Alan Turing. The test asked users to communicate by text only: if you were unable to tell whether you were talking to a computer or a human, then the computer 'won'. About 32,000 people took part and 'spoke' to either 'Sam', 'Chris' or 'Liz' before they voted. Results showed that one person in six was fooled, with people usually thinking that the humans were robots, rather than vice versa. Although some people were fooled, the test proved that the computer was not intelligent enough to fool a majority of users.

Above
MAGNUS is a lap top with attitude: it is one of the world's few computers with a mind of its own. Here it demonstrates to Professor Igor Aleksander of Imperial College, London, UK, how it can 'think' of a butterfly and then represent the image on screen.

▶ Insectoid robots can learn to be clever

Robobiologists at the Los Alamos National Laboratory, USA, are designing robots based on the behaviour of animals and insects. The resulting 'biomorphic' robots have basic brains and nervous systems. By emulating evolution, the makers are creating simple robots that even schoolchildren could build. The robots can then be taught a variety of tasks. Despite their primitive 'brains' and poor computing power the robots learn quickly – at the Department of Cybernetics, Reading University, UK, researchers under Professor Kevin Warwick have built a robot named 'Elma' that learns to walk in 12 minutes. @ *robots p28*

⏸ Six-legged walkers tackle tough terrain

Researchers at the Massachusetts Institute of Technology (MIT), USA, have also been developing insect-based robots, which they find are much more successful at covering difficult terrain. Where the humanoid two-legged robots lacked stability and robots on wheels or tracks failed to mount steep

slopes, these six-legged robots continue walking even if some of their legs become damaged. One of the aims of the Mobile Robot Group at MIT is to create multi-legged robots that will be able to repair themselves. One robot, Genghis, has been fitted with sensors that allow it to learn why it falls over and to evolve ways to avoid doing it in future.

APPLICATIONS

⏭ Computers that can pick you out of a crowd

A computer system that can recognize individual faces is under development at MIT in the US. The facial recognition software is also being developed to determine the meaning of sounds and gestures. The system, which works by drawing a picture of the subject's face and then matching this to images in a database, could be used for security systems access, police files, therapy and entertainment. @ *policing p62*

⏭ Getting pleasure out of a virtual environment

Artificially smart systems could mean that one day it will be possible to become a character in a virtual world. Bruce Blumberg of the MIT Media Lab is developing a system called Virtual Dog, in which people, standing in front of a large screen, would see simulated video images of themselves on the screen. When the real person moves, so does the on-screen creation. There is also a computer generated dog, which can interact with the virtual person. The real person can even train it and teach it to play 'fetch'. @ *virtual reality p158*

Above
Joshua Bers's research at MIT involves finding ways to communicate with machines as we would with humans – through speech, gesture and eye contact. If successful, computer keyboards and mice could give way to cybergloves and eye sensors. ⏭

▶ "Open the pod bay door, please Hal"

An intelligent computer system has been built for use on board the NASA *Discovery* Space Shuttle, and for the space stations to be used in the next millennium. The system is called dMars, and will be built by the Australian Artificial Intelligence Institute in Melbourne. Unlike the machine from which it drew inspiration, Hal, the rogue computer in Stanley Kubrick's movie *2001: a Space Odyssey,* dMars will definitely not be programmed to become self aware. @ *space stations p146*

♻ Back to the future

Backgammon-playing computer

In 1979, the world backgammon champion, Luigi Villa, was defeated in a specially-arranged tournament in Monte Carlo, Monaco, by the US Carnegie-Mellon University's computer, 'Mighty Bee'.

Computer speak

In 1970, artificial intelligence computer programs were used for the first time to understand language. Known as 'MTRANS', 'ATRANS' and 'ATTEND', they foreshadowed the voice recognition softwares in use today.

Chess-playing computer

Bell Telephone Laboratories designed an artificial intelligence computer program to play chess in 1959. The programs are now so complex they can beat Grand Masters.

1959	Dr Richard Feynman introduces the idea of manufacturing at the atomic level
2030	Nanomachines able to travel through the human body collecting raw materials and atoms, create new micro-machines

Left
Micromechanics manufactures scientific components on a tiny scale, as this electron micrograph of a selection of micromechanic devices seen next to a fly's leg demonstrates. But even these tiny artefacts may come to seem enormous when nanotechnology is fully able to manufacture devices as small as atoms.

NANOTECHNOLOGY

THE SCIENCE

▶ **Nanotechnology is the science of tomorrow**

Modern computers are made by reducing the design of a microchip thousands of times through a camera, resulting in the smallest components being about 2 mm

across – the size of bacteria.
To nanotechnologists, however, these are gigantic structures. The 'nano' in nanotechnology refers to a nano-meter or a thousand millionth (a billionth) of a metre. Nanotechnology involves moving single atoms and creating molecular machines thousands of times smaller than human cells and the smallest microchip. Building

atomic structures in the past has been a bit like fitting Lego together with boxing gloves on. With nanotechnology, the gloves are off.

▶▶ **What nanotechnology aims to achieve in future**

The aim of nanotechnology is to create new atomic structures consistent with the laws of science, using the smallest and most precise tools ever created. Nanomachines are so tiny that trillions of them would occupy a space equivalent to the size of a pinhead. Because this new science deals with matter on an atomic level, production costs are very low and raw materials go a long way. Nanotechnology also aims to develop tiny devices that can reproduce on site. Many believe that nanotechnology will replace current manufacturing technology.

▶▶ **Nanotechnology could mean a cleaner environment**

Nanotechnology is also good for the environment, as clean and productive nanomachine manufacturing simply involves rearranging a variety of atoms and molecules. In this way, fewer natural

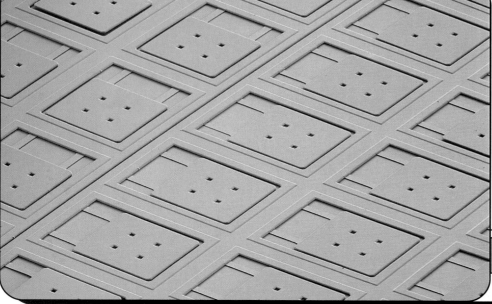

Left
This micrograph shows a series of minute pivoting flaps, designed to disrupt airflow over a surface. One possible role for them is on aircraft, replacing the huge flaps currently in use, to manage the airflow over the wings much more efficiently.

resources are used and waste is nothing more than a few leftover molecules. The predictions are that nanotechnology will be able to create cheap and efficient solar cells, ending the need for power stations.

APPLICATIONS

▶▶ The rise of the truly supercomputer

Nanotechnology will launch a new era of computational capacity, where a personal computer could have as many as a trillion transistors with the current CPU's (Central Processing Unit) power in each transistor. One observer says that the future of computing is having a "supercomputer behind every pixel on your screen". The speed of nanomachines could be in the region of a billion cycles per second, making machines much more productive. Also, nanotechnology will probably lead to much cheaper computers than those produced by conventional technology.

▶ Electronic devices await nano-revolution

Linked nanotubes, microscopic tubes usually made up of C60 (60 carbon molecules), nitrogen and boron, could be used in a nanocomputer system in a way similar to the neuron links in human brains. Special C60 tips for scanning probe microscopes (SPM) which would be used to engrave features onto a silicon surface are being developed by NASA. Called nanotube lithography, it will be used to create minute semiconductors which will revolutionize the electronics market. Scientists are also looking at ways to use synthesized DNA/enzyme techniques and diamonds for storing data.

▶ Ultra-light space vehicles and lifts into the cosmos

NASA is investigating creating light launch (single-stage-to-orbit) vehicles from carbon nanotubes which have a structural strength comparable to diamond. Scientists at NASA are also looking into building a space elevator which would feature a 70,000-km (43,497-mile) long cable extending from Earth up into space. It would need to be built from extremely strong materials, and once again carbon nanotubes could come to the rescue. To improve the safety of the trip, researchers envision 'active materials', to detect and repair flaws in the cable.

NANOMEDICINE

▶▶ Disease may be stopped in its tracks

Nanomedicine is a new science which aims to produce tiny internal robots to check on our bodies, looking for viruses and bacteria and destroying them on site. Others could scan our cells for degenerative changes and replace damaged components. This technology may become a reality by 2030.

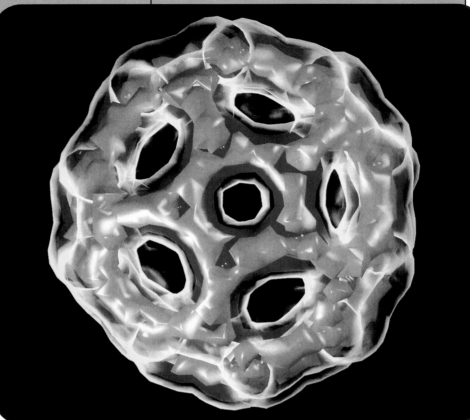

Above
This supercomputer simulation shows the electron distribution in a single molecule of C60. The colours gold, purple and pink denote areas of increased electron density, while the rings represent the molecule's atomic structure.

⏸ Minute machines could blast through blood clots

How do you open up clogged arteries? The same way as you clear blocked drains – by sending in an excavator. A tiny machine, small enough to float through blood vessels, is being developed in the US. Guided by sensors, the nano-surgical machine finds its way to the source of the problem and blasts away areas of blood clot and disease with a laser.

▶▶ Stretching arteries back to shape with mini-modules

The design of a tiny nanotechnology module is much like the design of a space-craft. Both are self-contained and operate in alien environments. Heart surgeons hope to perfect a tiny craft that could cruise through the body, easing collapsed blood-vessels back into shape. An inflatable collar around the middle would be filled with pressurized fluid, expanding collapsed blood-vessels back to their proper diameter.

▶ Machines that are able to replicate themselves

Nanotechnology modules would be made of familiar atoms – including oxygen and carbon, silicon and iron, which are all abundant in the human body. Scientists plan to make nanotechnology devices that could reproduce themselves where necessary. By collecting raw materials as they travel through the body, they could

create new micro-machines as they go. One day, these tiny machines will patrol our bodies, monitoring our vital systems and checking for disease. This type of technology is not too dissimilar from that envisaged by the 1966 film *Fantastic Voyage*, although these modules would not be crewed by miniaturized scientists.

♻ Back to the future

Eric Drexler:

MIT graduate K Eric Drexler is the leading proponent of nanotechnology, following where physicist Dr Richard Feynman left off in his 1959 lecture which introduced the basic idea of manufacturing on an atomic level. Drexler's book *Engines of Creation* (1986) proposes the development of programmable molecular assemblers and replicators and explores the idea of nanomachines travelling around the body as a form of medicine. Drexler, who currently heads the non-profit organization, The Foresight Institute in California, USA, stresses the difference between nanotechnology, which is still mainly theory, and microtechnology. Where nanotechnology involves manufacturing molecular machines from the bottom up, atom by atom, microtechnology is a top-down process involving making devices smaller and smaller.
@ artificial life p152

| 1924 | First frozen food company founded by Clarence Birdseye |
| 2050 | First cyrogenically preserved 'body' is brought back to life |

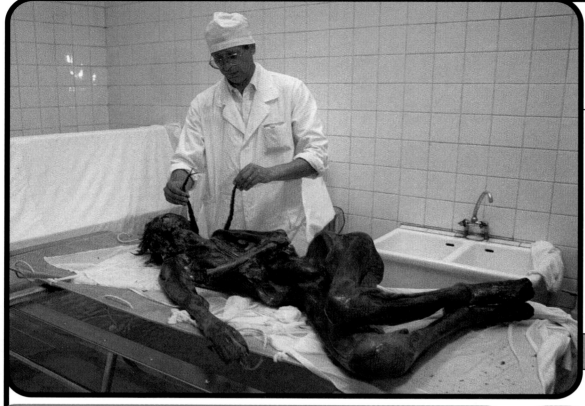

Left
A 2,500-year-old mummified man was discovered in the Altai Mountains of Siberia, more than 2 m (7 ft) below the permafrost. His internal organs had been removed and his skin, muscles and hair were in good condition – archaeologists could even make out a tattoo of a deer on his right shoulder.

CRYOGENICS

PRESERVATION

While living microbial cells can be stored at -70°C (-94°F) for years, even at this temperature metabolic activity is only slowed down. Life does not come to a complete standstill until -130°C (-202°F), below which temperature cultures can apparently be stored and preserved for a thousand years. Cryogenic specimens are best stored in liquid nitrogen containers, which maintain a steady temperature of -196°C (-321°F).

▶ Bodies await technology to bring them back to life

People are signing up to have their bodies frozen after death, in the hope that future generations will devise the technology to resuscitate them. As soon as a person is pronounced medically dead, circulation is restarted artificially to keep the brain supplied with oxygen, and to infuse the blood with an anti-freeze-like substance, which also protects the brain. Gradual cooling leads up to immersion in liquid nitrogen, taking the body temperature down as low as -200°C (-328°F).

⏸ Cryonic preservation does not come cheap

The Alcor Foundation in Arizona, USA, is the largest human cryonics organization, and has pioneered research for over 20 years. Bodies are injected with preservative solutions and stored in liquid nitrogen in cold storage at the Scottsdale laboratory.

The cost of cryonic suspension ranges from $50,000 to $120,000 (£30,000 to £72,000), depending on whether you want head or full body preservation, and there is a student rate of $180 (£108) per year. In the UK, there are no freezing or storing facilities, so bodies are normally flown to the US packed in dry ice.

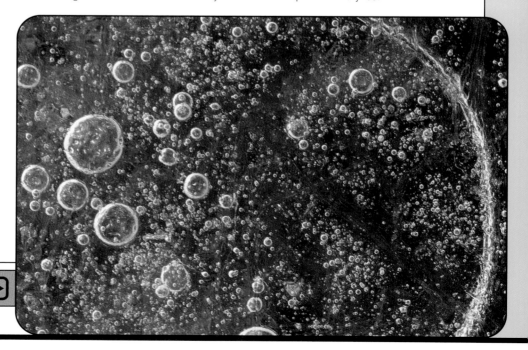

Right
Existing methods of freezing cannot prevent water seeping from the cells and forming crystals, so those waiting to have their bodies frozen must hope for a technological breakthrough in the future. Alternatively, it may be possible to clone new bodies.

Biological specimens preserved for future research

The development of cryogenics has led to a new branch of science called cryobiology, which allows specimens of blood and skin, spermatozoa, heart valves and other biological materials to be preserved at, or below, temperatures obtained using liquid nitrogen. Corneas can be preserved for only a few weeks, and research is under way to cryopreserve cartilage and arteries. Kidneys and hearts cannot survive cryonic freezing.

When the police arrested Dora's Head

On 11 Dec 1987, Dora Kent's head was put into cryonic storage in the US. The coroner ruled it was not certain whether or not she had been recorded as dead, and ordered an autopsy. Nobody would reveal where the head was stored, and police and a SWAT team attempted to recover it. After years of wrangling, charges were dropped. Dora Kent's head still awaits revival, and possibly a body transplant, in the future.

RESUSCITATION

Reviving patients' brains could be a possibility

The Alcor Company in the US has never tried to revive any of its patients frozen in liquid nitrogen, and many wonder if it could ever be done in practice. Alcor research technicians have cooled dogs to within 1°C (33.8°F) above freezing point. They were kept in this 'lifeless' state for four hours and were then revived. The dogs appeared to have sustained no measurable damage.

The drawbacks of cryogenic preservation

One of the main drawbacks of cryogenic preservation is that, when cells are frozen, water seeps out and collects between them. As this water turns to ice, it forms crystals which damage cell membranes. Consequently, it is hoped that by the time brains are defrosted, scientists will be able to clone replica bodies, although it is not certain whether the brains will still be functional or retain any memory.

Nanotechnology could help frozen bodies recover

Scientists predict that minute self-replicating medical robots, small enough to be injected into the blood stream, could be developed to aid cryogenic resuscitation. These nanobots would be designed to follow a programme enabling the repair of all kinds of cell, tissue or organ damage, whether caused by ice crystals, age, or fatal illness, and thus eliminate the need for a new, cloned body. @ *nanotechnolgy p154*

Tests show microbes can cope with being frozen

School students in Ventura County, California, USA, have shown that bacteria preserved by freezing seem to adapt to sub-zero conditions. Cultures that were frozen were sampled at intervals and grown on petri dishes where the colonies were measured. It was discovered that, although the unfrozen bacteria grew the best, samples that had been frozen for a long time grew better than the stored samples that has been frozen for a short time.

Anti-freeze used to help mammals survive the chill

Experiments in cryogenics have now shown that vertebrates can survive freezing if less than 60% of their body water is turned to ice, although a lower upper limit of 50% is considered safer. To achieve this, 35% of the body's tissue water must be replaced with a non-freezing liquid – glycerol and propanediol have shown the greatest promise so far.

Hextend technique enables long-distance space travel

In the US, Californian company Biotime has successfully revived near-frozen baboons using a revolutionary plasma replacement fluid called Hextend, which prevents bodily deterioration. The baboons were cooled to 1°C (33.8°F), and they were injected with Hextend as the blood was drained from their bodies. Scientists predict that this could be used in humans to delay ageing, postpone the treatment of diseases which are currently incurable, and avoid blood loss during complex surgery. In the future, this suspended animation technique could also be used to send astronauts on space missions many light years away. @ *longevity p116*

RESEARCH

Cryosurgery techniques aid doctors in tumour treatment

New freezing techniques can now help the living. Doctors have successfully treated colon cancer, and researchers are investigating the technology's suitability for treating tumours in other organs. Cryotherapy has successfully been used to destroy surface tumours and can also be used on internal organs. Doctors are developing cryotherapy for use with key-hole surgery, introducing liquid nitrogen to the tumour at -196°C (-321°F) on the tip of a thin probe. @ *equipment p104*

Cryogenics used to refine crystalline structure of steel

A company called Cryo-Tech, based in Michigan, USA, uses a dry cryogenic

Above
Advances in cryogenics have benefited the medical profession. Cryosurgery is being used to control pain and bleeding, and has proved to be an effective and relatively inexpensive way of treating malignant tumours, destroying them by superfreezing.

process to treat a variety of industrial steel components, from lathe tools to moulds, for the rubber and plastics industry. They claim this improves the product's durability. The material is gradually exposed to temperatures as low as -195.5°C (-320°F) which establishes a more uniform chemical microstructure. Research has shown that other products including aluminium baseball bats, skate blades, gun barrels and golf club heads have been similarly enhanced by cryogenic treatment.

Back to the future

Frozen food

Between 1912 and 1915, Clarence Birdseye, an American naturalist and fur trader, observed Indians fishing in sub-zero temperatures. He noticed that the frozen fish were fresh enough to eat when thawed. In 1924, he set up a company in Massachusetts, USA, to produce quickly frozen food. He later sold the company, which still retains the name 'Birds Eye'.

Ice

Both the Romans and the Greeks were known to have gathered ice and snow in the winter and stored it in pits covered with straw. As recently as the 19th century, ice was still preserved in the same way: natural ice was shipped all the way to England from the US, where it had to be cut from frozen rivers in the winter and stored before being exported across the Atlantic.

| 1971 | Redifon Ltd. manufactures flight simulators with computer graphic displays |
| 1989 | VR pioneer Jaron Lanier designs the first virtual reality head-mounted goggles |

Left
The traffic jams of the future will all be virtual ones, as this demonstration of German car-maker Opel's driving simulator indicates at the 1997 Tokyo Motor Show. The head-mounted display produces audio and visual stimulation, and the seats vibrate as the 'car' changes gear or encounters obstacles.

VIRTUAL REALITY

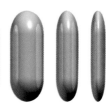

ENTERTAINMENT

From virtual vision to the sensation of touch

SensAble Technologies of Cambridge, Massachusetts, USA, is developing a device that will create the sensation of touch in a virtual environment. The unit, called the Phantom, looks somewhat like a desk lamp with a thimble for the user's finger. Using what is called force-feedback technology you feel as though you are actually touching and manipulating objects.

Kids combat hospital isolation through Starbright

Starbright World is a fully navigable virtual reality (VR) playspace on a broadband network that links seriously ill children from their hospital beds across the US. An 18-month trial linking seven hospitals showed that a virtual playground gives children kept in isolated hospital conditions the chance to recapture the joy of being a kid. Young patients can go on-line, meet their peers as cartoon-like avatars, and chat and have fun. The system seems to help lessen children's pain and loneliness, and improves their self esteem. From this year, it is being set-up in an extra 100 hospitals, with expanded activities and content (http://www.starbright.org/).

The silicon-safe way to get inside a tornado

Researchers at the University of Illinois, USA, are using VR technology to simulate the dynamics of violent storms. The system under development, the Cave Automatic Virtual Environment (CAVE), could help scientists predict which storms will produce tornadoes by studying them from the inside. Users step into a white-screened cave onto which animated images are projected, and wearing a simple headset and wielding a control wand, they experience the evolution of a 3-D tempest. Robert Wilhelmson, an atmospheric scientist who helped develop the system, claims that although the

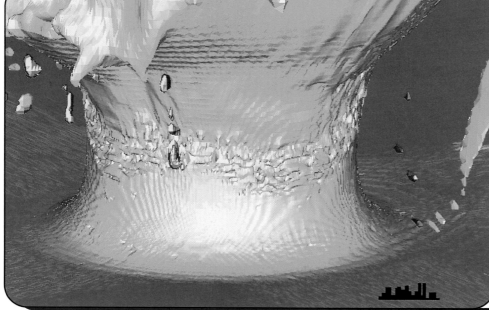

Left
A simulated moment of impact as a comet hits Earth. The US-based experiment estimated that the comet's impact would equal more than ten times the power of all Earth's nuclear weapons — and that such impacts are a statistical certainty.

technology is in its infancy, it will be able to offer a completely immersive virtual experience by 2002. @ climate p122

Digital models and world-wide flights in under an hour

Supercomputers are being used for aerodynamic modelling at NASA's Ames Research Centre in California, USA, where virtual wind tunnels are helping design the next generation space shuttle, the X34, to be in use by 2005. The digital models can indicate features such as surface pressure on the craft and airflow in the extreme conditions of outer space. The research could also lead to the development of spaceplanes able to fly at Mach 25, which would mean an hour-long trip from London to Sydney. @ spacecraft p144

Counteracting height anxiety in the real world

People whose lives are severely restricted by fear of heights – or acrophobia – could find help through VR. Researchers at the Graphics, Visualization and Usability Center at Georgia's Institute of Technology in the US have developed VR 3-D simulations for sufferers which enables them, using head-mounted displays and electromagnetic hand sensors, to experience ascending 49 storeys in a glass elevator, standing on a bridge 24 m (80 ft) above water or looking over a balcony 20 floors up. This development could open up the technology to a wide variety of therapeutic uses.

SCIENTIFIC STUDY

Visualizing a comet's impact on the Earth

A supercomputer at Scandia National Laboratories in the US has created a 3-D simulation of the effect of a massive comet hitting the Earth. An Intel Teraflop computer took 48 hours to perform the complex calculations. If a comet weighing one billion tonnes, 1 km (2/3 of a mile) in diameter and travelling at 60 km per second (37 miles per second) entered the Earth's atmosphere at a 45° angle, the simulation showed that the impact (equivalent to 300 gigatons of TNT) would throw enough debris into the atmosphere to seriously affect Earth's climate. The probability of a celestial body hitting the Earth is about one in 300,000.

Nuclear weapons research moves into simulation

If the US Senate ratifies a Comprehensive Test Ban Treaty, nuclear weapons may never be detonated for test purposes again. The only way countries will know if their existing weapons are still effective, and for new nuclear weapons to be tried, will be through virtual testing. The US Department of Energy is proposing to set up "a science-based stockpile stewardship", where information on weapons and experimental data from explosions is fed into a computer which then draws up highly detailed 3-D simulations. @ warfare p68

Training doctors using virtual reality programs

Virtual Reality technology is helping to improve doctors' understanding of a variety of conditions, surgery techniques and the effectiveness of prosthetics. A Virtual Reality in Medicine and Biology Group at Sheffield University, UK, has already designed a sensor-packed glove which a patient puts on, allowing a 3-D image to be transmitted to a screen. This can help doctors evaluate the degree and nature of a deformity, like rheumatoid arthritis, without causing discomfort or pain to the patient. The glove can also be used to assess the performance of artificial knuckles, which have one of the highest failure rates in prosthetics. A VR training simulator for key-hole surgery on the knee is also under development.

Internet2 to lead virtual conferencing into the future

Live remote conferencing over the Internet's successor, the more powerful Internet2, is set to link up with VR in the next century. The National Tele-Immersion Initiative could allow users in separate locations to interact in a visually-continuous, three-dimensional conference room, which could also include virtual documentation. Heading the project is VR pioneer, Jaron Lanier, of Advanced Network and Services, who designed the first VR head-mounted display in 1989. Aside from company meetings, Tele-Immersion will also have a role to play in doctor-patient consultations. @ communication p24

Deep-sea diving without the 'bends'

The most sophisticated simulation of a marine environment was unveiled at the

Above
One application of VR technology is for military use. In this example the user is able to enter a variety of situations – air-to-air, land-based and land-to-air – and direct troops and equipment around the battlefield. The advantage of this system is that it can recreate real terrain using digital maps.

Lisbon Expo in May 1998. The Virtual Oceanarium allows visitors to explore the photorealistically-created sea life of four of the world's oceans – even allowing them to interact with and feed virtual sharks. Each creature has been designed to resemble and behave like a real animal. Equipped with a headset and a spatial interaction device, visitors could navigate freely around the real-time digital environment, swimming in and out of schools of fish and avoiding angry sharks, while natural underwater sounds created a suitably aquatic mood.

Back to the future

Up, up and away

In the 1930s, inventor Edwin Link built a carnival ride from a model of an aeroplane cockpit fixed to a rotating platform, allowing users to pretend they were flying a real plane. The ride evolved into the flight simulator.

In the realm of the senses

The Sensorama was a big-screen simulator designed by Morton Heilig in 1956 that used sights, sounds, movement and even smells to take 'passengers' on motorbike rides or trips through Brooklyn's city streets.

Virtual pollution

In 1990, the US-based National Center for Supercomputing Applications (NCSA) designed an award-winning VR representation of smog descending on Los Angeles, USA, which helped influence the implementation of air pollution legislation in California.

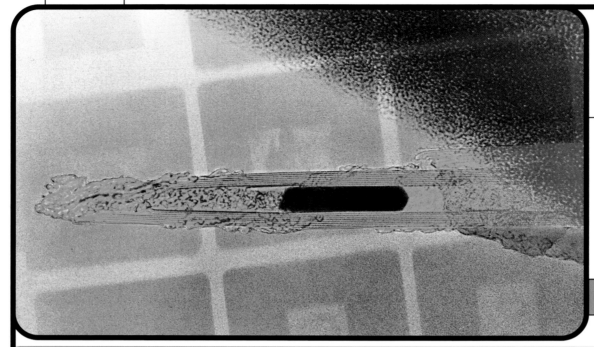

Left
This nanomagnet is a single crystal of nickel inside a nanotube, which is made of sheets of carbon atoms arranged hexagonally and wrapped around each other to form a cylinder with a hollow core up to 15 nanometres wide. Nanotubes could be used as molecular-scale wires for microscopic circuits.

MATERIALS SCIENCE

NEW DESIGNS

▶ **Versatile micro-tubes are as strong as steel**

Nanotubes are tiny elongated molecules only a few atoms in diameter. They are formed by condensing carbon vapour into a sheet one atom thick and rolling it up. If the seams of the tube line up, the tube can conduct electricity as well as any metal, and, if not, it acts as a semiconductor. As strong as steel, the tubes could serve as the basis for networks of nanocomputers capable of performing complex tasks and reconfiguring themselves to improve their own efficiency.

▶▶ **Gold clusters lead the way to miniature machines**

Silicon chips cannot get any smaller using current manufacturing processes. If they did, they would be unable to conduct current without overheating or breaking. Now US scientists have succeeded in constructing chips molecule by molecule using gold. These stay cool by allowing electrons to 'hop' one at a time between clusters of gold molecules. This is called a 'linked cluster network' and paves the way for the construction of nanoscale machines.
@ *nanotechnology p154*

▶▶ **Faster flight with new superlight insulator**

Planes will fly further and faster in the future thanks to a radical new superlight insulation material made from sand. The new material,

aerogel, is the result of NASA-funded research. It is produced by heating pure sand (silicon dioxide) with liquid carbon dioxide in a vacuum at very high pressure. The carbon dioxide is then removed, leaving a pliable pure silicone material, able to withstand enormous temperatures and almost as light as air.

⏸ **Glasses frames that remember their shape**

You've just sat on your glasses and now they are bending back into shape before your very eyes. The frames of these glasses are made from a shape memory alloy which has two distinct molecular structures at different temperatures. When manufactured, the materials can be programmed with a shape which they will resume if deformed.

▶ **Precision vehicle engineering by laser**

Prototype parts can be built in a fraction of the usual time by using powerful lasers to guide and melt metal powder. UK and German scientific researchers are 'growing' metal components by directing these laser-guided jets of molten metal onto a computer driven baseplate. They believe the new supremely precise technology will allow them to double the power of a car engine if it is modified with laser generated parts.

Right
The B-2 Stealth Bomber is the world's most advanced aircraft. This manned bomber features revolutionary aerospace technologies and low-observable characteristics such as radar-evasion.

▶▶ Diamond simulation heralds new age in space travel

Cheap space travel may one day become reality thanks to new composite materials containing diamond fibres. Artificial diamonds have been made for several years but scientists could not align the molecules in any particular way. Recent advances in nanotechnology have enabled researchers to build artificial polycrystalline diamond structures at molecular level, which can be made into composite materials.

▶ Recyclable submarines made from plastic composites

Composite materials are very strong and light, but expensive, and are usually made by embedding them in a matrix of thermoset polymers. Now, thermoplastic polymers are being used. They are recyclable and can be manufactured more quickly. The US Navy hopes to use thermoplastic composites to make submersible craft but the first use will be in the soles of running shoes – where it improves the wearer's ability to turn quickly.

▮▮ New phase-change gear keeps hikers cool

Phase change occurs in melting ice and most other materials, and it is now being harnessed to keep walkers cool. Outcast, a fabric originally developed for NASA, contains millions of microscopic phase change spheres. When they reach 35°C (95°F), the most comfortable temperature for walkers, they melt, keeping the wearer cool by locking up any excess heat created.

▶ New plastic keeps your cola fizzy for longer

A group of US researchers have found what they believe is the answer to dull, flat, lifeless cola: liquid crystalline polymers. Bottles made from these new plastics have high barrier properties, so the gas won't seep out and that vital slug of cola will stay fizzy after all. It also keeps external contaminants out, preventing bad tastes from developing and extending the shelf life.

▶ Bathrooms that clean themselves under UV light

At last – the self-cleaning toilet. A Japanese company, Toto, has invented a coating for tiles, toilets and washbasins that becomes active under ultraviolet light. Used under flourescent light, it kills over 99 per cent of some bacteria in an hour. The active ingredient in the coating is titanium dioxide and the light-prompting reaction is called photocatalysis. @ houses p88

HEALTH AND SAFETY

▶▶ Soldiers could be safer in smart suits

Scientists promise that there is no danger of the soldier of the future becoming

cannon fodder when clothed in his 'intelligent uniform'. A US Army research programme is proposing new fabrics with chameleon-like qualities: uniforms made from the fabric will sense ambient temperature changes and change camouflage colour accordingly. Coatings are also being developed that could be able to absorb or neutralize chemical and biological warfare agents. These superlight materials could also be bullet proof and fire resistant. @ fashion p14

▮▮ New life for sensitive teeth with glass compounds

US dental researchers have found a solution to sensitive teeth in the form of a substance called Bioglass, a non-toxic glass compound which bonds chemically with the tooth when brushed on. The bond between the Bioglass and the tooth has proved to be extremely strong and stable. Repeated use will gradually build up a shield preventing pain from the sensitive tooth. An estimated 40 million stateside sufferers can now drink hot coffee after ice cream without discomfort.

▶▶ Radical new material makes life safer for bodyguards

Stretch an elastic band between your hands and it will get thinner and thinner. Stretch a strip of auxetic material and it will actually get fatter – the more you pull it the fatter it will become. Not only that, but if it is struck, auxetic grows thicker at the point of impact. This unexpected response is caused by arranging the molecules in patterns that open outwards when pulled, rather like an umbrella, increasing the width as well as the length of the material. Proposed applications for auxetic range from synthetic arteries to bullet-proof clothing and car bumpers.

Above
A shape memory metal alloy has been developed by Memory Corporation, Connecticut, USA, for golf clubs. The metallurgical structure of the club changes as it hits the ball, keeping the ball on the club-face longer, and giving more control and spin.

▮▮ Road-running safety with electric trainers

Piezoelectrics are very useful compounds that generate electrical currents when put under mechanical stress. They are used by sportswear manufacturers who embed them in trainers to power LEDs (light-emitting diodes) in the sole, and can be used to turn vibration in snowboards into harmless heat. In reverse, battery-powered piezoelectrics move to counter vibrations in mountain-bike shock absorbers.

♻ Back to the future

Light-sensitive glass

In 1937, R. H. Dalton of the Corning Glass Works, USA, found that if glass is exposed to ultra-violet radiation while it is still cold, the colour it eventually acquires is darker. This was the basis for the development of light-sensitive glass.

Nylon

Nylon was first launched in 1938 after Dr Wallace Carothers and Du Pont had spent $27 million (£16 million) over 13 years researching methods to mass-produce it. At first, it was twice as expensive as silk, but it was also twice as durable.

Dayglo colours

In 1933, Joe and Bob Switzer developed fluorescent inks at their father's drugstore in Los Angeles, California, USA, with the help of chemist Dick Ward. They founded a lithography company on the success of their discovery.

1973	Californian skateboarder Frank Nasworthy invents urethane plastic wheels for use on skateboards
2020	Sports stars use computer chips to measure the efficiency of their equipment

Left
Speed skating is not just about trying to go very fast without slipping over. Manufacturers and skaters are constantly looking at new ways to shave those vital hundredths-of-a-second off the records – although the latest innovation, skates hinged at the toe end, was first patented back in 1894.

SPORTS SCIENCE

PERFORMANCE

▶ Heartbeat machine gives archers a straighter shot

The sporting world's most skilled archers have developed a shooting technique that enables them to release their arrows between heartbeats, because the slight movement caused by their pulse is amplified by the bow and can mean the difference between hitting a bull's eye or an outer. To bring this subtle skill to spectators' attention, US scientist Gene Greneker has invented a machine that can detect human heartbeats from 100 m (333 ft) away and display the signal on a TV screen.

▶ The perfect swing predicted by a computer

Rolls-Royce aeroengine professor Alan Turner has used computer modelling to find the perfect golf swing. For the first time, he has successfully modelled the combined forces in the shoulder, arm, wrist and hand. Curiously, the ideal swing, according to the computer, is identical to that used by legendary US golfer, Ben Hogan.

▶ Climb a mountain without being far from the ground

The sport of climbing was revolutionized by indoor artificial walls. Now, new walls have been developed that are automatically adjusting structures, with faces mounted on moveable frames that allow the wall's angle to be moved from a shallow slab to a fierce roof. Some walls are continuous belts so that, no matter how high you climb, you are never more than 1m (3 ft) from the floor.

⏸ Cut down your paintball hits with this new device

Paintball enthusiasts have a problem. The most common way of being eliminated is to get splatted on the obtrusive ammunition hopper on top of the gun. A British student,

Left
If you meet this woman in a darkened swimming pool, don't bother trying to outswim her – US swimmer Amy van Dyken won gold at the 1998 World Swimming Championships, 50 m freestyle, wearing Speedo's innovative new swimming cap.

Simon Stevens, has cunningly invented a hopper that sits beneath the weapon and feeds in ammunition from below. What's more, the mechanism accurately counts how many rounds have been fired and does not jam.

▶ Mini-sensors take games into the high-tech field

Sports people will be able to get instant readouts of how fast their equipment is moving – whether its a racquet, a ball or a javelin – thanks to a tiny acceleration sensor. Built into a silicon chip with a radio signal, the sensor transmits the forces it experiences from inside the equipment to a laptop computer on the edge of the playing area. The computer immediately converts the data into a graph, which it displays on screen, showing the equipment's speed.

▶▶ Wired stadium keeps spectators in the picture

Docklands Stadium in Melbourne, Australia, will give spectators an unprecedented experience when it opens in 1999. Apart from being the only stadium with both a movable roof *and* seating, it has also been constructed so that it can be 'wired'. In the back of each seat there is the space and capacity to house a small screen, so that spectators can watch instant replays and highlights of all the action from the angle of their choice or, at half time, they could switch over and watch other matches being played elsewhere.

Rubber warmers go from racetrack into orbit

Formula One tyres grip the road best when the rubber is heated to between 90°C and 95°C (194°F to 203°F). Any colder and they will slide. Tyres stored in the pits ready for a wheel change are wrapped in special electric blankets to warm them up to the optimum temperature. Now, the same warmers, but bigger, will be used to heat the massive tyres of the space shuttle before routine safety tests.

Nostril dilator for horses increases oxygen flow

If sports people can wear sticking plasters across their noses to keep their nostrils flared and so increase their oxygen flow, then why not racehorses? Because they don't have bridges to their noses to act as fulcrums, that's why. But an equine nostril dilator has now been patented, using a pair of soft rubber inserts that keep the horse's airways wide open. A winner by a nose.

MATERIALS

Smart fabric changes shape with temperature

Fabrics that expand and contract according to temperature changes could become a reality following research being conducted on high performance materials. Whether or not this type of fabric would make it into the mass market is debatable, but it is something sporting stars would welcome.

Shield protects horses from tendon injuries

Every year the US racing industry loses around $500 million (£312 million) through horses injuring their front fetlock tendons. Now, Irish designer Andrew Daly has invented a carbon fibre shield that protects the fetlock from impact injuries (caused by hitting the ground hard) and strike injuries (when the rear hoof kicks the front fetlock). The 270 g device costs £250 a pair.

Titanium racquets cut weight with improved strength

Titanium is one of the lightest, strongest and most expensive metals ever used. It has been used in cycle components for a long time but has only just found its way into tennis racquets. In 1997, the Austrian manufacturer Head successfully built titanium strands into carbon fibre composite frames, increasing strength but reducing weight. Others are following but none has yet beaten Head's unstrung minimum weight of 230 g.

Innovative easy-bat just isn't cricket

A carbon fibre composite cricket bat would allow every amateur to hit sixes at will, according to computer simulations at Newcastle University, UK. The problem with traditional willow is that it absorbs some of the ball's energy when the two collide. Carbon fibre reinforced plastic, however, is very stiff and virtually all the energy is transmitted to the ball, sending it flying. Trouble is, it's just not cricket.

NEW GEAR

Century-old design still tops for skaters

Speed skating records have tumbled since Dutch manufacturer Viking perfected the slap skate. The blade stays on the ice longer than a conventional skate because it is hinged at the toe end. This gives the skater a vital amount of extra time to exert more push and go faster before the blade springs back into position. However, the idea is not new: it was patented in 1894.

Robo-Leg puts World Cup ball to the test

To prove that it was the best product available, the World Cup soccer ball was subjected to repeated tests by a robotic leg. From 30 m (99 ft), Adidas's Robo-Leg can kick a soccer ball to land within a 1 m (3 ft) circle every 20 seconds, all day and all night. It has articulated joints and computer-braked spring mechanisms, so it can mimic every kind of human shot. The single mechanical leg cost £150,000.

Swedish power boat catches up with catamaran

Swedish designer Ocke Mannerfelt revolutionized power boat racing when he

Above
The Slam Man is a punch bag with a human face. Unveiled at the Atalanta Super Show, USA, in early 1998, it is one of a range of new interactive sports equipment designed to keep users interested in exercising at home.

came up with a single hull craft that could go as fast as a catamaran. He discovered that, if he added a set of specially-designed wings to the stern of the boat, they could trap a cushion of air underneath and so rise out of the water, thus causing less friction and more speed. His new design has left a lasting impression: his boats have won world championships and a new class of racing has been created for them.

Back to the future

Tennis racquets

In 1980, Dunlop Sports Co. Ltd in Yorkshire, UK, became the first company to manufacture injection-moulded carbon-fibre tennis racquets. They quickly replaced the traditional wooden racquet since they were much lighter, stronger and more powerful.

Skateboard wheels

In 1973, a Californian skateboard enthusiast Frank Nasworthy developed urethane plastic wheels for use on skateboards. The result meant a smoother, faster ride, indirectly leading to the mid-1970s skateboard craze.

Grass skis

In 1969, a knitting-machine manufacturer, Kurt Kaiser, became the first person to make grass skis. He then became the moving force behind a new sport: running down grassy slopes on skate-like 'caterpillar-track' skis.

Left
Fractals were once all the rage among Chaos theorists, but even though few people mention Chaos theory these days, its general principles still influence many physicists. Fractals clearly demonstrate the idea of the inherent order underlying chaotic events – a key concept for some theoretical scientists.

NEW THEORIES

UNIFICATION THEORIES

In search for the principle binding the Universe together

Physicist Gene Stanley is convinced that there is one law which could help advance the scientific understanding of a wide range of fields, from traffic jams to earthquakes, showing how different and complex systems can behave similarly. Crucial to the principle of universality is the idea of a system in a critical state – for example, when a magnet is heated to 770°C (1,418°F), the critical point between magnetic and non-magnetic states, its microscopic domains arrange themselves in mathematically identical patterns. These self-similar patterns are the defining characteristics of a critical state and can be found in water poised between a liquid and gaseous state as well as in the dynamics of extinction. In layman's terms, the theory proves the old adage that the more things change, the more they stay the same. In this argument, order spreads across a system, regardless of the precise physical elements that make it up. What is important are the connections between the elements, rather than the number of elements themselves – thus a number of different systems will all behave identically at the critical point.

Finding the meaning of life, the universe and everything

Science writer Ian Stewart believes that looking for a Theory of Everything to unite the four forces of nature (gravitational, magnetic, strong and weak forces) is misguided, as such a unification may not exist in nature. This, he says, is an example of asking the wrong question in the first place. There are, after all, things that science will probably never be able to explain, such as the complex process of protein folding. One particular human protein, cytochrome c, takes just one second to fold, but trying to work out how it does this requires complicated calculations using a computer model which will take an outrageous 10^{127} years on a supercomputer. Maybe just knowing there are limits to scientific study will help enhance our understanding within those boundaries.

Where the quantum meets the classical

Experimentalists are investigating the changeover between quantum and classical realms of physics, which is where much of the cutting-edge work in

theoretical physics is being done. According to quantum physics, particles can exist in several places at once (as shown by Erwin

Right
Even in chaotic events, such as avalanches, there may be a very ordered process at work – and it is this underlying process that some physicists feel may provide the as-yet elusive answer to what it is that holds the Universe together.

Schrödinger in 1935 with his theoretical cat-and-poison-in-a-box experiment), and can jump from point to point and appear to communicate with each other at speeds faster than light – even though in our everyday world this rarely applies to large objects like pianos or cats. David Pritchard of MIT and other researchers have created minute versions of Schrödinger's cats in the form of electrons and atoms made to reside in two places at the same time, as well as an electromagnetic field which can vibrate in two different ways simultaneously. In quantum-speak, this indefinite state is called superposition – Schrödinger's cat is both dead and alive at the same moment. Wojciech Zurek of Los Alamos National Laboratory, USA, advocates the theory of decoherence. This states that environment affects quantum coherence. Thus, larger objects, such as cats, cannot enter a superposition because the particles making up the cat influence other systems within the environment, making it impossible for coherence to exist.

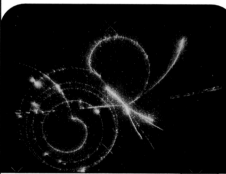

Above
This illustration shows a chain of electrons in decay as they are attacked by antiprotons. The circular pattern indicates that the electrons decay in an ordered fashion and that there is, therefore, a form of control at work in even the most chaotic and disorderly events.

▶ Putting Einstein's theory before taking a quantum leap

Many theorists hope one day to come up with one theory, one magic equation, that encompasses both quantum physics and the theory of relativity and the four known forces of nature. One physicist, Mark Hadley of the University of Warwick, UK, has presented a theory of the Universe which claims that quantum theory is actually a consequence of the hitherto incompatible classical theory of general relativity. While in classical theory objects behave in distinct and definite ways, in quantum theory, subatomic particles can be in more than one place simultaneously. Where Einstein saw gravity as a warped region of space and time, Hadley's theory goes even further, claiming that a subatomic particle is a distorted region of space and time that bends back on itself like a loop. This time and space loop means that particles interact with each other in the past and future, enabling general relativity to reproduce quantum effects. Hadley's radical theory overturns the traditional notion of cause followed by effect, and he is currently working on how to produce a particle-like solution for general relativity.

PUZZLES

▶ Are we really victims of Murphy's Law?

Robert A.J. Matthews has investigated a number of manifestations of Murphy's Law (if something can go wrong it will), including why toast always falls butter-side down, why it hardly ever rains when you take an umbrella with you and the proliferation of odd socks at the bottom of your drawer. He has found, using probability theory, that these annoying events do have a basis in fact. For example, Matthews claims that toast falls butter-side down because the Universe is designed that way. The average height of man has determined most kitchen tables and worksurfaces are built at a certain height. If the toast were to fall from an extremely high table, then it would probably have more of a chance of landing butter-side up. But because toast normally falls from a height of around 1 to 2 m (3 to 6 ft) above the ground, it does not have the opportunity of turning around 360° as a result of the force of gravity and surface friction working on it.

▶ We may exist in one of many parallel universes

While in our everyday lives light appears to travel in a straight line, on closer inspection – shining a torch through a narrow slit, for instance – it is clear that light does in fact bend. This fact has led quantum physicists like David Deutsch of Oxford University, UK, to propose that this may point to the existence of parallel universes. Deutsch claims that light particles (photons) are being deflected by other, invisible, particles which behave exactly like their visible counterparts. This extends quantum theory – which predicts that for each neutron and electron there are corresponding shadow particles – to light. This world of shadow particles could be called a parallel universe which has some effect on the tangible universe. For Deutsch, physical reality is a place where many universes exist at the same time – meaning that there could be numerous versions of 'you' currently wandering around the multiverse.
@ time travel p174

⏸ Mathematical puzzle generates profound interest

In the interests of stimulating an interest in mathematics, millionaire Texan Andrew Beal offered a reward of $50,000 (£31,250) in Nov 1997 to anyone who could solve a maths problem he had formulated. With thousands of entries pouring in, the 'Beal Problem' is a successor to the 17th century's 'Fermat's Last Theorem', set by the French mathematician Pierre de Fermat,

Above
In 1935, the physicist Erwin Schrödinger developed the theory that atoms can exist in two places at the same time and illustrated his argument by claiming that a cat drinking poison could be dead and not dead simultaneously.

which was finally solved in 1994 by Andrew Wiles. Beal's equation looks like this: $x^m + y^n = z^l$, where six whole number solutions to the equation must be found with x, y and z having no common factor. It remains to be seen if the solution will be found by a computer or a combination between humans and computer programs. In the event of no solution, Beal will reward the person who can provide mathematical proof that no solution exists.

♻ Back to the future

The Big Bang

UK astronomer Fred Hoyle first coined the term 'Big Bang' to describe a theory of creation that argued that all matter, space and time in the Universe was created in a gigantic explosive release of energy 15 billion years ago. The theory claims that everything in the Universe – the planets, stars, suns, galaxies and black holes – was originally compressed into a single atom of unimaginable density, called a singularity, that for some reason erupted into activity, creating billions of planets and stars.

Einstein explains it all

In 1905, to the acclaim of his peers, the Swiss-German physicist Albert Einstein published his *Special Theory of Relativity*, which explained the Universe as a constantly expanding entity. Ninety years on, his ideas still form the cornerstone of modern physics.

SCIENCE FICTION

FUTURESCOPE

- **Science fiction can often anticipate and predict future developments** in science and technology. Genetic engineering, autonomous aircraft technology, nanotechnology, intelligent robots and virtual battlefields were previously the stuff of science fiction, but all of them are now existing scientific disciplines. Much of what is being written about today – vacuum energy, synthetic foods, 38,000-km high skyscrapers, brain-memory audio-visual discs – may well become reality tomorrow.

- **In television, superheroes have always had their own particular gadgets** with which to confound their enemies. Batman used to be able to cut out the electrics of his enemy's cars using one of his weapons and Dr "Bones" McCoy in *Star Trek* used his tricorder to analyse a patient's vital signs. Today, the US police have developed a device that uses electromagnetics to stop cars and the US Army has developed something similar to the tricorder. Spacecraft designs, even in model form, were first seen in TV adventures: the Space Shuttle was prefigured by *Thunderbird 3* from *Thunderbirds*.

- **Films have introduced plenty of ideas for the first time:** 'replicants' in *Blade Runner*, cyborgs in *Terminator* and space tourism in *The Fifth Element*. Although not yet fully developed, robotic and artificial intelligence systems are areas of rapid growth and by the end of the next century there should be the technologies for prostheses and exoskeletons to allow humans to become at least part machine. Certainly, computers that can think for themselves, similar to *HAL* in *2001: A Space Odyssey*, may one day be available in our high street shops.

- **New divisions between people may be created by technology such as the Internet.** Some people will not have access to it. For others, the problem will be too much information, available via the Net, television and other media, leading to 'analysis paralysis' and the inability to make decisions. Genetic mapping also might eventually lead to discrimination on the basis of genes, the patenting of genes and the cloning of humans. The next hundred years will offer much, but at the same time we should all be aware of the negative potential of much of this new science.

CULT TV

FILM

NOVELS & COMICS

TIME TRAVEL

TECHNO UTOPIAS

DYSTOPIAS

TECHNO-BABBLE

BIOPUNK
Like the term cyberpunk, it is a genre of Science Fiction that concerns itself with the world of biological enhancements and globalization.

CYBERSTYLE
General writing style in cyberspace. Features include abbreviations, acronyms, and little attention to grammar.

EXTROPIANS
People looking for ways of prolonging life and using biotechnology on the body.

FUTURE-PROOF
Technology that allegedly cannot become obsolete.

MEATSPACE
The opposite of cyberspace – the real world.

MEME
Carrier of reproduction information for an idea.

S & F
Novels, films and lifestyles that rely on shopping and sex for a large part of their content.

1967	First ever interracial kiss shown on *Star Trek*
1999	The year a lunar-based colony was founded – according to the TV programme

CULT TV

CAMP CLASSICS

▮▮ Batman

The 1966 Batmobile remains the ultimate gadget. Its many gizmos included a Mobile Crime Computer stored in the boot, linked to the main Bat Computer, plus the Bat

Photoscope, which printed out digitized pictures on the dashboard. The Batmobile could also be remotely voice-activated and featured a host of cool weapons, like the Bat ray, which zapped out the electrics on the baddie's car. An electromagnetic device which does just that is now being tested by US police forces.

▮▮ Star Trek

Sadly, *Star Trek* science is far in advance of our own. To beam someone up – vaporizing them and reconstituting them at the other end – would involve processing more data than there are atoms in the universe. Warp speed is also a tricky one, due to the

Left
Batman's belt did more than hold his trunks up. It was packed with gadgets, like the Batrope and the Batshield, designed to get the Caped Crusader out of any tricky situation.

impossibility of exceeding the speed of light. But Trekkies can take heart. The tricorder, which Spock uses for on-the-spot planet analysis, has just hit the shops.

▮▮ Thunderbirds

International Rescue was set up in 2026 by ex-astronaut Jeff Tracy, and manned by his sons (all named after real US astronauts). The five Thunderbird craft all anticipate vehicles invented after the show's 1964 debut. Thunderbird 3 prefigured the space shuttle, while Thunderbird 5, the space station, incorporated satellite technology which has since become ubiquitous.

▮▮ The HitchHiker's Guide to the Galaxy

Douglas Adams's tragi-comic tale of Arthur Dent's deep space meanderings is full of humourous absurdities – and grains of technological possibility. The 'babel fish', a tiny alien which acts as a universal translator when popped into the ear, anticipates current developments in machine translation. One system is available via Altavista's web site (http://altavista.digital.com), performing (occasionally hilarious) on-line translations.

▮▮ The Time Tunnel

Two American scientists are lost "in the infinite corridors of time" during experiments on a top secret time tunnel in this 1967 show. Luckily they have been coated in radiation, so they can be tracked through time, though not brought back home. Their fist-fighting antics at the siege of Troy, the sinking of the *Titanic* and other great disasters happily ignore the complex problems of cause and effect which makes this vision of time travel an impossibility.

MIND BENDERS

▐▐ The X Files

Like all good conspiracy theory-based dramas, the *X-Files* exploits real events. The 'Greys', who, along with the 'Shapeshifters', are an alien race involved in the struggle for world control, are based on actual descriptions given by people who claim to have been abducted by aliens. In addition, the series' defining event is the 1951 Roswell Incident, in which an alien craft is supposed to have crashed in the New Mexico desert – and the evidence covered up by the US government.

Above
Star Trek: the Next Generation has updated the 1960s TV series, taking full advantage of 1990s technology. Now the show includes an almost-human android and a revamped *USS Enterprise* able to zip through space at greater speeds than ever before.

▐▐ The Prisoner

When a government spy tries to resign from the secret service he is kidnapped and held prisoner in a village. Renamed 'number six' he undergoes a series of tests and mind games to make him repent. Although cool, camp and very confusing, *The Prisoner* also addresses serious issues, such as the cold war rumours of government drugs and detention centres, such as the MK-Ultra project, in which the US army experimented with LSD and other mind-altering drugs. It also foresaw current fears about a society based on surveillance and control.

SPACE CADETS

▐▐ Flash Gordon

In the 1930's, Buster Crabbe's Flash Gordon was the Luke Skywalker of his day. The evil Emperor Ming's planet-vaporizing ray foresaw US attempts in the 1980s to

build space weapons in the Star Wars project. Like Ming the Merciless, Ronald Reagan's Star Wars was doomed to fail.

▐▐ Lost in Space

The Space Family Robinson fought some of the fiercest rubber aliens that 1960s special effects technology could throw at them as they careered through space in their gadget-packed spaceship. But at least one of their gizmos, the jetpack, has made its appearance in reality. Powered by rocket fuel, a one-man manoeuvrable jetpack was memorably seen at the opening ceremony of the 1984 LA Olympics in the US.

▐▐ Battlestar Galactica

When the evil Cylon empire attempts to wipe out humanity in a distant galaxy, the survivors set off on a long trek through space to find a mythical planet where they can settle: Earth. While intergalactic travel is not feasible yet, the International Space Station (http://station.nasa.gov) project is well underway, and will provide valuable information on the viability of living in space.

▐▐ Space 1999

Few TV shows caught on like the tale of the Moonbase Alpha, which, along with the Moon itself, is blasted into an unscheduled trip across the galaxy. However, although 1999 is just around the corner, there is no sign of a colony on the moon just yet, and while we have the space shuttle, it's not half as funky as the Eagle ships used by the Alphans. NASA has considered building a Moonbase, but there is little public support for such an expensive project.

Above
The X-Files is a stylish mix of clever conspiracy theorizing and UFO-invasion paranoia. According to the show's protagonists, Mulder and Scully, the aliens are already here, living amongst us and planning to colonize the planet.

▐▐ Babylon 5

The Babylon 5 station, a kind of interstellar UN, is where the five main alien races meet to negotiate a settlement in the aftermath of a major war. The idea of hostile aliens launching an attack on the Earth has always haunted science fiction writers, from HG Wells to the makers of *Independence Day*, but modern scientists are more concerned with the possible dangers presented by alien viral or bacteriological life than attack by fleets of laser-zapping starships.

 Back to the future

Orson Welles

The most controversial science fiction broadcast ever was probably Orson Welles's 1938 radio version of *War of the Worlds*, which caused terrified US citizens to flee their homes and left several dead.

Trek kiss

Star Trek made history in 1967 by screening US TV's first interracial kiss, between Captain Kirk and Lt. Uhura. Although Kirk had already kissed scores of alien women, all had been remarkably humanoid-like – and white.

Sightings

'Real' UFO encounters have always had a strong relationship to science fiction trends. Before the exploration of Mars, the red planet was seen as the aliens' most likely home. Now, planets well outside the solar system are usually cited as possible alien bases.

1926	Fritz Lang releases his vision of a future society with *Metropolis*
2001	The computer HAL on board the spacecraft in the film *2001* starts making its own decisions

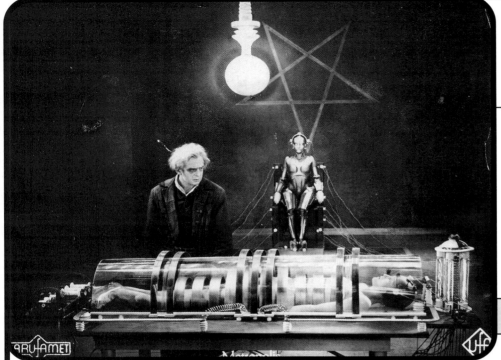

Left
Fritz Lang's *Metropolis* still has the ability to amaze modern audiences with its wonderfully stylized imagery. Unfortunately, the brave new world it predicted looks no nearer now than then, and his vision of a peaceful, society has been labelled as a typical, if visually-stunning, product of the pre-WWII mind.

FILM

FUTURE SHOCK

Metropolis

Fritz Lang's classic film is typical of 1920's hope for the future, where a city of toga-clad citizens commutes by raised roadways and personal rocketships. This optimistic vision of a rational technological tomorrow was largely destroyed by the horrors of WWII and the post-war awareness of the environmental impact of industrial society. Now, Lang's film seems to say more about its own age than about the future.

A Clockwork Orange

Stanley Kubrick's disturbing film about a futuristic society includes scenes in which Alex, violent young gang leader, is 'reconditioned' to curb his antisocial behaviour. He is shown images of sex and violence and stimulated to feel pain and sickness instead of excitement. Scientists have performed animal tests which show that such reconditioning is possible, but the ethical implications of this method of crime control make its introduction unlikely.

Blade Runner

In a run-down future city, Harrison Ford hunts down rogue 'replicants' – androids created to undertake dangerous jobs on Earth's space colonies. To stop them 'evolving', they are built to die after five years. Now, biologists have found a cell mechanism that 'tells' the cell when to die, perhaps a key part of the ageing process.

Strange Days

This tale of a world addicted to replaying its own memories reflects a fantasy common among futurologists. Many, such as BT's Peter Cochrane talk about 'downloading' the contents of their brains onto some kind of storage medium. However, this picture of the way the brain stores and accesses memories is, at best, dubious. The idea that memory is some kind of home video tape makes for a good story, but bad science.

Tron

When a computer game designer gets trapped inside one of his own machines, he has to take part in digital gladiatorial combat in order to find his way out. *Tron* is obviously a pure fantasy, but like *Metropolis* is a fascinating document of its time, 1982. Its wireframe computer

Right
Beneath the 1960s psychedelic effects, Stanley Kubrick's *2001: a Space Odyssey* was a serious attempt to bring to the screen the science-fiction writer Arthur C. Clarke's ideas on how human civilization was created with extraterrestrial help.

graphics are now historical relics, and the film's video game spin-off set a trend for film-based computer games.

▶ THX1138

The 1970 first film from George Lucas, director of *Star Wars*, is a true cult classic. Essentially an updated remake of *1984*, *THX1138* examines the use of computers as a tool for social control. With increasing governmental use of networked databases, surveillance cameras and bio-informatics, computers today have the potential to be used both for liberation and enslavement.

▶ Terminator

Cyborg technology was first proposed in the 1950s as a way of 'augmenting' humans to allow them to travel in space. The advanced technologies which create Arnold Schwarzenegger and his opponent in the *Terminator* films are coming ever closer, as experiments on prosthetics, exoskeletons and artificial intelligence are conducted, leading to ever-more sophisticated developments in robotics. However, the liquid metal cyborg seen in *Terminator 2* is pure Hollywood fantasy. @ *artificial life 152*

Above
The four *Alien* films explore a wide variety of scientific possibilities, including finding alien life on other planets, cryogenics, deep-space travel and advanced robotics. The most recent film, *Alien Resurrection,* deals with human cloning and the cross-transplantation of alien and human cells.

▶ The Fifth Element

The Fifth Element envisions a future of massively overcrowded cities, from which the elite escape to an orbital holiday camp. Space tourism is already being seriously considered by organizations such as the American-based STA (Space Transport Association), while the Association of Autonomous Astronauts (AAA), a global lobbying group, is trying to wrest the control of space away from governments.

SPACE VISIONS

▶ 2001: a Space Odyssey

The story of first contact with an advanced alien civilization, *2001* contains many plausible suggestions about the technology

of the near future. The HAL computer, which takes on a life of its own and begins making its own decisions, is far in advance of the machines which will be available by the real 2001. But, through neural network computers, there are now machines capable of 'thinking' for themselves.

▶ Alien

The *Alien* films' xenomorphs are some of the nastiest extraterrestrials ever seen on screen, yet their biology is based on some Earth creatures, including certain parasitic plants. Another of the films' futuristic pieces of hardware is the exoskeleton Ripley wears in *Aliens*. Similar strength-augmenting devices are currently being developed.

▶ Star Wars

The most exciting and successful SF film of the 1970s is, sadly, only fantasy. The fast-manoeuvring space ships of the rebels and the Imperial Fleet could never exist in real life. Tight turns are impossible in space, as there is no friction to push against. Light sabres, on the other hand, are theoretically possible as laser technology advances.

UNNATURAL ACTS

▶ Soylent Green

New York, USA, in 2022 is a ghetto of oppressed, starving people. Inquisitive cop Charlton Heston starts asking questions about 'soylent green', the synthetic food the authorities feed to the population. Many solutions have been proposed to the problem of starvation, but the most plausible are usually based on soya beans, rather than recycling people, as Heston discovers to his horror in the film.

▶ Demon Seed

This 1977 film is a horrific vision of the possible consequences of computer-

Above
In *The Fifth Element* exotic aliens entertain guests on board a space-based pleasure palace. While feasible, the technology is in its infancy, and real space stations like Russia's MIR bear little resemblance to Hollywood's idealized versions.

controlled living. Scientist's wife Julie Christie is trapped in her home by a psychotic machine, intent on impregnating her with its 'brain child'. While biologically implausible, the film does raise the idea of 'ubiquitous computing', where intelligence is built into every area of human living space, rather than confined to PCs.

▶ Jurassic Park

Steven Spielberg's dinosaur fantasy is a response to contemporary concerns about genetic engineering and the reanimation of dead tissue. Through Jeff Goldblum's chaos mathematician character, the film makes many references to the impossibility of controlling complex natural processes in the way that foolish theme park-owner Richard Attenborough tries to do. @ *genetics p112*

♻ Back to the future

Countdown

The 10...9...8... countdown made famous in US rocket launches was originally used in a German silent science fiction film, *Die Frau im Mond* (*The Woman in the Moon*). There is no logical reason for counting backwards, other than to heighten anticipation.

Strauss in space

The most popular music taken into space by US astronauts is *Also Sprach Zarathustra* by Richard Strauss, a piece of music made famous as the theme from *2001: a Space Odyssey*. John Denver and Roberta Flack tunes also seem popular.

Propaganda

In an attempt to make the 'Star Wars' space defence project palatable to the public, US president Ronald Reagan hired science fiction writers to produce promotional material. However, the end of the cold war after 1989 rendered the project obsolete.

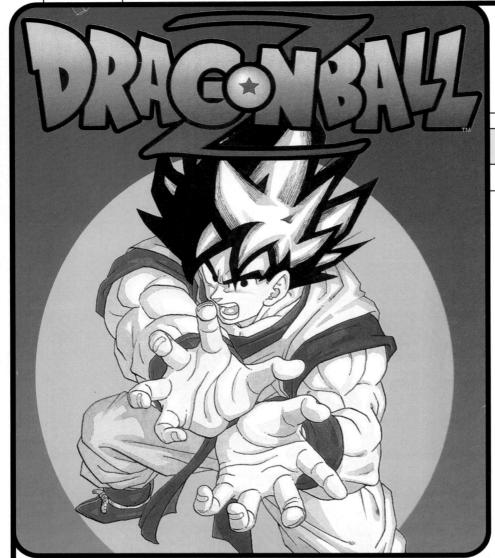

 Left
Japanese Manga comics have earned a worldwide fan base. Animated TV versions of the comics have become valuable advertising vehicles in Japan, successfully promoting a broad range of products from eye drops to curry rice.

▶▶ Sci-Fi writer campaigns for space colonies

Space travel and faster-than-light speed ships are a staple of science fiction. Larry Niven, often in collaboration with scientist Jerry Pournelle, has been writing novels for years in which he has invented a space drive, the Bussard ramjet, for interstellar travel. A good example is described in *A Gift from Earth*. Niven and Pournelle also propose a space elevator as a way of getting into orbit. Niven believes that the ramjet is technologically feasible and uses his novels to campaign for human space colonies whether they be on the Moon, Mars, or space stations orbiting Earth.

▶▶ Aliens often get bad press in science fiction.

The Vogons in Douglas Adams's *HitchHiker's Guide to the Galaxy* demolish Earth in order to make room for a space highway. In Keith Laumer's *A Plague of Demons*, aliens use the Earth as a farm to harvest human brains for installation in giant war robots. For a change, Arthur C. Clarke

NOVELS & COMICS

OUTER SPACE

▶ Heading towards a cyberspace existence

William Gibson's cyberpunk trilogy – *Neuromancer*, *Count Zero* and *Mona Lisa Overdrive* – imagine a world in which people can work and communicate in cyberspace using virtual reality headsets called 'trodes'. The Internet, which developed at the same time as Gibson was writing his novels, mirrors the trilogy, although we cannot yet immerse ourselves in cyberspace completely. However, though still in its infancy, research conducted into interfacing the human brain directly with computers is beginning to produce results. Gibson's books are also populated by 'superhackers', outlaw cyberspace cowboys with whom many real

life hackers such as Kevin Mitnick and the Datastream Cowboy no doubt identify.

▶▶ Relocating to Mars may be a real possibility

Kim Stanley Robinson's *Mars* trilogy begins with a manned expedition to Mars in 2027 and traces the story of a group of 100 people carving out a life on the planet. In *Red Mars*, *Blue Mars* and *Green Mars,* over a period of 200 years colonists turn the hostile environment into a world where it is possible for human beings to breathe the air and grow food – a process called 'terraforming'. The 1997 NASA Pathfinder mission to Mars sent back pictures eerily like Robinson's vision of the planet. Recent reports of the possibility of a NASA-funded manned mission to the red planet indicate that her ideas may yet become reality.

wrote a novel called *Childhood's End* in which aliens arrive on Earth with a mission to show humanity the way to spiritual maturity and bring them into the Galactic Consciousness, though the twist in the tale is that these saviour aliens look like stereotypical devils. While man continues to search for extraterrestrial life, it remains to be seen whether aliens will be friendly or hostile. @ alien life p148

▶ Aliens share autonomous aircraft technology

Julian May's *Galactic Milieu* trilogy – *Jack the Bodiless*, *Diamond Mask* and *Magnificat* – starts off in 2037, a few decades after a benevolent federation of advanced alien races have revealed themselves to Earthlings, sharing their technology and higher-mind powers. One of the technologies Earth gains is small flying machines called 'rhocraft', colloquially referred to as 'eggs'. The rhocraft's destination is punched into a computer and they take charge of the flying, even liaising with air traffic control. While personalized family aircraft are still a long way off, an automated highway system for cars is scheduled to begin trials in the US in 2002.

TECHNOLOGY

▶ When nanotechnology gets out of control

In Greg Bear's *Queen of Angels,* tiny machines which are as small as living cells perform tasks ranging from constructing buildings to modifying people's body shape or colour. His novel *Blood Music* considers the implications of these tiny biological machines becoming intelligent and literally taking over the world to remake it in their own image. Whilst nothing as sinister as Bear's vision is likely in the near future, micromachines which act as air pressure sensors in car tyres, and look for leaks and cracks in power plants, are already being tested. @ *nanotechnology p154*

Below
Judge Dredd has the massive task of maintaining law and order in Megacity One, a megalopolis in the US. As cities continue to expand, we may yet be in need of a real-life Judge Dredd.

⏸ The predicted science of cloning has arrived

Genetic engineering has been widely predicted in science fiction and Robert Heinlein's *Time Enough for Love* explores the use of cloning to grow spare bodies. David Brin's *Glory Days* envisions a future in which women rule the world and clone themselves, and men are simply an aid in the process. The recent creation of Dolly the sheep is a major breakthrough in this field, prompting governments worldwide to debate the ethics of human cloning. @ *genetics p112*

⏸ Get on-line for a 3-D virtual battle

Larry Niven's *Dream Park* series features games which seamlessly mix virtual reality and real action. The characters play war games in a 3-D virtual environment which is a cross between computer games and Paintball. Already, computer games Quake and Quake 2 from id Software have a following of players going on-line to battle against other players in real time, and the race is on between games companies to produce affordable virtual reality headsets for gamers. @ *gaming p50*

▶ Real-world communications outdoes Sci-Fi predictions

Novelist Ursula le Guin's 'ansible', which allows instantaneous voice and visual communication anywhere in the Universe, may still be a long way off, but it is already possible to communicate with video in real time over the Internet. The *Encyclopedia of Science Fiction* notes that the vidphone – a telephone which transmits pictures – is one of the oldest and most commonly used technologies in the genre. In this respect, real life has overtaken fiction: the convergence of cellular phones, notebook computers and satellite communications via the satellite phone, means it will soon be possible to telephone from anywhere on Earth – even Mt Everest.

▶▶ Thinking machines set to become part of our lives

Yukito Kishiro's Manga comic *Gunnm* (*Battle Angel Alita*) is the story of a battle-trained cygorg – part human, part machine – in search of her identity. Fujiko Fujio's *Doraemon*, another intelligent robot, is a cultural icon in Japan. Scientists are looking

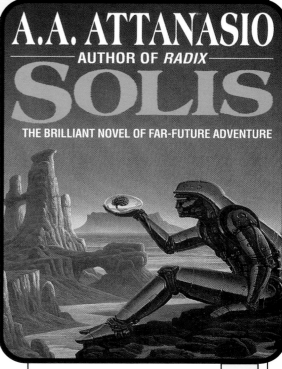

A.A. ATTANASIO
AUTHOR OF *RADIX*
SOLIS
THE BRILLIANT NOVEL OF FAR-FUTURE ADVENTURE

Above
A.A. Attanasio is an established science fiction and fantasy novelist. He has been publishing books for 15 years, and his work includes fantasy novels based on the historic myths of Camelot and Arthurian legend, as well as the far-future.

at ways of creating intelligence in robots and computers. @ *artificial life p152*

♻ Back to the future

Martian invasion

H.G. Wells' *War of the Worlds* introduced the idea of a monstrous alien invader, which quickly became a cliché in science fiction. But to US radio listeners on a Sunday night in 1938 the invasion was real. The first episode of a radio series based on the novel, narrated by Orson Welles, caused havoc as thousands of people panicked, running through the streets hysterically, and congregating in churches and police stations.

Atomic bomb

In 1944, legendary science fiction editor John W. Campbell published a short story by Cleve Cartmill, prompting a visit from the FBI because the story featured an atomic bomb and the US government feared there had been a leak of government secrets. At the time, the Allied powers were co-operating in top secret to develop the bomb.

Telecommunications satellite

In 1945, Arthur C. Clarke wrote a magazine article envisioning a network of communications satellites circling the Earth, which came about in the 1980s. Clarke correctly predicted that satellites would fly 22,300 miles above the Equator.

1895	H.G. Wells describes a machine than can travel into the future
2500	The laws of physics that allow for time travel are shown to be practically possible

METRO-GOLDWYN-MAYER PRESENTS THE SPECTACULAR **GEORGE PAL** PRODUCTION OF **H.G. WELLS'**

THE TIME MACHINE

WHIRLS YOU TO A WORLD OF AMAZING ADVENTURE IN THE YEAR 800,000!

IN FUTURISTIC METROCOLOR

starring **ROD TAYLOR · ALAN YOUNG · YVETTE MIMIEUX · SEBASTIAN CABOT · TOM HELMORE**

Screenplay by **DAVID DUNCAN** Based on the Novel by H. G. WELLS Directed by **GEORGE PAL**

Left
Time travel has long been the stuff of science fiction, but scientists now believe that some form of time travel could in theory be possible. In extreme gravitational fields, such as those created by black holes, space-time may collapse, effectively making a gateway connected by a wormhole to other universes.

TIME TRAVEL

THEORIES

Take a wormhole trip into time and space

The wormhole is a type of black hole time machine, based on the theory that hypothetical short cuts across the space-time continuum exist which could enable travel back and forth in time. A wormhole can be seen as a black hole in one universe connected to a black hole in another universe, although they appear to be based more in the imagination of science fiction writers than in fact. Albert Einstein and Nathan Rosen first realized in 1935 that the theory of general relativity allowed for the 'Einstein-Rosen bridge' (now referred to as wormholes), although initially this bridge was only thought to be possible through space, not time.

How to build your own time machine

In his book *Hyperspace*, New York physicist Michio Kaku describes how to construct a time machine, basing his calculations on Einstein's theory of relativity. Kaku's time machine consists of two chambers which each contain two parallel metal plates. In theory, the fabric of space-time is ripped apart by the phenomenal electric field created between the metal plates. This creates a hole in space that links the two chambers. One of the chambers is taken on a long and very fast journey and brought back, thus creating different rates of time at each end of the wormhole. Anybody tumbling into one end of the wormhole would then plunge into the past or future. One of the current logistical problems with this device is that we do not have the technology to create the intense electrical field which would be necessary.

Super strings and the theory of ten-dimensionals

While the basic idea of time travel is founded on the existence of the fourth dimension of time, the theory of super strings claims that there could be ten dimensions. While we exist in a three-dimensional world, this world exists in a multi-spatial dimensional manifold. Crossing over to another three-dimensional surface would mean crossing over into a new universe. The extra dimensions in this theory are those that link all the three dimensional surfaces together. While our current experience of time is one-dimensional and linear, the super string theory proposes that we could move into other lines of time by moving through the second temporal dimension. The vibrating 'strings' in this theory are what make up the resonance of the different particles which we can see in our everyday lives. The

Left
This computer graphic depicts the inside of a wormhole, with a planet at the end of the tunnel. It has been suggested that holes in space-time are connected by wormholes to distant points in our own Universe, or even to parallel universes.

strings, 100 billion times smaller than a proton, can vibrate only in space-time of ten dimensions.

▶▶ Technology to take advantage of wormhole travel

Gravitational theory expert Kip Thorne and his students Michael Morris and Ulvi Yurtsever, of the California Institute of Technology, USA, studied Einstein's theories in the mid-1980s and discovered that wormholes could also exist through time as well as space, thus opening up the possibility of time travel. Thorne maintains that, however bizarre it seems, time travel is nevertheless permitted by the laws of physics, so must be possible in some form. It is envisaged that in the future an advanced civilization may have sufficient technology to adapt naturally occurring wormholes for time travel purposes or even to create time machines.

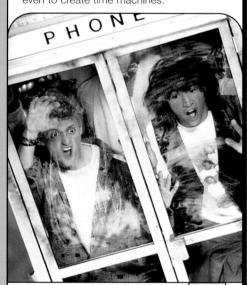

Above
Although scientists are now able to suggest how time travel might be accomplished, it is still a long way from becoming a reality. Today's technology has a lot of catching up to do before it could meet the demands of a time machine.

PARADOXES AND SOLUTIONS

▶ The problems with travelling faster than the speed of light

Unlike Gödel's early theory of time-travel speed, contemporary scientists have pointed out that to travel across time, one would have to travel at speeds *faster* than the speed of light. However, this is impossible. As you approach the speed of light, time slows down until you reach the speed of light itself, where time comes to an abrupt halt. It appears to be impossible to be able to continue travelling when time has actually stopped. It seems the only way to overcome this would be to travel through a wormhole with an electric charge which would keep the 'door' open for long enough, or else to travel through a rotating black hole. Then, travelling through the time tunnel would not have to involve speeds faster than that of light.

▶ Travelling back in time: the classic paradox

Travelling back in time gives rise to the classic paradox: if you can go back in time, you have the opportunity to change the past and thus alter the future. Although this may sound like a good idea, it in fact poses some problems. If you go back in time and murder your own grandmother, for example, this would make it impossible for you to ever have existed in the first place, and therefore your grandmother never died since you did not exist to kill her. This conundrum is explored in Steven Spielberg's film *Back to the Future*, when Michael J. Fox goes back in time and unwittingly prevents his parents ever meeting, and so nullifies his own existence.

⏸ Deutsch's 'multiverse' poses a solution

The problem of travelling back in time and being in a position to alter the past and thus affect the present can be theoretically solved using quantum physics and the concept of parallel universes. According to quantum physicist David Deutsch, of Oxford University, UK, quantum physics allows for the existence of many copies of the Universe. Therefore, if you were to go back in time, you would simply emerge in a copy of the original Universe and any changes made will not effect the original Universe. This alternative history approach maintains that there are different histories for every possible outcome of every decision, spreading out like the branches of an infinite tree. Another theory claims that the past is already defined and determined, and events cannot ever be altered, even by going back in time.

▶ Hawking disputes the possibility of time travel

The renowned physicist Professor Stephen Hawking of Cambridge University, UK, does not believe the Universe would allow for time travel, and invokes what he has called the Chronological Protection Conjecture (CPC) to support his theory. This is essentially a hypothetical law which prevents time travel and its accompanying set of paradoxes and fears. The CPC works by preventing you from making changes in your past. For example, if you tried to kill your grandmother, something which Hawking terms a 'cosmic censor' would stop you in your tracks and prevent this from happening. Although the laws of physics show that time travel is in theory possible, many people still maintain that the very idea goes against all common sense. This should not be taken too seriously though, since exactly the same argument was used in the past against space travel.

Above
Albert Einstein shaped scientific thought on time travel. He showed that space joined with time to form a fourth dimension – spacetime, which collapses under certain circumstances to make 'holes' through which we could travel.

▶▶ Further snags in the time travel theory

Another problem with time travel is that if it is possible, why have no travellers from the future come our way in the present? One neat explanation is that it seems as though you cannot use a time machine to go back in time before the machine was built, since the machine would not exist in the past and therefore neither would you. It seems time machines will only allow you to go forward in time and return to where you started.

♻ Back to the future

H.G. Wells

H.G. Wells's formative *The Time Machine* of 1895, described a time machine that could travel forwards into the future. Thus, Wells craftily avoided being weighed down with the paradoxes of changing the past.

Kurt Gödel

In 1949, the logician Kurt Gödel claimed that travelling back in time may indeed be possible according to Einstein's 1905 theory of relativity. He said, assuming that matter can be transformed into energy, it is theoretically possible in this Universe to travel into any part of the past or future. Gödel's theory proposed that a time machine would need to travel at a speed of 70.7% of the speed of light (about 800 million km/h) and relativity would do the rest.

Left
In the future everyone could be an astronaut. Organizations such as the Alternative Association of Astronauts are investigating low cost, private space travel in the hope that it could become available to all, and independent travellers will be able to journey to space without the help of organizations like NASA.

TECHNO UTOPIAS

Visions about the future of mankind based on technology have existed for a long time. As science and technology show no sign of slowing down in their race for innovation, techno utopias are blossoming as never before. Very often it is hard to draw the line between serious scientific efforts in conquering new territory, and ideologists or sectarian-like 'visionaries' who are using the same buzzwords to develop their brand of technology-inspired utopianism. Although not all utopianism is inherently bad, wrongheaded and biased utopias can be extremely harmful because they attempt to seduce mankind with false promises which can result in utopias collapsing into their opposite, dystopias.

THE CYBORG

Cybernetical organisms from present to future

The term Cyborg stands for Cybernetical Organism and was first used by Manfred Clynes and Nathan Kline to describe the technological enhancement of the human body for space travel. Employed by NASA, these two scientists proposed in 1960 that a combination of drugs and surgery would enable humans to survive within the harsh environment of outer space. Ever since, NASA has continued trying to find ways of making humans more adaptable to extreme conditions. The US Air Force is applying a similar range of medical, pharmaceutical, robotic and biotechnical techniques for supersonic jet pilots. The theme of humans merging with machine elements now appears in thousands of variations, from Mattel toys, Robotech by Matchbox or Mindstorm by LEGO, as well as in films such as *Robocop*, and TV series like *Captain Power* and *Soldiers of the Future*. Are we all going to become cyborgs? @ *film p170*

Extropians look for ways to extend life on Earth

A mixed group of like-minded people, headed by the Californian Max More, is organizing conferences about 'extropian issues'. Basically, they are looking for and discussing scientific methods or concepts about life-prolonging technologies and biotechnological optimization of the body with immortality as the ultimate goal. They think that in the near future we will be able to 'download' ourselves – to digitally capture a human mind and save it on a digital hard drive. @ *longevity p116*

Remodelling the human mind as a machine

The computer scientist Marvin Minsky claims in *Society of the Mind* that the human mind can be mechanically reproduced, and that it resembles a machine – a whole consisting of parts, which will be increasingly well understood by scientists and can therefore be re-modelled. Minsky's colleague Hans Moravec works on a similar basis. Moravec and his group are building large-scale autonomous robots, which can not only move but also 'think' and plan strategically on their own. He believes that robots will already have started replacing humans by the 21st century, and may eventually overtake human beings to create a robot society. @ *robots p28*

Right
The Heaven's Gate sect committed mass suicide in the belief that death was a passage into another level of reality. Among personal belongings found at the cult's home in California were these personal hair-cut kits.

THEORIES

⏸ Visualizing the process of idea evolution

The British biologist Richard Dawkins coined the term 'meme' in the 1970s. He suggested we try to understand the evolution of ideas in similar terms to the evolution of species. He talks about the Meme by analogy with the carrier of reproductive information, the Gene. The theory has had a lot of academic attention in the 1990s, and refined versions have since been developed. Richard Brodie, for example, speaks of the 'Ego-Gene', the meme which is responsible for the reproduction of the idea of the 'self'.

▶ Improved problem solving with a global meta-conscious

The term 'Collective Intelligence' was coined by French anthropologist Pierre Lévy, and is now widely in use with many meanings. For example, enhanced speed and quality of communication flows through the World Wide Web would contribute to a new kind of global meta-consciousness. This could be used to help us become better at problem solving and quicker at finding solutions for urgent global threats such as the potential climate catastrophe.

⏭ The emergence of a World Wide Super-Brain

Closely related to the notion of collective intelligence is the idea of a kind of meta-system emerging to form a World Wide Super-Brain. Communications systems such as the World Wide Web are seen as early forms of 'nervous systems' of a future superhuman being. The British Physician Peter Russel has pioneered this line of thought, which is now a widely recognized metaphor which attracts much interest. Work has been added by Howard Bloom, Francis Heylighen, Joel de Rosnay, Gregory Stock and others exploring the 'global brain' from the perspectives of neuro-sciences, computer sciences, linguistics and other related fields.

⏭ Welcome to the cerebral noosphere

The French scientist and Jesuit priest Teilhard de Chardin was probably the first person to discuss evolution towards a super-human integration. For the global network of ideas, information and communication he coined the term 'noo-sphere', the sphere of mental activity.

▶ Humanity evolves towards natural systems

In his book *Out of Control,* Californian writer Kevin Kelly compares human-made systems, such as economies and machines, with natural systems such as beehives and termite societies. He foresees a new economy called 'bionomics' evolving through the merging of people, information technology and cybernetical self-control, which resembles a natural system much more closely.

⏸ Cult's mass suicide aimed at a new level of reality

Members of the Californian sect Heaven's Gate committed mass suicide in 1996. The computer literate young men and women, who had all made their living from web-design, believed that death was just a transformation to another level of reality, and that they could achieve interstellar travel once they reached it. Lately, there have been rumours of e-mail messages emerging from the dead cult members claiming they had arrived 'on the other side', and are now continuing their interstellar trip. Needless to say, these e-mail messages appeared on mailing lists of affiliated sects.

▶ Joe Soap lines up for stellar existence

Alternative Association of Astronauts (AAA) is now a large movement, and aims at providing space travel without NASA or ESA. It holds international conferences to discuss ways of building low cost spaceships and establishing privately funded orbital space stations. @ *space stations p146*

⏭ Implanted computer chip records your life

Scientists at the British Telecom Laboratories, UK, estimate that by the year 2025 they will have produced a computer chip tiny enough to be implanted into the nerves behind a person's eye. The memory chip will record a person's lifetime data – estimated at 10 terrabytes. Every sight, thought, sensation and emotion, in the form of neuron pulses in the brain, gets stored

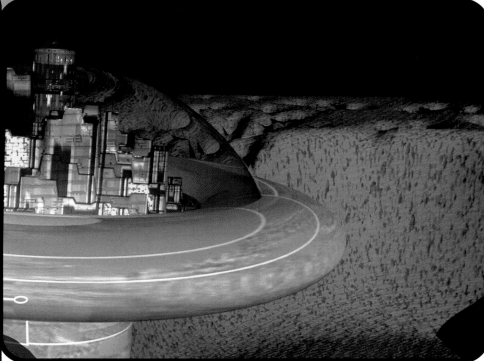

Above
This proposed colony on Mars would be built in a crater on an extinct volcano, Pavonis Mars. It could support 500 inhabitants, and is covered by a dome to protect them from Mars' thin atmosphere of carbon dioxide.

on the chip and can later be downloaded onto a computer. This information, combined with a record of a person's genes, will enable scientists to recreate a human being. The estimated 10 terrabytes of data produced during an 80-year life is equivalent to the storage capacity of 714,285,714,286,000 floppy disks.

♻ Back to the future

The Cyborg

Robots, iron men and other artificial people have enlivened our mental landscapes since ancient Greece. The Indian national epic, the *Mahabharata*, which was composed about 300 BC, features a lion automaton. Legendary automaton builder Wolfgang von Kempelen built a chess-playing tin Turk and became the toast of Napoleonic Europe.

Man as a machine

The French doctor Julien Offroy de La Mettrie published his text *L'Homme Machine* (*Man as Machine*) in 1748, quite a radical statement to make at the beginning of the age of enlightenment.

Cybernetics

In the 20th century, Norbert Wiener coined the term cybernetics (from the Greek term for 'pilot' or 'governor') and laid the basis for it as a research discipline with his book *Cybernetics: Or Control and Command in the Animal and the Machine* (1948).

1948	George Orwell publishes *1984* which predicts a future mind-controlled society
2000	Y2K Bug causes the world's computers to crash, triggering nuclear apocalypse

Left
George Orwell's vision of a future society in his novel *1984* predicted a less-than-rosy future for mankind, especially in his idea that there will always be a 'Big Brother' watching you. Today's surveillance devices are so well developed that we can even be monitored by satellites watching us from space.

DYSTOPIAS

COMMUNICATION BREAKDOWN

▶ Losing contact with the information underclass

Thousands of people join the Internet every day. Whilst this is a good thing, it has its pitfalls. One major problem is bandwidth logjam, where there is too much traffic flowing through the veins of cyberspace. Everywhere, demand for bandwidth space outstrips supply. For many users the Internet has become the Internot. But whilst cyberspace may help break down barriers of race, class and gender, other boundaries are being set up. The future may see two types of people: those with access to the Net and an underclass of those without. Although 100 million people use the Internet, the harsh reality is that two-thirds of the world's population does not even have access to a telephone.

▶ Satellite could bring nuclear apocalypse in 1999

On 15 Oct 1997 NASA launched its Cassini space probe to investigate Saturn. While this is a standard enough procedure, there is one small problem: to get to Saturn, Cassini must slingshot itself around Venus, a maneouvre that will send it hurtling back past the Earth in 1999 at a staggering 68,000 km/h (42,254 mph). Even worse, the probe is fuelled by 33 kg (72 lb) of throbbing plutonium, and if something goes wrong and Cassini crashes back to Earth, that's enough to poison everyone on the planet.

▶ The great satellite traffic jam in the sky

With over 500 satellites currently orbiting Earth, and more being launched every year, experts predict it is only a matter of time before they start colliding into each other. To make matters worse, most space missions leave debris behind them. There are said to be over 9,000 large items of

 Left
Director Ridley Scott's film *Blade Runner* (1982) showed a society where technology was out of control, in the form of androids that were so sophisticated that they became self-aware and wanted to live like 'normal' humans.

junk up there (ranging in size from a mobile telephone to a space station) and countless numbers of smaller pieces of flotsam and jetsam. To add insult to injury, from Nov 1998 the Earth will experience a series of extensive meteor showers. These will be especially hazardous to any spacecraft orbiting Earth, and while the more modern satellites are fitted with technology that allows them to manoeuvre themselves out of danger, the older machines cannot do this and will be little more than sitting ducks.

Information Fatigue Syndrome

The Information Superhighway puts billions of bytes of data at our fingertips – and for some, that is just too much information. Trying to keep track of our PIN codes, fax details, passwords, telephone numbers, e-mail addresses and web site URLs can lead to Information Fatigue Syndrome. The UK firm Benchmark Research conducted a survey of businessmen and found that many complained of 'analysis paralysis', the burn-out caused by the need to constantly monitor data sources. Other symptoms include greater levels of stress and anxiety, a tendency to blame others and self-doubt. As the Internet and other information networks continue to pump out yet more information, overworked managers may find it harder and harder to cope.

Pre-millennial tension: the end is nigh

Millenniums always see an increase in apocalyptic prophets convinced the world is about to end. One recent soothsayer – a Japanese scientist, in fact – calculates that it will all end on 18 Aug 1999, with the sun and planets aligning in the shape of a fiery cross as mankind destroys itself in a cataclysmic war. More worrying is the Y2K problem: many computers were not set up to recognize the year 2000 on their operating systems and it is predicted that many will crash just after midnight on 31 Dec 1999. According to some, this could trigger an unintentional nuclear holocaust as missiles are accidentally launched by confused computers in the US and Russia.

BIOHAZARDS

Biotech: genetic discrimination

The 1997 movie *Gattaca* depicted a future society where citizens were DNA-scanned at birth for signs of genetic or congenital weaknesses. Those whose genes did not make the grade were condemned to a slave-like life of manual labour. Although it is a work of fiction, the moral of *Gattaca* is relevant. Whilst discrimination on the basis of one's genes is still illegal in most places, it is possible that some companies with access to genetic information about potential employees or clients would exploit it. There are also religious and philosophical arguments which claim that any attempt to artificially alter mankind's genetic pattern is an offence against God or nature.

Biotech: cracking the Human Code

Can a company own the blueprint to life? If a company engineers a gene and then patents it, does it mean that those who carry it – and any offspring they pass the gene on to – are 'owned' by the company? Another area of genetic engineering that is just as controversial concerns the idea that, as more becomes known about human genes, the chances of selective abortions or other eugenic processes increases: once the gene for intelligence is found, the argument goes, why not terminate all those embryos which do not have it?

Biotech: clone yourself to grow spare parts

Cloning presents the most anxieties in gen-ethics. Since the cloning of Dolly the Sheep in 1997, most geneticists agree that the cloning of humans is not far off. It could even lead to the cloning of bodies, perhaps without a head, for the sole purpose of providing spare organs if and when required. The definition of life itself could become blurred as identities become confused, whilst cloned humans may be treated as freaks or second-class citizens.

Biotech: interfering in the food chain

The genetic engineering of food has caused much unease and some UK supermarkets, as well as environmental groups, are making a vocal stand against chemically altering food products. As yet, the very-long-term effects of genetically altering food are unknown, both on human health and in the food chain generally. Some feel that it could lead to genetically-altered organisms being released into the environment, or that

Above
Protests against cloning have reached up as far as the European Parliament in Strasbourg, France, where these Green Party deputies donned identical white masks in March 1997 as a protest during an EC debate on cloning experiments.

certain genetically-engineered plants may become antibiotic-resistant. Another problem could be the development of 'mutant' crops, as genetically-altered seeds become mixed with weeds or poisonous plants – a development recently confirmed by scientists in the UK. Finally, there is the sensitive issue of xenotransplantation – the transfer of animal organs to humans. Pig organs have already been successfully transplanted to humans, but there is a wealth of medical and ethical issues to overcome before the practice becomes commonplace and widely accepted.

Back to the future

TV troubles
In Dec 1997, 600 children suffered seizures while watching the *Pokemon* cartoon on Japanese TV. The children's fits began during the transmission of an explosive light effect, causing epilepsy-like symptoms and fainting.

Culture clash in the New World
When the Spanish conquistadors landed in the New World in 1518 they brought more than western civilization to the Aztec Empire: they also brought the common cold virus, killing thousands of immune-deficient natives.

Pre-millennium tension
As the year AD 1000 approached there was an explosion in apocalyptic religious and social groups convinced the world was about to end – just like now, in fact.

INDEX

Picture Acknowledgements

Placement key: t = top; l = left; r = right; b = bottom

The publisher would like to thank the following individuals, companies, and picture libraries for their kind permission to reproduce their photographs. Special thanks to Julia Kamlish, Seymour Yang and Andrew Entwhistle at Science Photo Library for their assistance with this project.

American Civil Liberties Union:@www.aclu.org 42b, 43t;
Allsport: Agence Vandystadt/Patrick Passe 6tc, 9, 17; Al Bello 162b;
Alton Towers: 56b;
AP Photo: 95r; Auburn University/ Mitch Emmons 70b; Frank Augstein 127r; Robyn Beck, Pool 110b; Bell Boeing 83l; Harry Cabluck 54t; Franki Chan 97; Jack Dempsey 67; Mike Derer 206t; Richard Dew 4tr; El Paso Times/Rudy Gutierrez 160b; Halifax Daily New/-Darrell Oake 138t; Handout 16b,38t; Kent C.Horner 176b; Eugene Hoshiko 118t; Sergei Karpukhin 156t; Katsumi Kasahara 75, 80t, 158t; Isabel Leon 65; Lockheed 145;Christian Lutz 5br, 179; Remy de la Mauviniere14t; Win McNamee, Pool 68b; Martin Mejia 122b; Doug Mills 6br,162; Jasper Mortimer 96b; Alan Mothner 163; Adam Nadel 23; Dolores Ochoa 84b; Michael Poche 16t; Denis Poroy 72t; Princeton Plasma Physics Laboratory, Dietmar Krause 125l; Pavel Rahman 30b; Sakchai Lalit 129l; Sikorsky Aircraft/Richard Zellner 72b; Joao Silva 118b; Pat Sullivan 129r; Barry Sweet 148t; C.F.Tham 4tc,34t; Elaine Thompson 40t; University of Florida/Thomas Wright 128b; Roberto Velazquez 66t; Carl D.Walsh 126t;
Ron Arad Associates: 5tl, 88b;
Arcaid: John Edward Linden/Architect Christian de Portzamoarc 90b;
Art+Com GmBH: www.artcom.de/projects 53;
B+W Loudspeakers Ltd.: 47;
BBC Natural History Unit: Jurgen Freund 103;
BDDP.GGT/Equitable Life: 116t;
Chris Bagot: 88t;
Car Cosy: 78b;
Channel 4: 36t;
Channel 4 PR: 33, 39;
CNAP Chrita Sommerer & Laurent Mignoneau 1995: Collection Musée d'Art Contemporain Lyon France 48b;
Corbis: James L. Amos 98t; Patrick Bennett 99; Bettman 175r; Eye Ubiquitous/John Dakers 87, 90t; Philip Gould 127l; Richard T. Nowitz 124b,125r; Pat O'Hara 156b; The Purcell Team 80b; Roger Ressmeyer 149, 167, 176t; Galen Rowell 164b; Leif Skoogfors 157; Grant Smith 98b; Richard Hamilton Smith 161; Brain Vikander 119;
Coventry School of Art and Design and Society of Motor Manufacturers and Traders: 77;
CTN Independant: 135;
Cyberlife: 55t;
Delia's Splash: www.gURL.com 41t;
Digicom: 130t;
Digital Amsterdam: www.dds.nl 43b;
Eden Project: 6bc,11t;
eff.org/pub/EFF: 26t/b, 27;
Egmont Fleetway Ltd.: Judge Dredd©1998 Egmont Foundation, all rights reserved/Cliff Robinson 173l;
Eidios Games: 55b;
EMap Construction: 95l;
Epic Megagames: 50t;
ESP Electronics: David Bunnell 36b;
Ford Motors: 76b;
Christopher Foss: Lockheed Martin Vought Systems 70t; Martin Marietta 71; United Defense Design 73t;
Fosters & Partners: 91; Richard Davies 93;
Future Systems: 13;
Genesis Space Photo Library: 146b;
Reproduced by permission of Hodder and Stoughton Ltd. ©1994 by AA Attanasio: 173r;
Richard Horden: 89;
Hotwire Productions: Lynn Hershman Leeson 49; IC Parc/William Penney Laboratory/Imperial College/Neville Miles 153l;
The Image Bank: John Banagan 30t; Robert Holland 116b; Jeff Hunter 124t; Tom Hussey 5bl,102t; Dominique Sarraute 4bl, 24t;

Interface Radio: 37;
courtesy of Jaguar and Ryanair: 38b;
Jubilee Line Extension Project: QA Photos 96t;
Knowbotic Research/Mediale Hamburg: C.Wirsing 48t;
Kobal Collection: Columbia 178t; Columbia Tristar /Digital Domain 171r; Fox/ABC 168b; Ladd Company/Warner Bros 178b; MGM1968 170b; MGM 174t; Nelson Entertainment/Orion 175l; New Line 1994 59; Paramount Television 168t,169l; 20th Century Fox 1997/Suzanne Tenner 171l; 20th Century Fox 1996 45, 58t; 20th Century Fox Television 169r; UFA 1927 170t; Universal 61, 64t;
Mathmos LTD: 64b;
MGM: 66b;
Miralab, University of Geneva: 58b;
Mitsubishi Motors: 78t;
Natural History Museum, London: 130b:
Nokia/Red Consultancy: 206b;
O.Decq-B.Cornette Architects, Paris: 92b;
Phoenix Resort: 18b;
Okupi: 35;
Pentagram Design Ltd: 12t;
Dag Pike: 73b, 85l;
Reading University: Dave Keating 152b;
Retna Pictures: Chris Taylor 46b;
Rex Features: 4br, 76t;
Richard Rogers Partnership: 94b;
Science Photo Library: Agstock/Ed Young 4tl,10t; American Science & Engineering 63; Aumer/Dr Bob Stepney 105; George Bernard 31; BSIP, VEM 104b; Manfred Cage 154t; Scott Camazine 111; Mark Clark 208t; Tony Craddock 174b; Ron Church 132t; DLR 83r; David Ducros 146t; East Anglia Genetics Service/L.Willatt 115; Eurelios/P.Gontier 46t; Eurelios/PH. Plailly 15l, 19, 28b, 107, 109t, 121, 122t, 134b; Simon Fraser 113l; GE Astro Space 69; J.G. Golden 133; Tommaso Guicciardini 128t; Victor Habbick Visions 177; Y.Hamel 5tc,126b; Daudier Jerrican 12b; Dr Rosalind King 68t; James King-Holmes 14b,113r; Mehau Kulyk 165r; Lawrence Livermore National Laboratory 82b; Peter Menzel 6bl, 28t, 57,62t/b,114t,152t,153r; Hank Morgan 11b,104t,114b; NASA 5bc, 10b, 137,139, 141t/b, 142t/b, 144t/b, 147; NASA/JPL 143; NASA/Space Telescope Unit 138b,140t/b; North Carolina State University/J.Bernholc et Al 151, 155; Claude Nuridsany & Marie Perennou 6tl,134t; Sam Ogden 15r, 22t, 84t; David Parker 22b, 79b,123, 131, 148b; Prof.G.Piragino 165l; J.C. Revy 6tr,106t/b,112t/b; Rosenfeld Images Ltd 21, 25; Gregory Sams 5tr,164t; David Scharf 154b; Dr. Jurgen Scriba 109b; Sandia National Laboratory 158b; Geoff Tompkinson 108t; Wellcome Dept. of Cognitive Neurology 108b; VLA 110t; Sinclair Stammers 117,132l; Taheshi Takahara 81; S.C.Tang 160t; Geoff Tompkinson 159; US Department of Energy 29; Erik Viktor 82t,102b;
Shueisha Publishing/Akira Toriyama: 172t;
Solar Tune Electronics: 54b;
Spymaster Communications and Surveillance Systems Ltd/New Media: 24b;
Starbright Foundation: 42t;
Suzuka Circuitland: 56t;
T3: 79t;
Takenaka Corporation: 94t;
Teledesic Corporation: 34b;
Westdeutsche Immobilien Holding GmbH: 92t;
www.bbc.co.uk/the mirror: 52b;
www.hip.atr.cp.jp/~ray/tiera/tiera.html: 4bc,40b;
ValokuvaamoSaaristo KY: Jouni Saaristo 85r;
Virgin Interactive: 50b, 51r;
Wimberly Allison Tong & Goo: 18t;
www.worldsaway.com: 52t;
Zablac Entertainment: 51l.